Model Based Fuzzy Control

Springer
Berlin
Heidelberg
New York
Barcelona
Budapest
Hong Kong
London
Milan
Paris
Santa Clara
Singapore
Tokyo

Rainer Palm Dimiter Driankov
Hans Hellendoorn

Model Based Fuzzy Control

Fuzzy Gain Schedulers and Sliding Mode Fuzzy Controllers

With 86 Figures

Springer

Dr. Rainer Palm
Dr. Hans Hellendoorn

Siemens AG
D-81730 München, Germany

Prof. Dr. Dimiter Driankov

University of Linköping
S-58183 Linköping, Sweden

Library of Congress Cataloging-in-Publication Data

Palm, Rainer.
Model-based fuzzy control : fuzzy gain schedulers and sliding mode fuzzy control / Rainer Palm, Dimiter Driankov, Hans Hellendoorn.
p. cm.
Includes bibliographical references and index.
ISBN 3-540-61471-0 (hardcover : alk. paper)
1. Automatic control. 2. Fuzzy systems. I. Driankov, Dimiter. II. Hellendoorn, Hans. III. Title.
TJ213.P222 1996
629.8'9--dc21 96-47571
CIP

ISBN 3-540-61471-0 Springer-Verlag Berlin New York Heidelberg

Typesetting: Camera-ready copy produced from the authors' output file using a Springer TEX macro package

Cover design: Künkel + Lopka, Ilvesheim
SPIN 10543385 45/3142 – 5 4 3 2 1 0 – Printed on acid-free paper

Foreword

Despite the excitement about its capabilities, and its success in some challenging applications, fuzzy control is still young and hence some important questions arise: In what situations, or for what applications, is fuzzy control superior to conventional control methods? Is it possible to combine some of the best ideas from the conventional methods with ideas from fuzzy control to provide more effective control solutions? How do we measure the success or failure of the methods? For many applications, simulations and experimental evaluations are not sufficient to verify the behavior of a control system, and in such situations there is a need for mathematical analysis of closed-loop system properties such as stability, performance, and robustness to determine whether a fuzzy control system is successful. Verification of such properties may be especially important for "safety-critical applications" (e.g., an aircraft or nuclear power plant) where the engineer must gain as much confidence in the closed-loop system as is possible before implementation.

Conventional control focuses on the use of models to construct controllers for dynamical systems. Fuzzy control focuses on the use of heuristics in the construction of a controller. While each of these seemingly disjoint approaches uses some ideas from the other, there has been relatively little work on how to more closely combine them to exploit the best characteristics of each. This book helps to remedy this problem by providing schemes that allow for the incorporation of heuristics and mathematical models. It also provides important ideas on how to marry some very successful conventional control ideas (e.g., sliding mode control and gain scheduling) with ideas from fuzzy control. While the past lack of focus on the use of mathematical models in fuzzy control systems development resulted in researchers ignoring mathematical analysis of stability, the basic approach used allows the authors to confront this important problem.

Overall, this book makes important steps toward bridging the apparent gap between fuzzy and conventional control. I would expect the techniques studied here to be quite useful for a wide range of challenging applications and would expect these ideas to form a foundation on which more research in this promising area will be based.

Columbus, Ohio, USA, 1996 — *Kevin M. Passino*

Preface

During the past few years two principally different approaches to the design of fuzzy logic controllers (FLC) have emerged: heuristics based design and model based design.

The main motivation for the heuristics based design is given by the fact that many industrial processes are still controlled in one of the following two ways:

- The process is controlled manually by an experienced operator.
- The process is controlled by an automatic control system which needs additional manual on-line "trimming" from an experienced operator.

In both cases it is enough to translate the operator's manual control algorithm in terms of a set of fuzzy if-then rules in order to obtain an equally good, or an even better, wholy automatic control system incorporating an FLC. This implies that the design of an FLC can only be done *after* a "control algorithm" already exists.

In the first case, the existing control algorithm may consist of sequential and/or parallel manual control actions performed by the operator upon a process whose mathematical model is either impossible to derive or of negligible utility for cost related reasons. In this case the FLC simply makes explicit the existing manual control knowledge, and consequently automates the use of this knowledge thus becoming a part of the closed loop system. In the second case, the existing control algorithm is a conventional control algorithm in need of additional manual "trimming". An FLC is then again used to automate the manual "trimming" algorithm employed by the operator and thus acts as a supervisor to the conventional closed loop system already in place.

It is admitted in the literature on fuzzy control that the heuristics based design is very difficult to apply to multiple-input/multiple-output control problems, which represent the largest part of challenging industrial process control applications. Furthermore, the heuristics based design lacks systematic and formally verifiable tuning techniques, and studies of stability, performance, and robustness can only be done via extensive simulations. Last but not least, there is a lack of systematic and easily verifiable knowledge acquisition techniques via which the qualitative knowledge about the process and/or available manual control algorithm can be extracted.

The above difficulties faced by the heuristics based design explain the recent surge of interest in the derivation of *black box* fuzzy models of the plant under control, in terms of the identification of a set of fuzzy if-then rules, by the use of conventional identification techniques, neural networks, genetic algorithms, or a mixture of these techniques.

This interest in the identification of fuzzy models is accompanied by a similar surge of interest in the model based design of fuzzy controllers. Model based fuzzy control uses a given conventional or fuzzy open loop model of the plant under control in order to derive the set of fuzzy if-then rules constituting the corresponding FLC. Interest then centers on the stability, performance, and robustness analysis of the resulting closed loop system involving a conventional model and an FLC, or a fuzzy model and an FLC. The major objective of model based fuzzy control is to use existing conventional linear and nonlinear design and analysis methods for the design of such FLCs that have better stability, performance, and robustness properties than the corresponding non-fuzzy controllers designed by the use of these same techniques. How to achieve this objective in terms of the design and analysis of sliding mode fuzzy controllers and fuzzy gain schedulers is the subject of this book.

In **Chapter 1** we introduce the basic notions and concepts in fuzzy control, the basic types of FLCs treated in the book, the major types of nonlinear control problems, and the existing methods for model based design and analysis of nonlinear control systems relevant for model based fuzzy control. We finally discuss informally the motivation for the design of fuzzy gain schedulers and fuzzy sliding mode controllers.

In Section 1.1 of this introductory chapter we present the basic fuzzy control related concepts used throughout the book involving the notions of a fuzzy state, fuzzy input, fuzzy output variables, and fuzzy state space.

In Section 1.2 we present the basic types of FLCs whose model based design and analysis is our subject. These include different types of Takagi–Sugeno FLCs (TSFLC) and the sliding mode FLC (SMFLC). We describe the open loop models used for the design of the different types of FLCs and the form of the fuzzy rules constituting these FLCs. We also present the control schemes incorporating an FLC that are relevant for model based fuzzy control.

In Section 1.3 we first describe the two basic types of nonlinear control problems considered in the book, namely nonlinear regulation and nonlinear tracking. Then, we discuss the specifications of the desired behavior of nonlinear closed loop systems in terms of stability, robustness, accuracy, and response speed.

In Section 1.4 we present the major existing methods for the model based design and analysis of nonlinear control systems and identify those of them whose fuzzy counterparts (with appropriate modifications) concern us.

In Section 1.5 we introduce and discuss informally the motivation for two basic types of FLCs, namely the Takagi–Sugeno FLC and the sliding mode FLC.

In **Chapter 2** we describe computation with an FLC and its formal description as a static nonlinear transfer element and thus provide the background knowledge needed to understand control with an FLC. We show the relationship between conventional and rule-based transfer elements and establish the compatibility between these two conceptually different, in terms of representation, types of transfer elements. We also introduce the basic stability concepts used in the model based design and analysis of FLCs.

In Section 2.1 we describe the computational structure of an FLC involving the computational steps of input scaling, fuzzification, rule firing, defuzzification, and output scaling.

In Section 2.2 we present the sources of nonlinearity in the computational structure of an FLC by relating them to particular computational steps.

In Section 2.3 we describe the relationship between conventional transfer elements and rule-based transfer elements. We show the gradual transition from a conventional transfer element to a crisp rule-based transfer element, and finally to a fuzzy rule-based transfer element. We also describe the computational structure of Takagi–Sugeno FLCs.

In Section 2.4 we present the stability concepts used in the model based design and analysis of an FLC including Lyapunov-linearization and the Lyapunov direct method for autonomous and nonautonomous systems.

In **Chapter 3** we make use of the similarity between the so-called diagonal form FLC and a sliding mode controller (SMC) to redefine a diagonal form FLC in terms of an SMC with boundary layer (BL).

In Section 3.1 we describe the control law of an SMC for an n-th-order SISO nonlinear nonautonomous system and its design for a tracking control problem with and without an integrator term.

In Section 3.2 we describe in detail the diagonal form FLC for a second order SISO nonlinear autonomous system and derive the similarities between the control law of a diagonal form sliding mode FLC and the control law of an SMC with BL.

In Section 3.3 we describe the design of the control law of a sliding mode FLC for an n-th-order SISO system for the tracking control problem, with and without integrator term.

In Section 3.4 we discuss the tuning of input scaling factors of a sliding mode FLC. In Section 3.5 we give an example of a force adapting manipulator arm for the design of a sliding mode FLC. In Section 3.6 we extend the sliding mode FLC design method to MIMO systems.

In **Chapter 4** we present the design methods for each of the different types of Takagi–Sugeno FLCs outlined in Chap. 1.

In Section 4.1 we present the Takagi–Sugeno FLC-1. We confine ourselves only to the presentation of the form of the open loop system, the form of the Takagi–Sugeno FLC-1, the form of the closed loop system and its stability properties, and an outline of a trial-and-error type of design method.

In Section 4.2 and 4.3 we present in detail the design of the Takagi–Sugeno FLC-2 and its use in local stabilization and tracking of a nonlinear autonomous system. With respect to local stabilization, a Takagi–Sugeno FLC-2 is able to stabilize a nonlinear autonomous system around *any* operating point without the need to change its gains. With respect to tracking, the FLC-2 performs gain scheduling on *any* reference state trajectory under the restriction that the reference state trajectories are slowly time varying.

In **Chapter 5** we illustrate in detail the design of fuzzy sliding mode controllers and fuzzy gain schedulers on a MIMO control problem concerning the control of a two-link robot arm.

Munich, 1996

Rainer Palm
Dimiter Driankov
Hans Hellendoorn

Table of Contents

1. Introduction to Model Based Fuzzy Control

A *fuzzy logic controller* (FLC) defines a *static nonlinear control law* by employing a set of *fuzzy if-then rules*, or *fuzzy rules* for short. The if-part of a fuzzy rule describes a fuzzy region in the state space. The then-part of a fuzzy rule specifies a control law applicable within the fuzzy region from the if-part of the same fuzzy rule. During control with an FLC a point in the state space is affected to a different extent by the control laws associated with all the fuzzy regions to which this particular point in the state space belongs.

The subject of this book is the model based design (synthesis) and analysis of FLCs, or in short, *model based fuzzy control.* Model based fuzzy control deals with the design of the set of fuzzy rules given a conventional, nonlinear open loop model of the system under control (a plant, or a process) and the consequent stability, robustness, and performance analysis of the resulting closed loop system. This is contrary to the *heuristic approach* to FLC design where the set of fuzzy rules is derived via a knowledge acquisition process and reflects the heuristic (shallow) knowledge of an experienced system operator. It is admitted in the literature on fuzzy control [5] that this approach is difficult to apply to *multiple-input/multiple-output* (MIMO) control problems. Though successfully applied in a wide range of basically *single-input/single-output* (SISO) control problems, the heuristic approach lacks systematic and verifiable tuning techniques, and studies of stability, robustness, and performance can only be done via extensive simulation.

In the design, we are given a nonlinear model of the plant to be controlled and some specifications of closed loop behavior, and the task is to construct an FLC, that is a set of fuzzy rules, so that the closed loop system meets these specifications. In the analysis, a nonlinear closed loop system involving an FLC is assumed to have been designed, and the task is to study its behavior in terms of certain characteristic features. In practice, design and analysis are interleaved and the design of a nonlinear controller is in effect an iterative process of analysis and design.

In Sect. 1.1 of this introductory chapter we first present the basic FLC related concepts to be used throughout the book involving the notions of a *fuzzy state, fuzzy input, fuzzy output variables*, and *fuzzy state space.*

In Sect. 1.2 we present the basic types of FLCs whose model based design and analysis are the subject of this book. These include different types of *Takagi–Sugeno* FLCs (TSFLC) and the *sliding mode* FLC (SMFLC). We describe the open loop models used for the design of the different types of FLCs and the form of the fuzzy rules constituting these FLCs. We also present the control schemes incorporating FLCs that are relevant for model based fuzzy control.

In Sect. 1.3 we first describe the two basic types of nonlinear control problems considered in the book, namely nonlinear regulation and nonlinear tracking. Then, we discuss the specifications of the desired behavior of nonlinear closed loop systems in terms of *stability*, *robustness*, *accuracy*, and *response speed.*

In Sect. 1.4 we present the major existing methods for the model based design and analysis of nonlinear control systems and identify those whose fuzzy counterparts (with appropriate modifications) are the subject of this book.

In Sect. 1.5 we introduce and discuss informally the motivation for the two basic types of FLCs that are the subject of this book, namely the Takagi–Sugeno FLC and the sliding mode FLC.

1.1 Fuzzy Concepts in Model Based Fuzzy Control

The essential feature of the notion of a *state* for a dynamical system is that it should contain all information about the past history of the system that is relevant for its future behavior. That is, if the state at a given instant of time is known, then its subsequent evolution can be predicted without any knowledge as to what has previously happened with the system. This means that when ordinary differential equations are used, the definition of the state must involve enough variables for all the equations to be of first order in the time-derivative. The dependent variables in these equations are called *state variables*, and they are usually denoted by $x_1, x_2, \ldots, x_n$, where n is the *order of the system.* Each state variable x_i is a function of time and takes pointwise, or *crisp values* in the domain of the reals and is thus called a *crisp state variable.*

Besides the crisp state variables, the equations also contain a number of externally specified variables which represent the driving forces acting upon the system from outside of the same system. These are known as *input variables* and are denoted as $u_1, u_2, \ldots, u_m$, where m is usually, though not neccessarily, less than n. Each input variable is also a function of time and takes crisp values in the domain of reals and is thus called a *crisp input variable.* For ease of notation the crisp state and input variables are assembled into the so-called *state vectors* and *input vectors* $\mathbf{x} = (x_1, x_2, \ldots, x_n)^T$ and $\mathbf{u} = (u_1, u_2, \ldots, u_m)^T$ respectively. We will call these vectors *crisp state vectors* and *crisp input vectors.*

In the context of control, it is also appropriate to distinguish another type of crisp variables called *crisp output variables* which represent aspects of the system's behavior that can be measured and controlled. These are usually a subset of the crisp state variables, but may in general depend on $\mathbf{u}$ and t as well. That is why they are collected in another vector called the *crisp output vector* $\mathbf{y} = (y_1, y_2, \ldots, y_p)^T$ where p is usually less than or equal to n.

In what follows we will present the fuzzy counterparts of the crisp state, input, and output variables.

1.1.1 Fuzzy Sets

A *classical (sub)set* C of the *universe of discourse*, or *domain* D, can be represented by using its *characteristic function* μ_C defined as follows.

Definition 1.1.1. *The function* $\mu_C : D \mapsto \{0, 1\}$ *is a characteristic function of the set* C *if and only if for all* d

$$\mu_C(d) = \begin{cases} 1 & \text{if } d \in C, \\ 0 & \text{if } d \notin C. \end{cases} \tag{1.1}$$

Figure 1.1 shows the characteristic function of a crisp set.

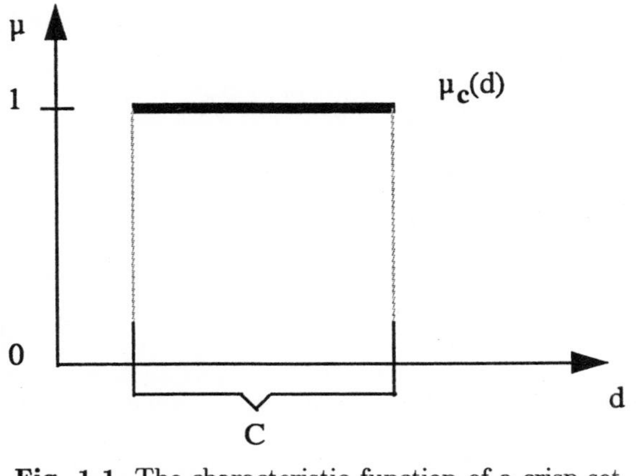

Fig. 1.1. The characteristic function of a crisp set

In *fuzzy set theory* classical sets are called *crisp sets* in order to distinguish them from *fuzzy sets*. Let C be a crisp set defined on the domain D. Then for any element d of D, we have that either $d \in C$, or $d \notin C$. In fuzzy set theory this property is generalized. Therefore, in a fuzzy set F, it is not necessary that either $d \in F$, or $d \notin F$. The generalization is realized as follows. According to the above definition, for any crisp set C it is possible to define a characteristic function $\mu_C : D \mapsto \{0,1\}$. In fuzzy set theory, the above characteristic function is generalized to a *membership function* which assigns to every $d \in D$ a value from the unit interval $[0,1]$ instead from the two-element set $\{0,1\}$. The set F, defined on the basis of such a generalized characteristic function, is called a fuzzy set.

Definition 1.1.2. *The membership function μ_F of a fuzzy set F is a function defined as*

$$\mu_F : D \mapsto [0,1]. \tag{1.2}$$

Thus every element $d \in D$ has a *membership degree* $\mu_F(d) \in [0,1]$. Then the fuzzy set F is completely determined by the set of tuples

$$F = \{(d, \mu_F(d)) \mid d \in D\}. \tag{1.3}$$

Figure 1.2 shows the membership function of a fuzzy set.

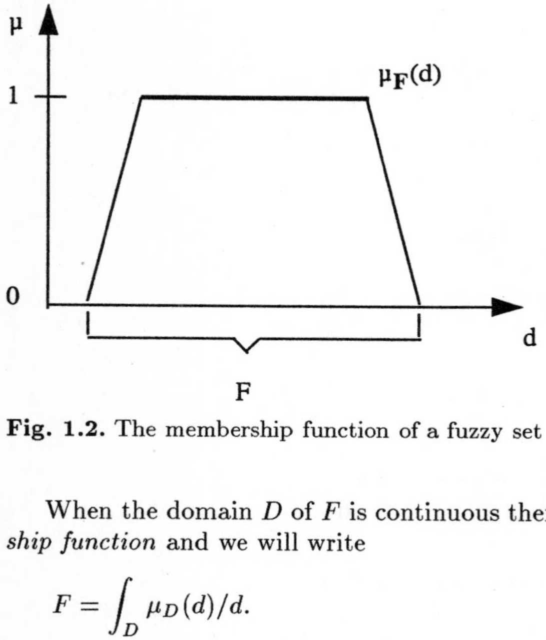

Fig. 1.2. The membership function of a fuzzy set

When the domain D of F is continuous then μ_F is a *continuous membership function* and we will write

$$F = \int_D \mu_D(d)/d. \tag{1.4}$$

Hence, the $\int$-sign denotes an infinite enumeration rather than integration over D. Throughout the rest of the book we consider fuzzy sets on continuous domains and thus defined with continuous membership functions unless stated otherwise. Figure 1.3 shows continuous and discrete membership functions.

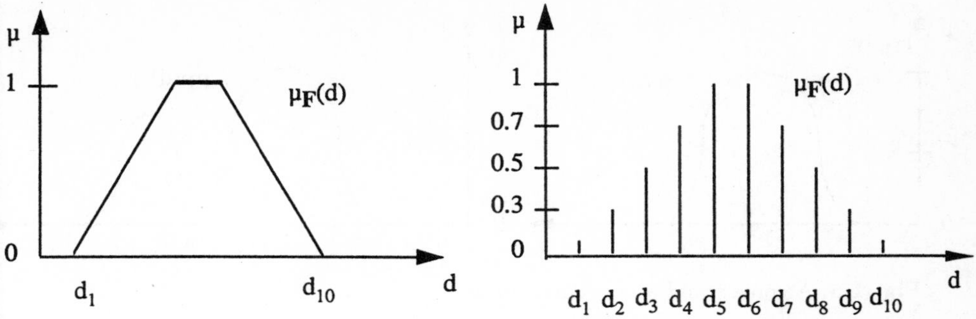

Fig. 1.3. Discrete and continuous membership functions

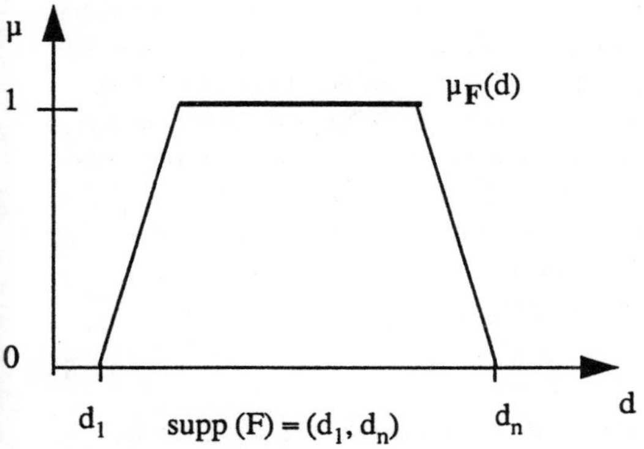

Fig. 1.4. The support of a fuzzy set

The elements of D that have degrees of membership to F different from zero form the *support* of F denoted as $\text{supp}(F)$. Figure 1.4 shows the support of a fuzzy set.

Finally, throughout the book we will consider only *convex fuzzy sets*, i.e., fuzzy sets with *convex membership functions.*

Definition 1.1.3. *A fuzzy set F is convex if and only if*

$$\forall x, y \in X\ \forall \lambda \in [0, 1] : \mu_A(\lambda \cdot x + (1 - \lambda) \cdot y) \geq \min(\mu_A(x), \mu_A(y)). \quad (1.5)$$

Figure 1.5 shows a convex and a *nonconvex fuzzy set.*

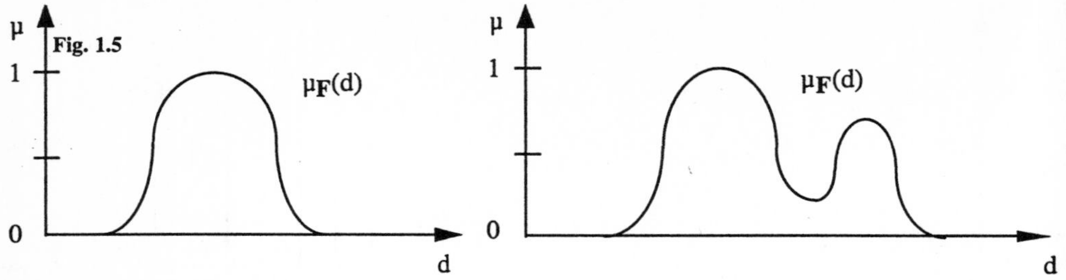

Fig. 1.5. A convex and a nonconvex fuzzy set

1.1.2 Fuzzy State, Input, and Output Variables

Let us consider the state variables $x_1, x_2, \ldots, x_n$, and let X be a given closed interval of reals. A *fuzzy state variable* is a state variable x_i the values of which are fuzzy sets defined on X. In what follows we will call these fuzzy sets the *fuzzy values* of x_i. The set of fuzzy values of x_i is called the *term-set* of x_i and is denoted as $\mathbf{TX_i}$. Each distinct fuzzy value in $\mathbf{TX_i}$ is denoted as LX_{ij} and represents the j-th fuzzy value of the i-th fuzzy state variable. Each LX_{ij} is defined by a membership function $\int_X \mu_{LX_{ij}}(x)/x$, that is $LX_{ij} = \int_X \mu_{LX_{ij}}(x)/x$, where $\mu_{LX_{ij}}(x)$ is the degree of membership of the *crisp value* x_i^* of x_i to the fuzzy value LX_{ij} of x_i (see Fig. 1.6)

Thus for each fuzzy state variable we have

$$\mathbf{TX_i} = \{LX_{i1}, LX_{i2}, \ldots, LX_{im_i}\}. \tag{1.6}$$

An arbitrary fuzzy value from $\mathbf{TX_i}$ will be denoted as LX_i, that is LX_i can be any one of $LX_{i1}, LX_{i2}, \ldots, LX_{im_i}$. In practical applications of FLCs we have normally that: (i) the term-sets of the different fuzzy state variables have the same cardinality, that is $m_1 = m_2 = \ldots = m_n$, and (ii) $LX_{1j} = LX_{2j} = \ldots = LX_{nj}$ for each j. In what follows we assume the cases (i) and (ii) unless stated otherwise. Figure 1.7 shows a term-set $\mathbf{TX_i}$ consisting of the seven fuzzy values $\{LX_{i1}, LX_{i2}, \ldots, LX_{i7}\}$.

The fuzzy value LX_{ij-1} is called the *left-neighbor* of the fuzzy value LX_{ij}, and the fuzzy value LX_{ij+1} is called the *right-neighbor* of the fuzzy value LX_{ij}. For the membership functions of LX_{ij-1} and LX_{ij} we have

$$\mathrm{supp}(LX_{ij-1}) \cap \mathrm{supp}(LX_{ij}) \neq \emptyset \tag{1.7}$$

and

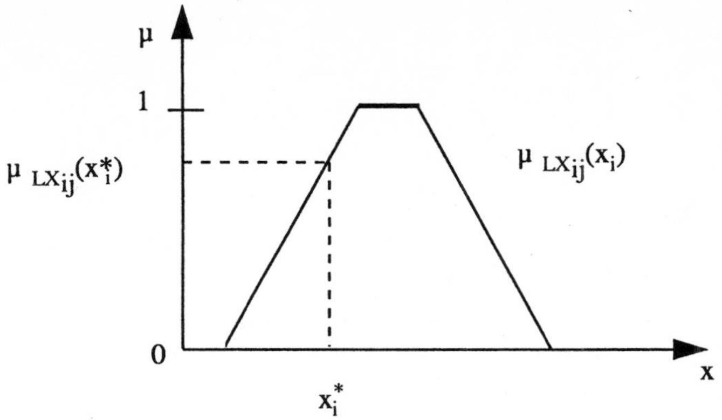

Fig. 1.6. The degree of membership of the crisp value x_i^* of x_i to the fuzzy value LX_{ij} of x_i

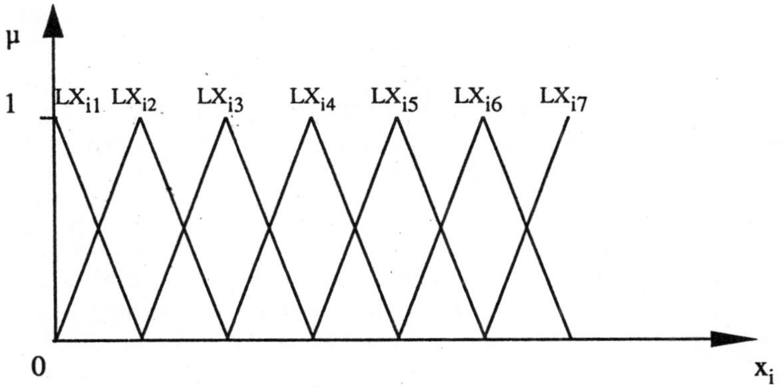

Fig. 1.7. The term-set of x_i

$$\forall x \in \mathrm{supp}(LX_{ij-1}) \cap \mathrm{supp}(LX_{ij}), \quad \mu_{LX_{ij-1}}(x) + \mu_{LX_{ij}}(x) = 1. \qquad (1.8)$$

For the membership functions of LX_{ij} and LX_{ij+1} we again have

$$\mathrm{supp}(LX_{ij}) \cap \mathrm{supp}(LX_{ij+1}) \neq \emptyset \qquad (1.9)$$

and

$$\forall x \in \mathrm{supp}(LX_{ij}) \cap \mathrm{supp}(LX_{ij+1}), \quad \mu_{LX_{ij}}(x) + \mu_{LX_{ij+1}}(x) = 1. \qquad (1.10)$$

In other words, it is required that each fuzzy value overlaps to a certain degree with its left and right neighbor (see Fig. 1.8).

In the same manner as above, we define the fuzzy counterparts of fuzzy input and output variables.

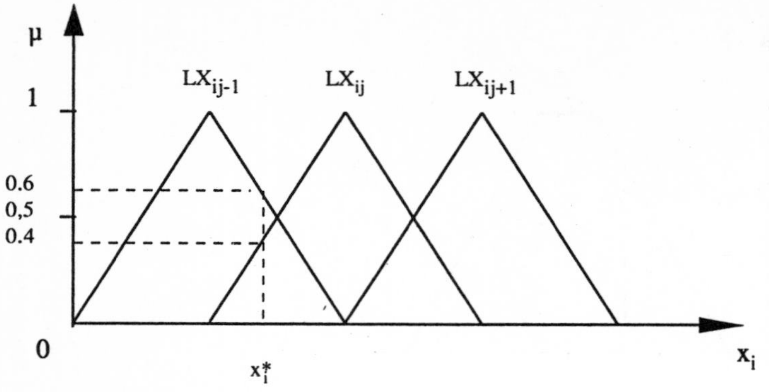

$\mu_{LX_{ij-1}}(x_i^*) + \mu_{LX_{ij}}(x_i^*) = 0.6 + 0.4 = 1$

Fig. 1.8. The neighboring fuzzy values of LX_{ij}

A *fuzzy input variable* is an input variable u_i $(i = 1, 2, \ldots, m)$ whose fuzzy values are defined on a closed interval U of reals called the domain of u_i. The term-set of u_i is denoted as $\mathbf{TU_i}$ and each distinct fuzzy value in $\mathbf{TU_i}$ is denoted as LU_{ij}. Each LU_{ij} is defined by a membership function $\int_U \mu_{LU_{ij}}(u)/u$, that is $LU_{ij} = \int_U \mu_{LU_{ij}}(u)/u$, where $\mu_{LU_{ij}}(u)$ is the degree of membership of the crisp value u_i^* of u_i to the fuzzy value LU_{ij} of u_i.

Thus for each fuzzy input variable we have

$$\mathbf{TU_i} = \{LU_{i1}, LU_{i2}, \ldots, LU_{ik_i}\}. \tag{1.11}$$

An arbitrary fuzzy value from $\mathbf{TU_i}$ will be denoted as LU_i, that is LU_i can be any one from $LU_{i1}, LU_{i2}, \ldots, LU_{ik_i}$. Here we have again that: (i) the term-sets of the different fuzzy state variables have the same cardinality, that is $k_1 = k_2 = \ldots = k_m$, and (ii) $LU_{1j} = LU_{2j} = \ldots = LU_{mj}$ for each j. Furthermore, the requirements on neighboring fuzzy values of a fuzzy state variable also hold in the case of neighboring fuzzy values of an input fuzzy variable.

A *fuzzy output variable* is an output variable y_i $(i = 1, 2, \ldots, p)$ whose fuzzy values are defined on a closed interval Y of reals called the domain of y_i. The term-set of y_i is denoted as $\mathbf{TY_i}$ and each distinct fuzzy value in $\mathbf{TY_i}$ is denoted as LY_{ij}. Each LY_{ij} is defined by a membership function $\int_Y \mu_{LY_{ij}}(y)/y$, that is $LY_{ij} = \int_Y \mu_{LY_{ij}}(y)/y$, where $\mu_{LY_{ij}}(y)$ is the degree of membership of the crisp value y_i^* of y_i to the fuzzy value LY_{ij} of y_i.

Thus for each fuzzy output variable we have

$$\mathbf{TY_i} = \{LY_{i1}, LY_{i2}, \ldots, LY_{ir_i}\}. \tag{1.12}$$

An arbitrary fuzzy value from $\mathbf{TY_i}$ will be denoted as LY_i, that is LY_i can be any one from $LY_{i1}, LY_{i2}, \ldots, LY_{ir_i}$. Again: (i) the term-sets of the different fuzzy output variables have the same cardinality, that is $r_1 = r_2 = \ldots = r_p$, and (ii) $LY_{1j} = LY_{2j} = \ldots = LY_{pj}$ for each j. Also, the requirements on neighboring fuzzy values of a fuzzy state variable also hold in the case of the neighboring fuzzy values of an output fuzzy variable.

1.1.3 The Fuzzy State Space

Consider the crisp state vector $\mathbf{x} = (x_1, x_2, \ldots, x_n)^T$. For given crisp values $(x_1^*, x_2^*, \ldots, x_n^*)^T \in X^n$ of its component state variables it provides the coordinates of a specific point in the n-dimensional state space.

In the case of a *fuzzy state vector*, each x_i takes a fuzzy value, i.e., x_i takes some fuzzy value $LX_i \in \mathbf{TX_i}$. Thus an arbitrary fuzzy state vector can be written as $\mathbf{LX} = (LX_1, LX_2, \ldots, LX_n)^T$. Since each LX_i is a fuzzy value defined by a membership function $\int_X \mu_{LX_i}(x)/x$ one can find the degree of membership of each crisp value $x_i^* \in X$ to its corresponding fuzzy value LX_i. This degree of membership is given as $\mu_{LX_i}(x_i^*)$. The smallest of these degrees of membership is called the *degree of satisfaction* of the fuzzy state vector $\mathbf{LX} = (LX_1, LX_2, \ldots, LX_n)^T$ by the crisp state vector $\mathbf{x}^* = (x_1^*, x_2^*, \ldots, x_n^*)^T \in X^n$.

Since each fuzzy state variable takes its fuzzy values amongst the elements of a finite term-set, there is a finite number of different fuzzy state vectors, denoted respectively as $\mathbf{LX^i}$ $(\mathbf{i} = \mathbf{1}, \mathbf{2}, \ldots, \mathbf{M})$.

Example 1.1.1. For example, let $\mathbf{x} = (x_1, x_2)^T$, $\mathbf{TX_1} = \{LX_{11}, LX_{12}, LX_{13}\}$, and $\mathbf{TX_2} = \{LX_{21}, LX_{22}, LX_{23}\}$. Then the total number of different fuzzy state vectors is $\mathbf{M} = 9$ and these state vectors are

1. $\mathbf{LX^1} = (LX_{11}, LX_{21})^T$.
2. $\mathbf{LX^2} = (LX_{11}, LX_{22})^T$.
3. $\mathbf{LX^3} = (LX_{11}, LX_{23})^T$.
4. $\mathbf{LX^4} = (LX_{12}, LX_{21})^T$.
5. $\mathbf{LX^5} = (LX_{12}, LX_{22})^T$.
6. $\mathbf{LX^6} = (LX_{12}, LX_{23})^T$.
7. $\mathbf{LX^7} = (LX_{13}, LX_{21})^T$.
8. $\mathbf{LX^8} = (LX_{13}, LX_{22})^T$.
9. $\mathbf{LX^9} = (LX_{13}, LX_{23})^T$.

Let the $\mathbf{i}$-th fuzzy state vector be $\mathbf{LX^i} = (LX_1^\mathbf{i}, LX_2^\mathbf{i}, \ldots, LX_n^\mathbf{i})^T$, where the upper index $\mathbf{i}$ in $LX_j^\mathbf{i}$ denotes the $\mathbf{i}$-th state vector to which an arbitrary fuzzy value LX_j of the fuzzy state variable x_j belongs. For example, with this notation, $\mathbf{LX^1} = (LX_{11}, LX_{21})^T$ from the above example will now be denoted as $\mathbf{LX^1} = (LX_{11}^\mathbf{1}, LX_{21}^\mathbf{1})^T$

Let also $\mathbf{x}^* = (x_1^*, x_2^*, \ldots, x_n^*)^T \in X^n$ be a given crisp state vector. As already said above, the degree of satisfaction $\mu^\mathbf{i}$ of $\mathbf{LX^i}$ by $\mathbf{x}^*$ is computed as

$$\mu^\mathbf{i}(\mathbf{x}^*) = \min(\mu_{LX_1^\mathbf{i}}(x_1^*), \mu_{LX_2^\mathbf{i}}(x_2^*), \ldots, \mu_{LX_n^\mathbf{i}}(x_n^*)). \tag{1.13}$$

For example, the degree of satisfaction of the fuzzy state vector $\mathbf{LX^1} = (LX^1_{11}, LX^1_{21})^T$ by the crisp state vector $\mathbf{x}^* = (x^*_1, x^*_2)^T \in X^2$ is computed as

$$\mu^{\mathbf{1}}(\mathbf{x}^*) = \min(\mu_{LX^1_{11}}(x^*_1), \mu_{LX^1_{21}}(x^*_2)). \tag{1.14}$$

In this context, for each fuzzy state vector $\mathbf{LX^i}$ there is a set of crisp state vectors $\{\mathbf{x}^*\}$, each one satisfying the given fuzzy state vector to a certain degree (different from 0). Thus for each fuzzy state vector $\mathbf{LX^i}$ one can construct a fuzzy set defined on the domain of these crisp state vectors. This fuzzy set is such that the degree of membership of a crisp state vector to it is equal to the degree of satisfaction of $\mathbf{LX^i}$ by this particular crisp state vector. This fuzzy set is called a *fuzzy region* and the number of fuzzy regions is equal to the number of fuzzy state vectors. For example, the fuzzy region corresponding to the fuzzy state vector $\mathbf{LX^1} = (LX^1_{11}, LX^1_{21})^T$ will be given by the fuzzy set $R^{\mathbf{i}}$ defined as

$$R^{\mathbf{i}} = \{(\mathbf{x}*, \mu_{R^{\mathbf{i}}}(\mathbf{x}^*)) \mid \mathbf{x}^* \in X^2\}. \tag{1.15}$$

Through the rest of the book we will consider the notion of a fuzzy region to be equivalent with the notion of a fuzzy state vector, since a fuzzy region is implicit in a given fuzzy state vector. As already explained, a fuzzy region is explicitly determined if all of the crisp state vectors that satisfy the given fuzzy state vector to a degree different from zero are available. Figure 1.9 is a graphical representation of some of the nine fuzzy regions from the previous example.

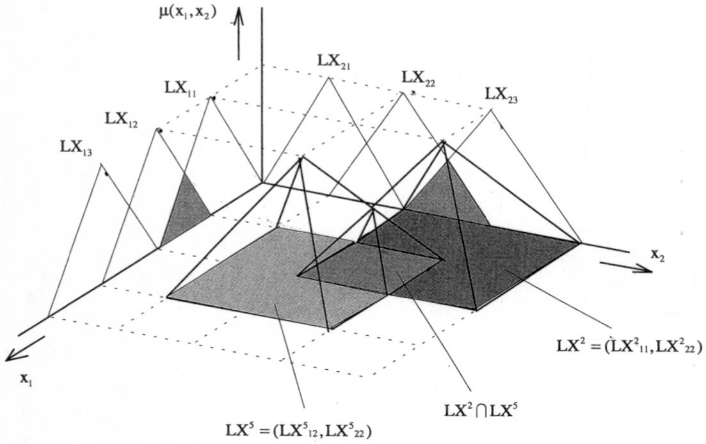

Fig. 1.9. Fuzzy regions

The *center of a fuzzy region*, $\mathbf{LX^i} = (LX^{\mathbf{i}}_1, LX^{\mathbf{i}}_2, \ldots, LX^{\mathbf{i}}_n)^T$, is defined as this crisp state vector $\mathbf{x^i} = (x^{\mathbf{i}}_1, x^{\mathbf{i}}_2, \ldots, x^{\mathbf{i}}_n)^T \in X^n$, where $x^{\mathbf{i}}_k$ are crisp values, such that

$$\mu_{LX_1}(x_1^{\mathbf{i}}) = 1, \mu_{LX_2}(x_2^{\mathbf{i}}) = 1, \ldots, \mu_{LX_n}(x_n^{\mathbf{i}}) = 1. \tag{1.16}$$

Thus the degree of satisfaction of $\mathbf{LX^i}$ by $\mathbf{x^i}$ is given as

$$\mu^{\mathbf{i}}(\mathbf{x^i}) = \min(1, 1, \ldots, 1) = 1. \tag{1.17}$$

Hence, the center of a given fuzzy region is each crisp state vector such that the degree of satisfaction of this fuzzy region by the crisp state vector is 1. If all the membership functions defining the fuzzy values in the term-sets of the state variables are *triangular membership functions*, i.e., only one crisp value in the support of any fuzzy value has a degree of membership 1 to this fuzzy value, then the centers of all fuzzy regions are single crisp state vectors (see Fig. 1.10). If we have instead *trapezoidal membership functions*, i.e., more than one crisp value in the support of a fuzzy value has a degree of membership 1 to this fuzzy value, then for each fuzzy region we have that its center corresponds to a set of crisp state vectors (see Fig. 1.11).

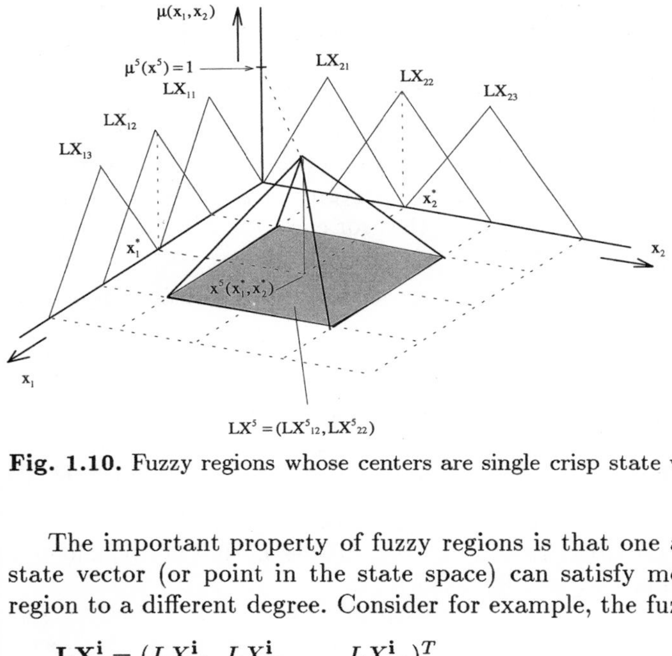

Fig. 1.10. Fuzzy regions whose centers are single crisp state vectors

The important property of fuzzy regions is that one and the same crisp state vector (or point in the state space) can satisfy more than one fuzzy region to a different degree. Consider for example, the fuzzy region

$$\mathbf{LX^i} = (LX_{11}^{\mathbf{i}}, LX_{21}^{\mathbf{i}}, \ldots, LX_{n1}^{\mathbf{i}})^T, \tag{1.18}$$

and let $\mathbf{x}^* = (x_1^*, x_2^*, \ldots, x_n^*)^T \in X^n$ be such that $\mu_{LX_{11}^{\mathbf{i}}}(x_1^*) = a_1$ and $\mu_{LX_{21}^{\mathbf{i}}}(x_2^*) = a_2, \ldots, \mu_{LX_{n1}^{\mathbf{i}}}(x_n^*) = a_n$.

Consider now a different fuzzy region

$$\mathbf{LX^k} = (LX_{11}^{\mathbf{k}}, LX_{21}^{\mathbf{k}}, \ldots, LX_{r1}^{\mathbf{k}}, LX_{r+12}^{\mathbf{k}} \ldots, LX_{n2}^{\mathbf{k}})^T, \tag{1.19}$$

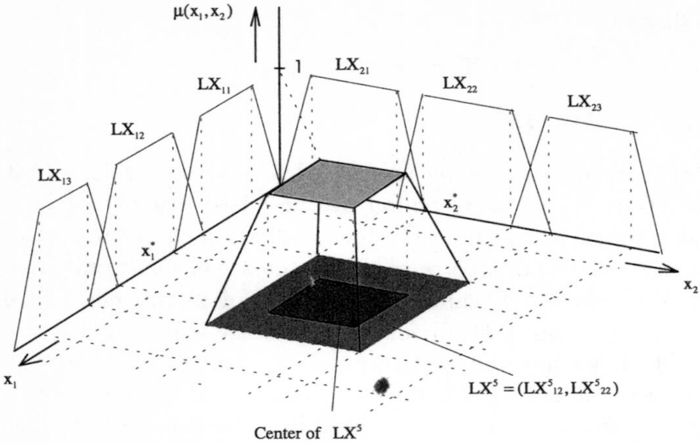

Fig. 1.11. Fuzzy regions whose centers are sets of crisp state vectors

i.e., a fuzzy region such that its fuzzy values $LX^{\mathbf{k}}_{j1}$ are equal to the fuzzy values $LX^{\mathbf{i}}_{j1}$ for $j = 1, 2, \ldots, r$ and the rest of the fuzzy values, namely $LX^{\mathbf{k}}_{j1}$ $(j = r+1, r+2, \ldots, n)$ are the right neighbors of $LX^{\mathbf{i}}_{j1}$ $(j = r+1, r+2, \ldots, n)$. Then for the same crisp state vector $\mathbf{x}^* = (x_1^*, x_2^*, \ldots, x_n^*)^T \in X^n$ we will have that for each $j = 1, 2, \ldots, r$, $\mu_{LX^{\mathbf{i}}_{j1}}(x_j^*) = \mu_{LX^{\mathbf{k}}_{j1}}(x_j^*) = a_j$, simply because these fuzzy values are equal. Furthermore, according to the definition of a neighbor of a fuzzy value, we will have that for each $j = r + 1, r + 2, \ldots, n$, $\mu_{LX^{\mathbf{i}}_{j1}}(x_j^*) = a_j$ and $\mu_{LX^{\mathbf{k}}_{j2}}(x_j^*) = 1 - a_j$, simply because for each such j, $LX^{\mathbf{k}}_{j2}$ is the right neighbor of $LX^{\mathbf{i}}_{j1}$. Thus the degree of satisfaction of $\mathbf{LX^i}$ by $\mathbf{x}^*$ will be

$$\mu^{\mathbf{i}}(\mathbf{x}^*) = \min(a_1, a_2, \ldots, a_r \ldots, a_n). \tag{1.20}$$

In the same way the degree of satisfaction of $\mathbf{LX^k}$ by $\mathbf{x}^*$ will be

$$\mu^{\mathbf{k}}(\mathbf{x}^*) = \min(a_1, a_2, \ldots, a_r, 1 - a_{r+1} \ldots, 1 - a_n). \tag{1.21}$$

Thus, in general, the above two degrees of satisfaction can be equal or different, but in any case the crisp state vector satisfies both fuzzy regions to a degree different from zero (see Fig. 1.12).

The fuzzy region $\mathbf{LX^i}$ is called the *neighboring region* of the fuzzy region $\mathbf{LX^k}$ and vice versa, if and only if there exists at least one crisp state vector that satisfies to certain degrees, different from zero, both fuzzy regions. It is easily seen that as long as two fuzzy regions share at least one and the same fuzzy value and the rest of the fuzzy values of the first fuzzy region are left or right neighbors of the rest of the fuzzy values of the second fuzzy region we have two neighboring fuzzy regions. Also, each fuzzy region has at least one neighboring region because for a given fuzzy state vector one can always find at least one other fuzzy state vector such that: (i) some of the fuzzy values in these two fuzzy state vectors are the same and (ii) the different fuzzy values in the two fuzzy state vectors are left or right neighbors of each other.

Example 1.1.2. Consider again a two-dimensional state space. Let the term-sets of the two state variables x_1 and x_2 be $\mathbf{TX_1} = \{LX_{11}, LX_{12}, LX_{13}\}$ and $\mathbf{TX_2} = \{LX_{21}, LX_{22}, LX_{23}\}$. Thus we have nine fuzzy regions, some of which are illustrated in Fig. 1.12.

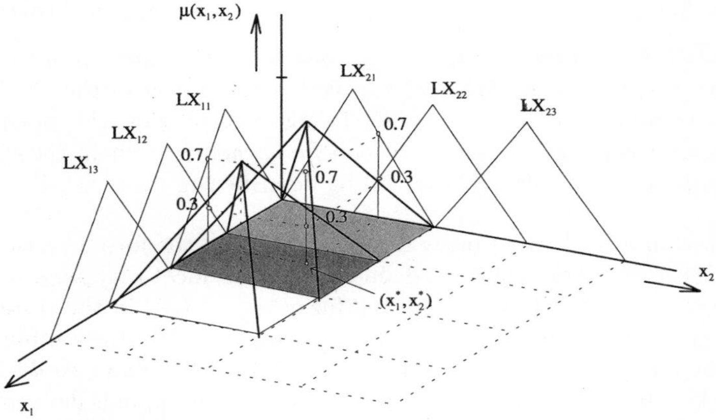

Fig. 1.12. Neighboring fuzzy regions and their degrees of satisfaction by a crisp state vector

In Fig. 1.12, the center of the fuzzy region, say $\mathbf{LX^4} = (LX_{12}^{\mathbf{4}}, LX_{21}^{\mathbf{4}})^T$, is the crisp state vector $\mathbf{x^4} = (x_1^{\mathbf{4}}, x_2^{\mathbf{4}})^T$. Furthermore, the crisp state vector $\mathbf{x}^* = (x_1^*, x_2^*)^T$ belongs to degree 0.3 to the fuzzy region $\mathbf{LX^4} = (LX_{12}^{\mathbf{4}}, LX_{21}^{\mathbf{4}})^T$ and to degree 0.7 to the fuzzy region $\mathbf{LX^1} = (LX_{11}^{\mathbf{1}}, LX_{21}^{\mathbf{1}})^T$.

The fact that for each fuzzy region there is at least one neighboring fuzzy region and that each crisp state vector belongs to a different degree (different from zero) to each one of two neighboring fuzzy regions guarantees a smooth transition from one fuzzy region to its neighboring region.

Finally, one can define the fuzzy input and output vectors (or fuzzy input and output regions) in exactly the same way as for fuzzy state vectors. Thus the $\mathbf{i}$-th fuzzy output vector is given as $\mathbf{LY^i} = (LY_1^{\mathbf{i}}, LY_2^{\mathbf{i}}, \ldots, LX_m^{\mathbf{i}})^T$ and the $\mathbf{i}$-th fuzzy input vector as $\mathbf{LU^i} = (LU_1^{\mathbf{i}}, LU_2^{\mathbf{i}}, \ldots, LU_p^{\mathbf{i}})^T$.

1.2 Control Schemes in Model Based Fuzzy Control

Let us consider a conventional *nonlinear autonomous open loop model* of a *forced system* given in the general form

$$\dot{\mathbf{x}} = \mathbf{f}(\mathbf{x}, \mathbf{u}), \tag{1.22}$$

where $\mathbf{f}$ is a $n \times 1$ nonlinear vector function, $\mathbf{x}$ is the $n \times 1$ state vector, and $\mathbf{u}$ is the $n \times 1$ input vector.

Let also the *nonlinear control law* be given as

$$\mathbf{u} = \mathbf{g}(\mathbf{x}). \tag{1.23}$$

Then the *closed loop system model* is of the form

$$\dot{\mathbf{x}} = \mathbf{f}(\mathbf{x}, \mathbf{g}(\mathbf{x})). \tag{1.24}$$

In model based fuzzy control the open loop equation is the same as in the case of conventional nonlinear control and is given at the outset of the FLC design. However, in control with the so-called Takagi–Sugeno FLC this open loop equation is approximated by an *open loop fuzzy model* given in terms of a particular type of fuzzy rules. These will be described in more detail in Sect. 1.2.1.

The control law in model based fuzzy control is given in the form of a set of fuzzy rules. The $\mathbf{i}$-th fuzzy rule then defines a specific local mapping, or *local control law* (linear or nonlinear) from the fuzzy region $\mathbf{LX^i}$ in the state space to the fuzzy input vector $\mathbf{LU^i}$, i.e., the fuzzy region $\mathbf{LU^i}$ of the input space. The set of fuzzy rules defines a global mapping, or a *global control law* from X^n to U^n, by a suitable aggregation of the local mappings defined by each fuzzy rule. Thus, in general, the global control law of an FLC is a combination of the local control laws for each fuzzy region, where each local control law is weighted by the degree of satisfaction of the present operating fuzzy region and the degrees of satisfaction of its neighboring fuzzy regions.

The fuzzy rules defining the local control laws are designed either using the open loop equation, or its approximation in the form of an open loop fuzzy model.

In what follows we present the control schemes relevant for model based fuzzy logic controllers.

1.2.1 FLC Control Schemes

In the following we present the control schemes relevant for model based fuzzy control. For each control scheme we describe in brief the type of fuzzy if-then rules consituting the FLC and the open loop model from which these fuzzy rules are derived.

Takagi–Sugeno FLC-1

The *open loop fuzzy model* [34] is given as a set of fuzzy rules, each fuzzy rule $R_S^{\mathbf{i}}$ being of the form

$$R_S^{\mathbf{i}}: \textit{if } \mathbf{x} = \mathbf{LX^i} \textit{ then } \dot{\mathbf{x}} = \mathbf{f_i}(\mathbf{x}, \mathbf{u}).$$

The then-part of the above fuzzy rule defines a linear autonomous open loop model representing the system dynamics within the fuzzy region $\mathbf{LX^i}$ specified in the if-part of the same fuzzy rule. This model is of the form $\dot{\mathbf{x}} = \mathbf{f_i}(\mathbf{x}, \mathbf{u})$, where $\mathbf{f_i}$ is a linear function normally obtained via an identification procedure.

The nonlinear expression for the global open loop system is given as

$$\dot{\mathbf{x}} = \sum_{\mathbf{i}} w^{\mathbf{i}}(\mathbf{x}) \cdot \mathbf{f_i}(\mathbf{x}, \mathbf{u}), \tag{1.25}$$

where $w^{\mathbf{i}}(\mathbf{x}) \in [0, 1]$ are the normalized degrees of satisfaction of the fuzzy regions $\mathbf{LX^i}$ $(\mathbf{i} = \mathbf{1}, \mathbf{2}, \ldots, \mathbf{M})$ by a particular crisp value of the state vector $\mathbf{x}$. That is, for an arbitrary crisp value $\mathbf{x}^*$ of the state vector $\mathbf{x}$, $\sum_{\mathbf{i}} w^{\mathbf{i}}(\mathbf{x}^*) = 1$.

The *Takagi–Sugeno FLC-1* is given as a set of fuzzy rules, each fuzzy rule $R_{\mathrm{C}}^{\mathbf{i}}$ being of the form

$$R_{\mathrm{C}}^{\mathbf{i}}: \textit{if } \mathbf{x} = \mathbf{LX^i} \textit{ then } \mathbf{u} = \mathbf{g_i}(\mathbf{x}).$$

The then-part contains the linear control law $\mathbf{u} = \mathbf{g_i}(\mathbf{x})$ intended to stabilize the system dynamics within the fuzzy region $\mathbf{LX^i}$ specified in the if-part of the same fuzzy rule.

The nonlinear expression for the global FLC-1 is

$$\mathbf{u} = \sum_{\mathbf{i}} w^{\mathbf{i}}(\mathbf{x}) \cdot \mathbf{g_i}(\mathbf{x}), \tag{1.26}$$

where $w^{\mathbf{i}}(\mathbf{x}) \in [0, 1]$ are the normalized degrees of satisfaction of the fuzzy regions $\mathbf{LX^i}$ by an arbitrary crisp value of the state vector $\mathbf{x}$. That is, for an arbitrary crisp state vector $\mathbf{x}^*$, $\sum_{\mathbf{i}} w^{\mathbf{i}}(\mathbf{x}^*) = 1$.

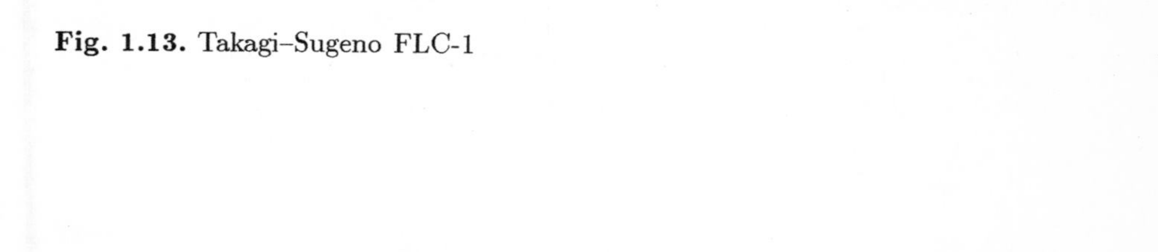

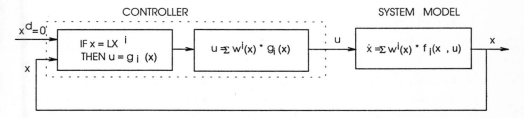

Fig. 1.13. Takagi–Sugeno FLC-1

When the fuzzy values in each of the fuzzy state vectors $\mathbf{LX^i}$ are defined via trapezoidal membership functions, the set $\{R_S^i\}$ of fuzzy rules defines a globally piecewise linear behavior for the open loop system. This is due to the following. In the case of trapezoidal membership functions the center of any fuzzy region $\mathbf{LX^i}$ is a set of crisp state vectors. For each such crisp state vector $\mathbf{x^i}$, the degree of satisfaction $w^\mathbf{i}$ of $\mathbf{LX^i}$ by $\mathbf{x^i}$ is equal to 1. Since the $w^\mathbf{i}$'s are normalized, this implies that each one of $w^\mathbf{j}$ ($\mathbf{i} \neq \mathbf{j}$) will be equal to 0. Thus every time the crisp state vector belongs to the set of crisp state vectors from the center of $\mathbf{LX^i}$ only the linear open loop model associated with $\mathbf{LX^i}$ will be activated with a constant $w^\mathbf{i}(\mathbf{x^i}) = 1$.

In between the centers of neighboring regions the overlapping of these fuzzy regions guarantees a smooth transition from the center of any fuzzy region to the centers of its neighboring regions. The dynamics of the smooth transition from one fuzzy region to another are nonlinear since no $w^\mathbf{i}(\mathbf{x})$ is equal to one, and instead $w^\mathbf{i}(\mathbf{x})$ is a nonlinear function of the state vector.

The fuzzy rules R_C^i of the Takagi–Sugeno FLC-1 are designed on the basis of the open loop fuzzy model rules R_S^i. Here again R_C^i defines a linear control law $\mathbf{u} = \mathbf{g_i}(\mathbf{x})$ (then-part) only at the center of the fuzzy region $\mathbf{LX^i}$ (if-part). In between the centers of neighboring regions the overlapping of these fuzzy regions guarantees the smoothness of the global control law. Again, the dynamics of the control law from one fuzzy region to another are nonlinear since no $w^\mathbf{i}(\mathbf{x})$ is equal to one and instead $w^\mathbf{i}(\mathbf{x})$ is a nonlinear function of the state vector.

The control scheme involving a Takagi–Sugeno FLC-1 can also be defined on the state space of *error*. Thus for $\mathbf{e} = \mathbf{x} - \mathbf{x^d}$, where $\mathbf{x^d}$ is a given operating point, the open loop fuzzy model is given as a set of fuzzy rules, each fuzzy rule R_S^i being of the form

$$R_S^i\text{: } \textit{if } \mathbf{e} = \mathbf{LE^i} \textit{ then } \dot{\mathbf{e}} = \mathbf{f_i}(\mathbf{e}, \mathbf{u}).$$

The nonlinear expression for the global open loop system is

$$\dot{\mathbf{e}} = \sum_\mathbf{i} w^\mathbf{i}(\mathbf{e}) \cdot \mathbf{f_i}(\mathbf{e}, \mathbf{u}), \tag{1.27}$$

where $w^\mathbf{i}(\mathbf{e}) \in [0, 1]$ and for an arbitrary crisp value $\mathbf{e}^*$ of $\mathbf{e}$, $\sum_\mathbf{i} w^\mathbf{i}(\mathbf{e}^*) = 1$.

The Takagi–Sugeno FLC-1 is given as a set of fuzzy rules, each fuzzy rule R_C^i being of the form

$$R_C^i\text{: } \textit{if } \mathbf{e} = \mathbf{LE^i} \textit{ then } \mathbf{u} = \mathbf{g_i}(\mathbf{e}),$$

and the nonlinear expression for the global FLC-1 is

$$\mathbf{u} = \sum_\mathbf{i} w^\mathbf{i}(\mathbf{e}) \cdot \mathbf{g_i}(\mathbf{e}), \tag{1.28}$$

where $w^\mathbf{i}(\mathbf{e}) \in [0, 1]$ and for an arbitrary crisp value $\mathbf{e}^*$ of $\mathbf{e}$, $\sum_\mathbf{i} w^\mathbf{i}(\mathbf{e}^*) = 1$.

The model based design of a Takagi–Sugeno FLC-1 in the case of a MIMO nonlinear system is presented in Sect. 4.1.

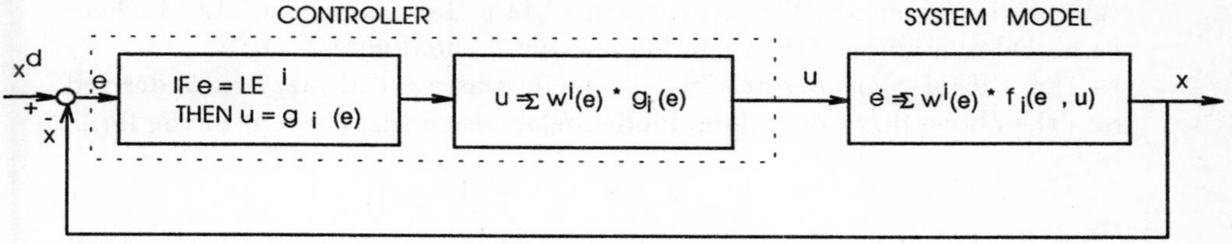

Fig. 1.14. Takagi–Sugeno FLC-1 on the state space of error

Takagi–Sugeno FLC-2

Here the open loop model is represented as a set of fuzzy rules derived from the original nonlinear autonomous open loop model, $\dot{\mathbf{x}} = \mathbf{f}(\mathbf{x}, \mathbf{u})$, by Lyapunov-linearization at the centers $\mathbf{x^i}$ of the fuzzy regions $\mathbf{LX^i}$ ($\mathbf{i} = \mathbf{1, 2, \ldots, M}$) . Thus each fuzzy rule of the open loop system is of the form

$$R^{\mathbf{i}}_{\mathrm{S}}\text{: } \textit{if } \mathbf{x^d} = \mathbf{LX^i} \textit{ then } \dot{\mathbf{x}} = \mathbf{f_i}(\mathbf{x}, \mathbf{x^d}, \mathbf{x^i}, \mathbf{u}, \mathbf{u^d}, \mathbf{u^i})$$

where $\mathbf{x^d}$ denotes an arbitrary operating point and "$\mathbf{x^d} = \mathbf{LX^i}$" denotes that $\mathbf{x^d}$ belongs to the fuzzy region $\mathbf{LX^i}$. Furthermore, $\mathbf{f_i}(\mathbf{x}, \mathbf{x^d}, \mathbf{x^i}, \mathbf{u}, \mathbf{u^d}, \mathbf{u^i})$ is the linear approximation of $\mathbf{f}(\mathbf{x}, \mathbf{u})$ at $(\mathbf{x^d}, \mathbf{u^d})$ obtained via Lyapunov-linearization of $\mathbf{f}(\mathbf{x}, \mathbf{u})$ at $(\mathbf{x^i}, \mathbf{u^i})$ where $\mathbf{x^i}$ is the center of the fuzzy region $\mathbf{LX^i}$ and $\mathbf{u^i}$ is the input corresponding to $\mathbf{x^i}$.

The linear expression for the global open loop system is given as

$$\dot{\mathbf{x}} = \sum_{\mathbf{i}} w^{\mathbf{i}}(\mathbf{x^d}) \cdot \mathbf{f_i}(\mathbf{x}, \mathbf{x^d}, \mathbf{x^i}, \mathbf{u}, \mathbf{u^d}, \mathbf{u^i}), \tag{1.29}$$

where $w^{\mathbf{i}}(\mathbf{x^d})$ is the *normalized degree* of satisfaction of the fuzzy region $\mathbf{LX^i}$ by a given crisp operating point $\mathbf{x^d}$. That is, $\sum_{\mathbf{i}} w^{\mathbf{i}}(\mathbf{x^d}) = 1$.

Observe here that the dynamics of the open loop system, as defined by the above equation, is linear not only for $\mathbf{x^d} = \mathbf{x^i}$, i.e., at the center of the $\mathbf{i}$-th fuzzy region, but also within the whole fuzzy region $\mathbf{LX^i}$. This is so, because for a fixed $\mathbf{x^d}$ the degree of satisfaction of $\mathbf{LX^i}$ by $\mathbf{x^d}$ is constant. Furthermore, the degree of satisfaction of each neighboring fuzzy region of $\mathbf{LX^i}$ by the fixed $\mathbf{x^d}$ is also constant. Thus, for a given $\mathbf{x^d}$ all $w^{\mathbf{i}}(\mathbf{x^d})$ are constant. Hence, the dynamics of the global open loop system, given a particular $\mathbf{x^d}$, is linear: it will simply be a linear combination of the open loop linear models associated with each fuzzy region and weighted by the degree of satisfaction of each fuzzy region by the given $\mathbf{x^d}$. This is in contrast to the Takagi–Sugeno FLC-1 where the global dynamics of the open loop system is nonlinear.

The *Takagi–Sugeno FLC-2* is also defined as a set of fuzzy rules derived from the above fuzzy open loop model, where each fuzzy rule is of the form

$$R_{\mathrm{C}}^{\mathbf{i}}: \textit{if } \mathbf{x^d} = \mathbf{LX^i} \textit{ then } \mathbf{u} = \mathbf{g_i}(\mathbf{x}, \mathbf{x^d}, \mathbf{x^i}, \mathbf{u^d}, \mathbf{u^i}),$$

and the above fuzzy rule defines a linear control law $\mathbf{u} = \mathbf{g_i}(\mathbf{x}, \mathbf{x^d}, \mathbf{x^i}, \mathbf{u^d}, \mathbf{u^i})$ such that $\mathbf{x^d}$ is an asymptotically stable equilibrium.

The linear expression for the global FLC-2 is

$$\mathbf{u} = \sum_{\mathbf{i}} w^{\mathbf{i}}(\mathbf{x^d}) \cdot \mathbf{g_i}(\mathbf{x}, \mathbf{x^d}, \mathbf{x^i}, \mathbf{u^d}, \mathbf{u^i}), \tag{1.30}$$

where $w^{\mathbf{i}}(\mathbf{x^d})$ is the normalized degree of satisfaction of the fuzzy region $\mathbf{LX^i}$ by a particular crisp operating point $\mathbf{x^d}$. Here again, the above control law is linear, for a given $\mathbf{x^d}$, within the whole fuzzy state space since each $w^{\mathbf{i}}(\mathbf{x^d})$ is constant. This is in contrast to the Takagi–Sugeno FLC-1 where the control law is linear only at the center of $\mathbf{LX^i}$, but nonlinear within the fuzzy state space.

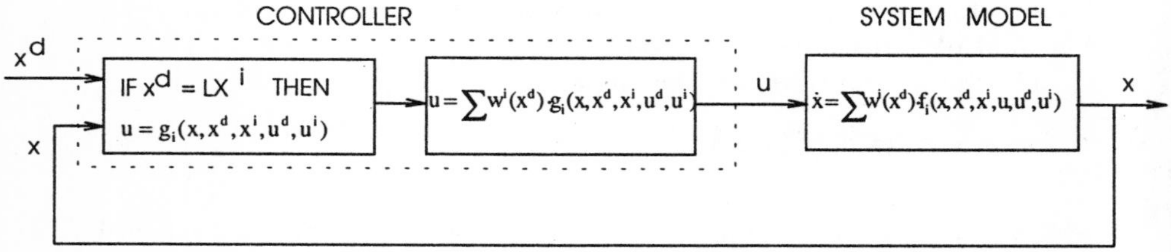

Fig. 1.15. Takagi–Sugeno FLC-2

The model based design of the Takagi–Sugeno FLC-2 in the case of a MIMO nonlinear system is presented in detail in Sect. 4.2.

Sliding Mode FLC

In sliding mode fuzzy control the nonlinear autonomous open loop model is given in the standard form

$$\dot{\mathbf{x}} = \mathbf{f}(\mathbf{x}, \mathbf{u}). \tag{1.31}$$

The SMFLC is given as a set of fuzzy rules, derived directly from the above nonlinear model, each fuzzy rule being of the form

$R^{\mathbf{i}}_{\mathrm{C}}$: *if* $s = LS^{\mathbf{i}}$ *then* $\mathbf{u} = \mathbf{LU^i}$,

or of the form

$R^{\mathbf{i}}_{\mathrm{C}}$: *if* $s = LS^{\mathbf{i}}$ *and* $d = LD^{\mathbf{i}}$ *then* $\mathbf{u} = \mathbf{LU^i}$,

where s is the distance between the state vector and the sliding surface, and d is the distance between the state vector and the normal vector to the sliding surface where the normal vector goes through the origin of the state space. See Fig. 1.19 for the graphical interpretation of s and d. Furthermore, $LS^{\mathbf{i}} \in \mathbf{TS}$ and $LD^{\mathbf{i}} \in \mathbf{TD}$ are the fuzzy values of the fuzzy state variables s and d in the $\mathbf{i}$-th fuzzy region of the fuzzy state space; $\mathbf{LU^i}$ is the fuzzy input vector corresponding to the $\mathbf{i}$-th fuzzy region of the fuzzy state space; **TS**, **TD**, and **TU** are the term-sets of s, d, and $\mathbf{u}$ containing the range of fuzzy values of s, d, and $\mathbf{u}$.

This type of FLC is an extension of crisp sliding mode control [38], and crisp sliding mode control with boundary layer [28, Chap. 7]. The control law of the SMFLC has a static transfer characteristic reflecting the relationship between the variables s and d and the input u.

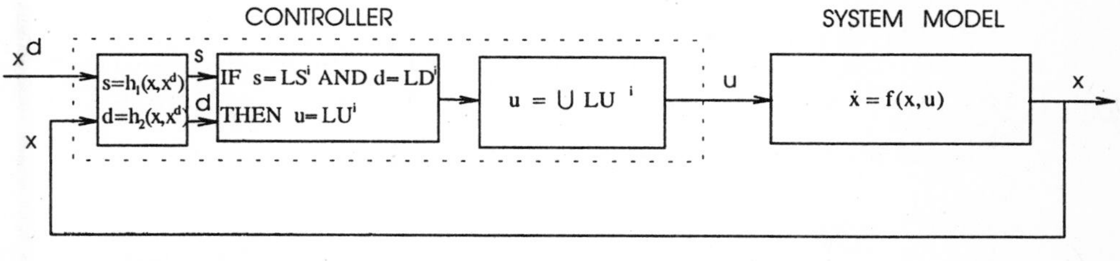

Fig. 1.16. Sliding Mode FLC

The model based design of SMFLC in the case of a MIMO nonlinear system is presented in detail in Chap. 3.

1.3 Nonlinear Control Problems

The objective of the design in model based fuzzy control can be stated as follows:

> Given a model of the physical system to be controlled and the specifications of its desired behavior, design a feedback control law in the form of a set of fuzzy rules such that the closed loop system exhibits the desired behavior.

In what follows we will define first the two basic types of nonlinear control problems, namely the *nonlinear regulation (stabilization)* and *nonlinear tracking.* Second, we will discuss the specifications of desired behavior in the context of nonlinear control. Finally, we discuss the place of model based fuzzy control in the context of the major methods available for the design of nonlinear controllers.

1.3.1 Stabilization and Tracking

In general, the tasks of a control system can be divided in two basic categories:

1. *Stabilization.* In stabilization control problems, an FLC, called a stabilizer, or regulator, is to be designed so that the state vector of the closed loop system will be stabilized around a point (operating point, or a set-point) of the state space.
2. *Tracking.* In tracking control problems, an FLC is to be designed so that the closed loop system output follows a given time-varying trajectory.

The descriptions of stabilization and tracking are given as follows [28, Chap. 1].

Asymptotic Stabilization

Consider a nonlinear autonomous system described by the open loop equation

$$\dot{\mathbf{x}} = \mathbf{f}(\mathbf{x}, \mathbf{u}), \tag{1.32}$$

or its approximation in terms of a fuzzy open loop model. The asymptotic stabilization control problem is to find a control law in terms of a set of fuzzy rules such that, starting anywhere in a region around $\mathbf{0}$, the state vector $\mathbf{x}$ of the closed loop system tends to $\mathbf{0}$ as t tends to infinity.

If the control law directly depends on measured signals, it is said to be a *static control law.* This is the type of control law that is the subject of this book. Furthermore, in the above definition, we allow both the size of the region around $\mathbf{0}$ to be small, i.e., the case of *local stabilization* which can be achieved by a linear control law, and large, in which case a nonlinear control law is required in order to achieve *global stabilization.*

Let the objective of asymptotic stabilization be to stabilize the closed loop system in a region around some setpoint $\mathbf{x^d}$ different from $\mathbf{0}$. Then, one can simply transform the asymptotic stabilization problem in a region around $\mathbf{x^d}$ into an asymptotic stabilization problem in a region around $\mathbf{0}$ by taking $\mathbf{x} - \mathbf{x^d}$ as the new state vector.

Asymptotic Tracking

Consider the nonlinear autonomous open loop equations

$$\dot{\mathbf{x}} = \mathbf{f}(\mathbf{x}, \mathbf{u}), \tag{1.33}$$

$$\mathbf{y} = \mathbf{h}(\mathbf{x}). \tag{1.34}$$

Furthermore, let $\mathbf{y^d}(t)$ be a desired output trajectory. The asymptotic tracking problem is then to find a control law in the form of an FLC such that starting from any initial state in a region around $\mathbf{0}$, the tracking error $\mathbf{y}(t) - \mathbf{y^d}(t)$ tends to $\mathbf{0}$ while the whole state vector remains bounded.

For this type of control problem it is usually assumed [28, Chap. 1] that the desired trajectory and its derivatives up to a sufficiently high order (generally equal to the system's order) are continuous and also that the desired trajectory and its derivatives are bounded. Observe here that in the case of fuzzy model based control the latter assumption always holds. This is because the fuzzy state space is bounded due to the fact that the fuzzy values of the fuzzy state variables are defined on a closed interval of the reals. We also assume that the desired trajectory and its derivatives are available via online computation. This assumption is satisfied when the desired trajectory is specified in advance and its derivatives can be easily obtained. In some tracking problems this latter assumption is not satisfied, however, and a so-called *observer* can be used to provide the required derivatives.

Let us also stress here that perfect tracking, i.e., when the initial states imply zero tracking-error, is not possible. Thus the design objective of achieving asymptotic tracking cannot be achieved. In this case, one should aim at bounded-error tracking, with small tracking-error to be achieved for trajectories of particular interest.

From a theoretical point of view, there is a relationship between the stabilization and the tracking control problems. Stabilization can be regarded as a special case of tracking where the desired trajectory is a constant. On the other hand, if (see for example [28, Chap. 1]) we are to design a tracker for the open loop system

$$\ddot{y} + f(\dot{y}, y, u) = 0, \tag{1.35}$$

so that $e(t) = y(t) - y_d(t)$ tends to zero, the problem is equivalent to the asymptotic stabilization of the system

$$\ddot{e} + f(\dot{e}, e, u, y_d, \dot{y}_d, \ddot{y}_d) = 0 \tag{1.36}$$

with state vector components e and $\dot{e}$. Thus the tracker design problem can be solved if one designs a regulator for the latter nonautonomous open loop system.

1.3.2 Specifications of Performance

In linear control, the desired behavior of the closed loop system can be systematically specified in exact quantitative terms. For example, the specifications of the desired behavior can be formulated in the time domain in terms of rise time and settling time, overshoot and undershoot, etc. Thus, for this type of control, one first postulates the quantitative specifications of the desired behavior of the closed loop system, and then designs a controller that meets these specifications, for example, by choosing the poles of the closed loop system appropriately.

As observed in [28, Chap. 2] such systematic specifications of the desired behavior of nonlinear closed loop systems, except for those that can be approximated by linear systems, are not obvious at all because the response of a nonlinear system (open or closed loop) to one input vector does not reflect its response to another input vector. Furthermore, a frequency domain description of the behavior of the system is not possible either.

The consequence of this is that in specifying the desired behavior of a nonlinear closed loop system one employs some qualitative specifications of performance including stability, accuracy and response speed, and robustness.

Stability

Stability must be guaranteed for the model used for design (the nominal model) either in a local or in a global sense. The regions of stability and convergence are also of interest.

One should keep in mind, however, that stability does not imply the ability to withstand persistent disturbances of even small magnitude. This is so since the stability of a nonlinear system is defined with respect to initial conditions, and only temporary disturbances may be translated as initial conditions. Thus stability of a nonlinear system is different from stability of a linear system. In the case of a linear system stability always implies the ability to withstand bounded disturbances, when of course the system stays in its linear range of operation. The effects of persistent disturbances on the behavior of a nonlinear system are addressed by the notion of robustness.

Accuracy and Response Speed

Accuracy and response speed must be considered for some desired trajectories in the region of operation. For some classes of systems, appropriate design methods can guarantee consistent tracking accuracy independently of the desired trajectory as is the case in sliding mode control and related control methods.

Robustness

Robustness is the sensitivity of the closed loop system to effects which are neglected in the nominal model used for design. These effects can be disturbances, measurement noise, unmodeled dynamics, etc. The closed loop system should be insensitive to these neglected effects in the sense that they should not negatively affect its stability.

We want to stress here that the above specifications of desired behavior are in conflict with each other to some extent, and a good control system can be designed only based on trade-offs in terms of robustness versus performance, cost versus performance, etc.

1.4 Methods in Nonlinear Model Based Control

It is a well known fact that there is no general method for the design of all classes of nonlinear control systems. Instead there is a collection of alternative and complimentary design methods, each method being best applicable to a particular class of nonlinear control problems. Fuzzy model based control is just one such alternative design method. Following [28, Chap. 4], we will briefly discuss the major existing methods for the design of nonlinear control systems such as *feedback linearization*, *robust control*, *adaptive control*, and *gain scheduling*. The purpose of this is to put model based fuzzy control in the context of these other major methods.

1.4.1 Feedback Linearization

The first step in the design of a control system for a given physical plant is to construct a (nonlinear open loop) model that captures the key dynamical aspects of the plant in some operational region of interest.

The principle idea behind *feedback linearization* is to transform the nonlinear system model into a fully, or partially, linear model and then use the powerful linear control design techniques to accomplish the design. In its simplest form, feedback linearization amounts to canceling the nonlinearities of a nonlinear open loop system system so that the closed loop system becomes linear. Thus the method of feedback linearization is concerned with techniques for transforming the original system model into equivalent models of a simpler form. For example, in input-state linearization the technique helps in finding a state vector transformation and an input vector transformation so that the nonlinear open loop model is transformed into an equivalent linear time-invariant open loop model. Then one can, for example, use pole placement to design the control law for the transformed open loop system.

Another type of feedback linearization technique, so-called *input-output linearization*, achieves a partial linearization of the original nonlinear open loop system. This method applies to an important class of nonlinear systems, namely the so-called input state linearizable, or minimum phase systems. The method requires full state vector measurement and can be used for both SISO and MIMO nonlinear systems. It can also be used as a model simplifying tool for the design of robust and adaptive control systems.

The limitations of the method are that it cannot be used for all nonlinear systems and no robustness is guaranteed in the presence of parameter uncertainty (the difference between the ranges of the model parameters and their actual physical ranges in the plant under control) and unmodeled system dynamics. For a detailed description of the limitations of the feedback linearization method the reader can refer to [28, Chap. 6] and [40, Chap. 7].

In fuzzy model based control there is no fuzzy counterpart of feedback linearization as observed in [13]. However, a principally different linearization method, the so-called Lyapunov linearization, in the context of the fuzzy state space, will be used in Chap. 4 for the systematic design of Takagi–Sugeno FLC-2. We will present the motivation for the Takagi–Sugeno FLC-2 based on the above type of linearization in Sect. 1.5.

1.4.2 Robust Control

In model based nonlinear control such as the feedback linearization method, the control law is designed based on a nominal open loop model of the physical plant under control. Thus how the control system will behave in the presence of model uncertainties (i.e., the differences between the nominal model and the actual physical plant) cannot be determined at this stage.

In robust nonlinear control, the method for the design of the control law, e.g., sliding mode control, is based both on the nominal model and some lower and upper bounds of the model uncertainties. As described in [28, Chap. 7], model uncertainties can be classified into two major types:

- *Structured uncertainties.* Structured uncertainties or *parametric uncertainties* are the differences between the model parameters and the actual physical plant. Thus they correspond to inaccuracies in the parameters included in the nominal model.
- *Unstructured uncertainties.* Unstructured uncertainties or *unmodeled dynamics* correspond to inaccuracies (i.e., underestimation) in the system's order. These uncertainties often stem from the deliberate choice of a simplified representation of the open loop model, e.g., modeling friction as linear.

A simple robust control method is the so-called sliding mode control. The method uses the concept of a sliding surface which divides the state space into at least two semi-surfaces and defines the distance to the sliding surface in terms of a *Lyapunov-like function.* Then a control law is formulated such that the squared distance to the sliding surface remains a Lyapunov-like function of the closed loop system. That is, the squared distance decreases along all system trajectories, which in turn makes the system trajectories converge towards the sliding surface; once on it, they cannot leave it. This is achieved despite model uncertainties and disturbances, which is the main characteristic of robustness.

In the presence of arbitrary parameter uncertainties, a "perfect" performance can be achieved, in principle, but is obtained at the price of very high control activity, i.e., fast changes in the input vector. This high control activity may excite the neglected dynamics if additional unstructured uncertainties are present. For example, it may result in the chattering of gears. Thus a modification of the control law is introduced: a boundary layer is designed near the sliding surface, which smooths out the input vector and ensures that the closed loop system remains within this layer. The introduction of a boundary layer results in an effective trade-off between stabilization versus tracking and robustness in the face of structured and unstructered uncertainties.

Problems with the sliding mode control method occur if no sound compromise between required tracking accuracy and restrictions limiting the amplitude of the input variable can be found. Another problem is due to the so-called *matching conditions* for MIMO systems which require that the parametric uncertainties of the system have to be in the range of the input matrix $\mathbf{B}$ for a nonlinear open loop model of the form, $\dot{\mathbf{x}} = \mathbf{f}(\mathbf{x}) + \mathbf{B} \cdot \mathbf{u}$.

In model based fuzzy control, the fuzzy counterpart of the crisp sliding mode method is the sliding mode FLC. It has a number of advantages over the crisp sliding mode control method.

- The possibility to design different transfer characteristics and thus to generate different behavior of the closed loop system in different fuzzy regions of the fuzzy state space,
- The possibility for adaptation and tuning of the transfer characteristic,
- The possibility for changing the velocity with which the closed loop system approaches the setpoint.

These possibilities allow for an improvement of the performance of the closed loop system while preserving its robustness.

The fuzzy sliding mode control method for the MIMO case is the subject of Chap. 3. However, we will briefly describe the motivation for this method in Sect. 1.5.

1.4.3 Adaptive Control

Many dynamic systems have a known structure, but uncertain or slowly varying parameters. Adaptive control is an approach to the control of such systems. Adaptive controllers, whether designed for linear or nonlinear systems, are inherently nonlinear. We distinguish between *direct* and *indirect* adaptive control methods. Direct adaptive methods start with sufficient knowledge about the system structure and its parameters. Direct change of controller parameters optimize the system's behavior with respect to a given criterion.

In contrast, the basic idea of indirect adaptive control methods is to estimate the uncertain parameters of the system under control (or, equivalently, the controller parameters) on-line, and use the estimated parameters in the computation of the control law. Thus an indirect adaptive controller can be regarded as a controller with on-line parameter estimation. There do exist systematic methods for the design of adaptive controllers for the control of linear systems. There also exist adaptive control methods that can be applied to the control of nonlinear systems. However, the latter methods require measurable states and a linear parametrization of the dynamics of the system under control, i.e., that parametric uncertainty be expressed linearly in terms of a number of adjustable parameters. This is required in order to guarantee stability and tracking convergence. However, when adaptive control of nonlinear systems is concerned, most of the adaptive control methods can only be applied to SISO nonlinear systems.

Since robust control methods are also used to deal with parameter uncertainty, adaptive control methods can be considered as an alternative and complimentary to robust control methods. In principle, adaptive control is superior to robust control in dealing with uncertainties in uncertain or slowly varying parameters. The reason for this is the learning behavior of the adaptive controller: such a controller improves its performance in the process of adaptation. On the other hand, a robust controller simply attempts to keep a consistent performance. Furthermore, an indirect adaptive controller requires little a priori information about the unknown parameters. A robust controller usually requires reasonable a priori estimates of the parameter bounds.

Conversely, a robust controller has features which an adaptive controller does not possess, such as the ability to deal with disturbances, quickly varying parameters, and unmodeled dynamics.

In control with an FLC there exist a number of direct adaptive control methods aimed at improving the FLC's performance on-line. The FLC's parameters that can be altered on-line are: the scaling factors for the input and output signals, the input and output membership functions, and the fuzzy if-then rules. An adaptive FLC whose adjustable parameters are the fuzzy values and their membership functions, is called a *self-tuning* FLC. An adaptive FLC that can modify its fuzzy if-then rules is called a *self-organizing* FLC. Detailed description of the design methods for these two types of direct adaptive FLCs can be found in [7, Chap. 5]. Descriptions of indirect adaptive FLCs can be found in [42].

The methods for the design of a self-tuning FLC can be applied independently of whether its fuzzy if-then rules are derived using model based fuzzy control or a heuristic design approach, and are thus applicable to the different types of FLCs presented in this book.

1.4.4 Gain Scheduling

A typical gain scheduling design procedure for a nonlinear autonomous system (see [26, Sect. 4.2] and [25]) goes as follows. First, several operating points covering the range of the system dynamics are selected. These operating points are usually specified by the values of one or more *exogenous variables*, where these variables would, in fact, be state variables in a complete model of the system under control, but this model is either not available or is not used for design because of its complexity. Gain scheduling can also be done on internal variables, for example, gain scheduling on a reference state trajectory. Then at each one of these operating points a linear time invariant approximation of the original nonlinear system is constructed. Finally, a linear controller for each linearized system is designed. In between operating points, the linear controller parameters are then interpolated (or scheduled), thus resulting in a global linear controller called a *gain scheduler*.

Since the local linear controllers are based on linear time invariant approximations of the original nonlinear system, the design guarantees that at each local operating point, the closed loop system is locally stable with guaranteed robustness and has the desired performance. However, since the original system is nonlinear the global closed loop system need not have any of the above mentioned properties of the local closed loop systems. As shown in [26, Sect. 4.2], in the case of gain scheduling on a reference input trajectory, the global closed loop system is locally stable if the reference trajectory is sufficiently slow. Furthermore it is also required that the reference input trajectory does not excite unmodeled dynamics. For example, if this trajectory has a significant frequency content in the region of unmodeled actuator dynamics, then one cannot make demands with respect to the stability and performance of the global closed loop system. In the case of gain scheduling on the reference output trajectory, [26, Sect. 4.2] gives exact conditions which essentially verify and formalize the two common gain scheduling guidelines of "scheduling on a slow variable" and "capturing the plant nonlinearities".

The conclusions arrived at in [26, Sect. 4.4], in the case of linear time invariant approximations of the original nonlinear system and scheduling on a reference state trajectory, is that the global closed loop system inherits the robustness, performance, and local stability properties of the local closed loop systems if the reference state trajectory varies "slowly". This stems from the fact that the design is based on *frozen-time values* of the reference state trajectory. A detailed exposition of the quantified version of the "slowness" condition on the variation of the reference state trajectory can be found in [26, Sect. 4.2] and [40, Theorem 15]. In Sect. 4.3 we consider the fuzzy counterpart of crisp gain scheduling on a reference state trajectory in terms of a Takagi–Sugeno FLC-2. The design of this type of FLC is based on linear time invariant approximations of the original nonlinear system. Furthermore, in Sect. 4.4 we study the conditions under which the local stability of the gain scheduled closed loop system can be extended to the whole fuzzy state space.

The main advantage of gain scheduling is that linear design methods are applied to the linearized system at the different operating points, and the whole power of linear control methods, in terms of performance measures, robust design, design intuitions, and computational tools, can be brought to bear on controller design for nonlinear systems. Other advantages include the fact that a gain scheduler has the potential to respond rapidly to changing operating conditions, and that real-time computation can be achieved.

Perhaps the major difficulty [25] in the design of a gain scheduler is the selection of the gain scheduling procedure, that is, the computation of the linear control laws at intermediate operating points given local linear control laws for fixed operating points. Normally, the linear control laws for intermediate operating points are determined as linear interpolations of the local linear control laws for the fixed operating points. However, as observed in [25], this has the effect that, in general, the eigenvalue locations of the closed loop system at intermediate operating points are incorrect. In this context, the advantage of the FLC based scheduler is that its gain scheduling procedure guarantees the correct locations of the eigenvalues for intermediate operating points.

1.5 Motivation for TSFLC and SMFLC

In what follows we will briefly outline the basic ideas providing the motivation for the different types of Takagi–Sugeno FLCs and the sliding mode FLC.

1.5.1 Takagi–Sugeno FLC-1

As already mentioned in Sect. 1.2, the Takagi–Sugeno FLC-1 design is based on the assumption that a fuzzy open loop model is provided where each fuzzy rule is of the form

$$R_S^{\mathbf{i}}\text{: } \textit{if } \mathbf{x} = \mathbf{LX^i} \textit{ then } \dot{\mathbf{x}} = \mathbf{f_i}(\mathbf{x}, \mathbf{u}).$$

Thus the existence of a fuzzy open loop model is crucial for the derivation of the Takagi–Sugeno FLC-1 (as well as for the design of FLC-2) and only in this case can the design of this type of FLC-1 be motivated.

The basic idea underlying the above type of fuzzy open loop model is as follows. Most industrial plants (or processes) are inherently nonlinear and cannot be described by a single linear model. Instead of constructing complicated open loop nonlinear models based on physical laws, one can decide on an alternative approach, namely the construction of a collection of open loop linear models. In this case, each open loop (local) linear model approximates locally the original nonlinear plant around different operating points and a supervisory scheduling system determines which particular local open loop linear model is the relevant one. Such an open loop scheme is called a *composite model* according to [27]. It is assumed that the parameters of a virtual open loop linear model of the plant change along the operating point trajectory, while the virtual model structure remains unchanged.

The operating point vector $\mathbf{z} = \{z_1, z_2, \ldots, z_{nz}\}$ consists, in general, of state, input, and output variables, and its structure is chosen via identification. The *supervisory scheduling system* uses a discriminant function $\mathbf{w} = \mathbf{f_d}(\mathbf{z})$. This function defines a weight vector $\mathbf{w} = \{w_1, w_2, \ldots, w_K\}$, with $w_i \in [0, 1]$, for each particular value of the operating point vector. The overall output $\mathbf{y}$ of the composite model is calculated as the weighted mean of the outputs y_i of the local linear open loop models

$$\mathbf{y} = \frac{\sum_{i=1}^{K} w_i \cdot y_i}{\sum_{i=1}^{K} w_i}, \tag{1.37}$$

where K is the number of local open loop linear models, and n_z is the dimension of the operating point vector.

Depending on the *discriminating function* $\mathbf{f_d}$ the local open loop linear models can be scheduled in two ways. Assume first that the discriminating function is such that $w_i \in \{0, 1\}$ and also if $w_i = 1$, then $w_j = 0$ for each $j \neq i$. This is the so-called crisp case since at each operating point only one local open loop linear model is active and the switching between any two such models is nonsmooth.

If the discriminating function is such that $w_i \in [0, 1]$ and more than one w_i is different from 0, then the transition from one open loop linear model to another will be smooth, and the global model will be nonlinear, since the weights themselves are functions of the operating point vector. For example, let the discriminating function $\mathbf{f_d}$ be given as min and the variables of the operating point vector take fuzzy values $LZ_1, LZ_2, \ldots, LZ_{n_z}$. Then for a particular crisp value $\mathbf{z} = \{z_1^*, z_2^*, \ldots, z_{n_z}^*\}$ of the operating point vector we will have

$$\mathbf{w} = \min(\mu_{LZ_1}(z_1^*), \mu_{LZ_2}(z_2^*), \ldots, \mu_{LZ_{n_z}}(z_{n_z}^*)). \tag{1.38}$$

In other words, we have that the discriminating function computes the degree of satisfaction of a fuzzy region by a crisp operating point vector. Thus we have exactly the case described by the Takagi–Sugeno FLC-1 with fuzzy operating point vectors in the if-part of the fuzzy rules describing the open loop fuzzy model.

However, the construction of a composite model from data is not a trivial problem. In [27] the construction of a (crisp) composite open loop model was proposed in terms of an on-line recursive identification procedure consisting of the following three main steps.

1. Choice of the open loop model structure and the components of the operating point vector.
2. Estimation of the discriminant function.
3. Estimation of the local open loop linear models.

The identification procedure is based on a fast tracking algorithm for the identification of the parameters of a linear model and a pattern recognition algorithm for constructing a crisp discriminant function. For more details the reader is referred to [27].

Recently in [1] a fuzzy variant of the above mentioned identification procedure was described. The identification procedure does not require any particular knowledge about the operating point vector structure and the number of local open loop linear models. The only parameter to be specified is an upper bound on the number of these models, which is related to the assumed nature of the plant's nonlinearities. The identification procedure is based on fuzzy clustering and a compatible cluster merging technique for determining an optimal number of local open loop linear models. The authors identify a composite model of a highly nonlinear pressure dynamics of a laboratory batch fermentor where its composite model is given as a set of fuzzy rules (see [1]) like:

if pressure $y(k)$ is *low and* valve $u_1(k)$ is *open and* input flow-rate $u_2(k)$ is *low*
then $y(k+1) = 0.85 \cdot y(k) + 0.00074 \cdot u_1(k) + 0.0053 \cdot u_2(k) - 0.45$,

if pressure $y(k)$ is *medium and* valve $u_1(k)$ is *half-closed and* input flow-rate $u_2(k)$ is *high*
then $y(k+1) = 0.76 \cdot y(k) + 0.00024 \cdot u_1(k) + 0.0049 \cdot u_2(k) + 0.04$,

if pressure $y(k)$ is *high and* valve $u_1(k)$ is *closed and* input flow-rate $u_2(k)$ is *very high*
then $y(k+1) = 0.52 \cdot y(k) + 0.00005 \cdot u_1(k) + 0.0032 \cdot u_2(k) + 0.44$.

1.5.2 Takagi–Sugeno FLC-2

A different type of fuzzy open loop model is used for the design of the Takagi–Sugeno FLC-2, The motivation for this type of fuzzy open loop model is as follows.

Let the nonlinear autonomous open loop model of the plant to be controlled be given as $\dot{\mathbf{x}} = \mathbf{f}(\mathbf{x}, \mathbf{u})$. Suppose that we want to design a linear control law $\mathbf{u} = \mathbf{g}(\mathbf{x}, \mathbf{x^d}, \mathbf{u^d})$ capable of locally stabilizing the closed loop nonlinear system $\dot{\mathbf{x}} = \mathbf{f}(\mathbf{x}, \mathbf{g}(\mathbf{x}, \mathbf{x^d}, \mathbf{u^d}))$ at a given operating point $\mathbf{x^d}$ and its corresponding $\mathbf{u^d}$.

We can achieve this goal by obtaining the open loop linear approximation of the original nonlinear model by Lyapunov-linearization of $\mathbf{f}(\mathbf{x}, \mathbf{u})$ at $\mathbf{x^d}$ and its corresponding input $\mathbf{u^d}$. Second, we design a linear control law $\mathbf{g}(\mathbf{x}, \mathbf{x^d}, \mathbf{u^d})$ such that $\mathbf{x^d}$ becomes an asymptotically stable equilibrium point of the closed loop linear approximation version of the original nonlinear model. This in turn will guarantee the local asymptotic stability of the original nonlinear system at $\mathbf{x^d}$.

Now suppose that $\mathbf{x^d}$ is not specified in advance, but we still want to design a linear control law $\mathbf{u} = \mathbf{g}(\mathbf{x}, \mathbf{x^d}, \mathbf{u^d})$ that can locally stabilize the same nonlinear plant whatever $\mathbf{x^d}$ may turn out to be. In order to cover all possible $\mathbf{x^d}$'s, and since we cannot Lyapunov-linearize $\dot{\mathbf{x}} = \mathbf{f}(\mathbf{x}, \mathbf{u})$ at every point in a continuous state space, we partition the state space into a finite number of fuzzy regions $\mathbf{LX^i}$. Then we can Lyapunov-linearize $\dot{\mathbf{x}} = \mathbf{f}(\mathbf{x}, \mathbf{u})$ at the center $\mathbf{x^i}$ of each fuzzy region $\mathbf{LX^i}$, thus obtaining the local linear open loop model $\dot{\mathbf{x}} = \mathbf{f_i}(\mathbf{x}, \mathbf{x^i}, \mathbf{u}, \mathbf{u^i})$. Finally, we can design a local linear control law $\mathbf{g_i}(\mathbf{x}, \mathbf{x^i}, \mathbf{u^i})$ such that the local linear closed loop model $\dot{\mathbf{x}} = \mathbf{f_i}(\mathbf{x}, \mathbf{g_i}(\mathbf{x}, \mathbf{x^i}, \mathbf{u^i}), \mathbf{x^i}, \mathbf{u^i})$ is locally asymptotically stable at $\mathbf{x^i}$. This will in turn imply that the original nonlinear model is also locally asymptotically stabilized at $\mathbf{x^i}$.

Now, let a particular operating point $\mathbf{x^d} \in \mathbf{LX^i}$ be given and let $\mathbf{x^d} \neq \mathbf{x^i}$ for each $\mathbf{i}$. Let $\mu^{\mathbf{i}}(\mathbf{x^d})$ $(\mathbf{i} = \mathbf{1}, \mathbf{2}, \ldots, \mathbf{M})$ be the degrees of satisfaction of $\mathbf{LX^i}$ and all of its neighboring regions by $\mathbf{x^d}$. Normalizing these degrees of satisfaction one obtains their normalized counterparts $w^{\mathbf{i}}(\mathbf{x^d})$. Then a control law such as $\mathbf{u} = \sum_{\mathbf{i}} w^{\mathbf{i}}(\mathbf{x^d}) \cdot \mathbf{g_i}(\mathbf{x}, \mathbf{x^d}, \mathbf{x^i}, \mathbf{u^d}, \mathbf{u^i})$ is a linear control law since the $w^{\mathbf{i}}$'s are not a function of the state vector $\mathbf{x}$, but are constant for the given $\mathbf{x^d}$. The question, of course, is whether such a control law can locally asymptotically stabilize the Lyapunov-linearized closed loop system at $\mathbf{x^d}$. If it can, then again the original nonlinear system will be also locally asymptotically stabilized at $\mathbf{x^d}$. This question is addressed in detail in Chap. 4.

A different motivation for the Takagi–Sugeno FLC-2 is its use as a gain scheduler. Consider a nonlinear autonomous open loop system and suppose one has to design a controller such that the closed loop system follows a given reference state trajectory. In this case one is concerned with stabilizing the closed loop system not around an operating point, but in making this system remain close to the reference state trajectory if perturbed slightly away from it. That is, we are concerned with the so-called *stability of motion.* As we will show in Chap. 2, the latter stability problem can be transformed in such a way that, instead of studying the deviation of the state vector from the reference state trajectory, one can study the stability of the transformed system around the origin. However, as the result of this transformation the original nonlinear autonomous system will become equivalent to a nonlinear nonautonomous system.

Now let us Lyapunov-linearize the transformed nonlinear nonautonomous system around the origin. The resulting linearized approximation will be a linear nonautonomous system. If one can now design a controller such that the closed loop linear nonautonomous system is locally uniformly exponentially stable around the origin, then this same controller guarantees the local uniform exponential stability of the transformed nonlinear nonautonomous system around the origin and thus, the local stability of the original nonlinear autonomous system around the given reference state trajectory [40, Theorem 15].

In this context, the major problem is then the design of the controller for the linear nonautonomous system such that the closed loop linear nonautonomous system is locally exponentially stabilized around the origin. This is the same as stabilizing the linear nonautonomous system around the reference state trajectory.

One approach to the design of such a controller would be gain scheduling on a given reference state trajectory. In this case (see [26, Sect. 4.2.1] and [25]) one selects a number of operating points in the state space and designs a linear autonomous controller for each such point. Then for any point in between operating points, the linear autonomous controllers are interpolated such that for all frozen-time values of the reference state trajectory the local feedback closed loop system has the properties of local stability, robustness to unmodeled dynamics, and robust performance. The condition, which guarantees that the global closed loop linear nonautonomous system will inherit the properties of the frozen-time linear autonomous closed loop systems, is that the linear nonautonomous system should be slowly varying. In terms of the reference state trajectory, the slowness condition on the dynamics of the linear nonautonomous system implies that the reference state trajectory itself should vary slowly.

The Takagi–Sugeno FLC-2 can be considered the resulting fuzzy counterpart of the gain scheduling design described above.

1.5.3 Sliding Mode FLC

FLCs for a large class of second-order nonlinear systems are designed by using the phase plane determined by error e and change of error $\dot{e}$ [22, 23, 37, 41]. The fuzzy rules of these FLCs determine a fuzzy value for the input u for each pair of fuzzy values of error and change of error, i.e., for each fuzzy state vector. The usual heuristic approach to the design of these fuzzy rules is the partitioning of the phase plane into two semi-planes by means of a *sliding (switching) line*. This means that the FLC has a so-called *diagonal form*. Another possibility, instead of using a sliding line, is to use a sliding curve like a time optimal trajectory [29].

$\dot{e}$ \ e	NB	NM	NS	Z	PS	PM	PB
PB	Z	NS	NS	NM	NM	NB	NB
PM	PS	Z	NS	NS	NM	NM	NB
PS	PS	PS	Z	NS	NS	NM	NM
Z	PM	PS	PS	Z	NS	NS	NM
NS	PM	PM	PS	PS	Z	NS	NS
NM	PB	PM	PM	PS	PS	Z	NS
NB	PB	PB	PM	PM	PS	PS	Z

P - positive
N - negative
Z - zero
S - small
M - medium
B - big

Fig. 1.17. An FLC in a diagonal form

A typical fuzzy rule for the FLC in a diagonal form is

$$\textit{if } e = \text{PS} \textit{ and } \dot{e} = \text{NB} \textit{ then } u = \text{PS},$$

where PS stands for the fuzzy value of error Positive Small, NB stands for the fuzzy value change of error Negative Big, and PS stands for the fuzzy value Positive Small of the input.

Each semi-plane is used to define only negative or positive fuzzy values of the input u. The magnitude of a specific positive/negative fuzzy value of u is determined on the basis of the distance $|s|$ between its corresponding state vector $\mathbf{e}$ and the sliding line $s = \lambda \cdot e + \dot{e} = 0$. This is normally done in such a way that the absolute value of the required input u increases/decreases with the increasing/decreasing distance between the state vector $\mathbf{e}$ and the sliding line $s = 0$.

It is easily observed that this design method is very similar to sliding mode control (SMC) with a *boundary layer* (BL) which is a robust control method (see [38] and [28, Sect. 7.2]). Sliding mode control is applied especially to control of nonlinear systems in the presence of model uncertainties, parameter fluctuations, and disturbances. The similarity between the diagonal form FLC and SMC enables us to redefine a diagonal form FLC in terms of an SMC with BL and then to verify its stability, robustness, and performance properties in a manner corresponding to the analysis of an SMC with BL. In the following, the diagonal FLC is therefore called SMFLC.

However, one is tempted to ask here what one gains by introducing the SMFLC type of controller. The answer is that SMC with BL is a special case of SMFLC. SMC with BL provides a linear transfer characteristic with lower and upper bounds while the transfer characteristic of an SMFLC is not necessarily a straight line between these bounds, but a curve that can be adjusted to reflect given performance requirements. For example, normally a fast rise time and as little overshoot as possible are the required performance characteristics for the closed loop system. These can be achieved by making the controller gains much larger for state space regions far from the sliding line than its gains in state space regions close to the sliding line (see Fig. 1.18).

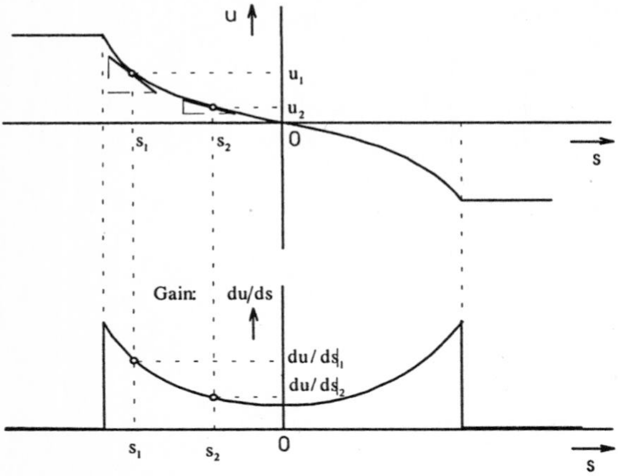

Fig. 1.18. The adjustable transfer characteristic of an SMFLC

In this connection it has to be emphasized that an SMFLC is a state dependent filter. The slope of its transfer characteristic decides the convergence rate to the sliding line and, at the same time, the bandwidth of the unmodeled disturbances that can be coped with. This means that far from the sliding line higher frequencies are allowed to pass through than in the neighborhood of it. The other function of this state dependent filter is given by the sliding line itself. That is, the velocity with which the origin is approached is determined by the slope λ of the sliding line $s = 0$.

Because of the special form of the rule base of a diagonal form FLC (see Fig. 1.17) each fuzzy rule can be redefined in terms of the fuzzy value of the distance $|s|$ between the state vector $\mathbf{e}$ and the sliding line, and the fuzzy value of the input u corresponding to this distance. This helps to reduce the number of fuzzy rules especially in the case of higher order systems. Namely, if the number of state variables is two and each state variable has m fuzzy values, the number of fuzzy rules of the diagonal form FLC is $M = m^2$. For the same case, the number of fuzzy rules of an SMFLC is only m. This is so, because the fuzzy rules of the SMFLC only describe the relationship between the distance to the sliding line and the input u corresponding to this distance, rather than the relationship between all possible fuzzy state vectors and the input u corresponding to each fuzzy state vector.

Moreover, the fuzzy rules of an SMFLC can be reformulated to include the distance d between the state vector $\mathbf{e}$ and the vector normal to the sliding line and passing through the origin (see Fig. 1.19). This gives an additional opportunity to further affect the rate at which the origin is approached. A fuzzy rule including this distance is of the form

if $s =$ PS *and* $d =$ S *then* $u =$ NS.

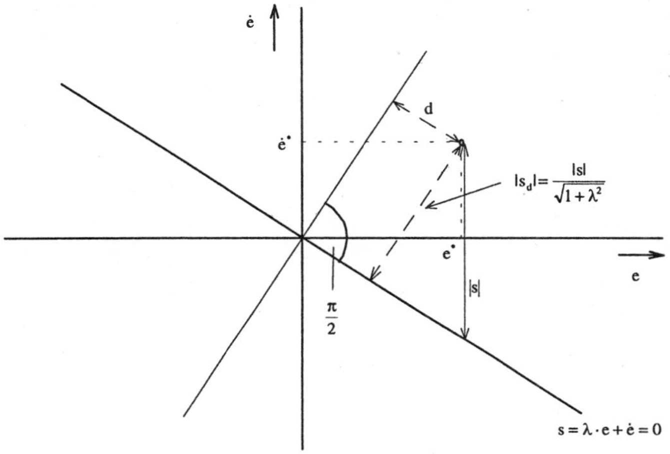

Fig. 1.19. The s and d parameters of an SMFLC

Despite the advantages of an SMFLC it poses a number of problems the solutions of which can improve its performance and robustness. One such problem is the addition of an integrator to an SMFLC in order to eliminate remaining errors in the presense of disturbances and model uncertainties. There are several ways to accomplish this. One option for example, is to treat the integration term in the same manner as the other parameters of the if-part of the SMFLC's fuzzy rules. This and other available options will be described in Chap. 3.

Another problem is the so-called *scaling* of the SMFLC parameters so that the domains on which their fuzzy values are defined are properly determined and optimized with respect to performance. This problem arises in the context of SMFLC since the real physical domains of the SMFLC parameters are normalized, i.e., their measured values are mapped on their respective normalized domains by the use of *normalization factors.* Thus a normalized input u is the result of computation with the SMFLC. This normalized u is then denormalized, i.e., mapped back on its physical domain, by the use of a *denormalization factor.*

The determination of the proper scaling factors, via which the normalization and denormalization of the SMFLC parameters is performed, is not only part of the design, but also important in the context of adaptation and on-line tuning of the SMFLC. The behavior of the closed loop system ultimately depends on the normalized transfer characteristic (control surface) of the SMFLC. This control surface is mainly determined by the shape and location of the membership functions defining the fuzzy values of the SMFLC's parameters. In this context one should pay attention to the following.

1. The denormalization factor for u has most influence on stability and oscillations. Because of its impact on stability the determination of this factor has the highest priority in the design.
2. Normalization factors influence most the SMFLC sensitivity with respect to the proper choice of the operating regions for s and d. Therefore, normalization factors have second priority in the design.
3. The proper shape and location of the membership functions and, with this, the transfer characteristic of the SMFLC can influence positively the behavior of the closed loop system in different fuzzy regions of the fuzzy state space provided that the operating regions of s and u are properly chosen through well adjusted normalization factors. Therefore, this aspect comes third in priority.

Thus one obtains the following three-level tuning hierarchy:

1. Tuning of the denormalization factor,
2. Tuning of the normalization factors,
3. Tuning of the membership functions.

In this book we deal with the second level of the above tuning hierarchy.

A third problem is the design of SMFLC for MIMO systems. The design for SISO systems can still be utilized though some new aspects and restrictions come into play when this design is extended to the case of MIMO systems. First, we assume that the MIMO system has as many input variables u_i as it has state variables x_i. Second, we assume that the so-called *matching condition* holds [28, Sect. 7.2]. This condition constrains the so-called *parametric uncertainties.* These are, for example, imprecision on the mass or inertia of a mechanical system, inaccuracies on friction functions, etc. *Non-parametric uncertainties* are unmodeled dynamics, neglected time delays, etc.

Let $\dot{\mathbf{x}} = \mathbf{f}(\mathbf{x}) + \mathbf{B} \cdot \mathbf{u}$, be the nonlinear open loop system to be controlled, where $\mathbf{f}$ is a nonlinear vector function of the state vector $\mathbf{x}$, $\mathbf{u}$ is the input vector, and $\mathbf{B}$ is the *input matrix.*

Then, the matching condition requires that the parametric uncertainties have to be within the range of the input matrix $\mathbf{B}$. Since $\mathbf{B}$ is assumed to be a square matrix, this means that $\mathbf{B}$ has to be invertible over the whole state space, which is a controllability-like assumption. A second condition required is that the estimate $\hat{\mathbf{B}}$ also is invertible.

2. The FLC as a Nonlinear Transfer Element

A fuzzy logic controller defines a control law in the form of a static nonlinear *transfer element* (TE) due to the nonlinear nature of the computations performed by an FLC. However, the control law of an FLC is not represented in an analytic form, but by a set of fuzzy rules. The *antecedent* of a fuzzy rule (if-part) describes a fuzzy region in the state space. Thus one effectively partitions an otherwise continuous state space by covering it with a finite number of fuzzy regions and, consequently, fuzzy rules. The *consequent* of a fuzzy rule (then-part) specifies a control law applicable within the fuzzy region from the if-part of the same fuzzy rule. During control with an FLC a point in the state space is affected to a different extent by the control laws associated with all the fuzzy regions to which this particular point in the state space belongs. By using the operations of *aggregation* and *defuzzification*, a specific control law for this particular point is determined. As the point moves in the state space, the control law changes smoothly. This implies that despite the quantization of the state space into a finite number of fuzzy regions, an FLC yields a smooth nonlinear control law.

One goal of this chapter is to describe computation with an FLC and its formal description as a static nonlinear transfer element and thus provide the background knowledge needed for the understanding of control with an FLC. Furthermore, we show the relationship between conventional and rule-based transfer elements, thus establishing the compatibility between these two conceptually different, in terms of representation, types of transfer elements. The chapter also introduces the basic stability concepts used in the model based design and analysis of FLC.

In Sect. 2.1 we first describe the *computational structure* of an FLC involving the *computational steps* of *input scaling*, *fuzzification*, *rule firing*, *defuzzification*, and *output scaling.*

In Sect. 2.2 we present the sources of nonlinearity in the computational structure of an FLC by relating them to particular computational steps.

In Sect. 2.3 we describe the relationship between conventional transfer elements and rule-based transfer elements. We show the gradual transition from a conventional transfer element to a crisp rule-based transfer element, and finally to a fuzzy rule-based transfer element. We also describe the computational structure of Takagi–Sugeno FLCs.

In Sect. 2.4 we introduce the stability concepts used in the model based design and analysis of an FLC including Lyapunov-linearization and the Lyapunov direct method for autonomous and nonautonomous systems.

2.1 The Computational Structure of an FLC

A control law represented in the form of an FLC directly depends on the measurements of signals and is thus a static control law. This means that the fuzzy rule-based representation of an FLC does not include any dynamics which makes an FLC a *static transfer element*, like a *state controller*. In addition to that, an FLC is, in general, a *nonlinear static transfer element* due to those computational steps of its computational structure that have nonlinear properties. In what follows we will describe the computational structure of an FLC by presenting the computational steps it involves.

The computational structure of an FLC consists of a number of computational steps and is illustrated in Fig. 2.1.

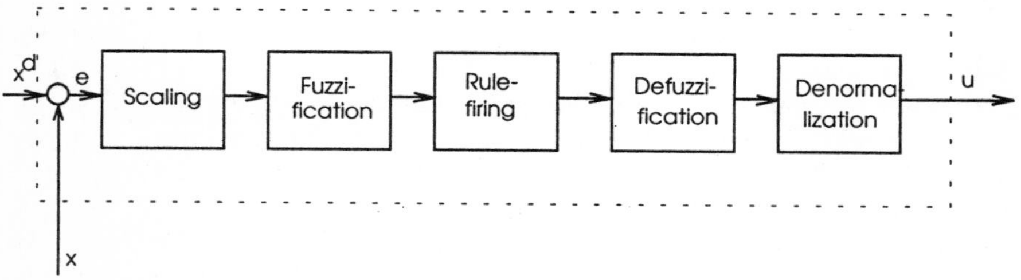

Fig. 2.1. The computational structure of an FLC

There are five such computational steps constituting the computational structure of an FLC. These are the following.

1. *Input scaling (normalization).*
2. *Fuzzification* of controller-input variables.
3. *Inference (rule firing).*
4. *Defuzzification* of controller-output variables.
5. *Output scaling (denormalization).*

We should remark here that the state variables $x_1, x_2, \ldots, x_n$ (or $e, \dot{e}, \ldots, e^{(n)}$) that appear in the if-part of the fuzzy rules of an FLC are also called *controller inputs.* The controller-input variables $u_1, u_2, \ldots, u_m$ that appear in the then-part of the fuzzy rules of an FLC are also called *controller outputs.* In the remainder of this chapter we will use controller inputs and controller outputs when referring to the state variables $x_1, x_2, \ldots, x_n$ and the input variables $u_1, u_2, \ldots, u_m$ respectively.

We will now consider each of the above computational steps for the case of a *multiple-input/single-output* (MISO) FLC. The generalization to the case of multiple-input/multiple-output FLC, where there are m controller outputs $u_1, u_2, \ldots, u_m$ instead of a single controller output u, can be easily done.

2.1.1 Input Scaling

There are two principle cases in the context of input scaling.

1. The membership functions defining the fuzzy values of the controller inputs and controller outputs are defined off-line on their actual physical domains. In this case the controller inputs and controller outputs are processed only using *fuzzification, rule firing,* and *defuzzification.* For example, this is the case of Takagi–Sugeno FLC-1 and FLC-2.
2. The membership functions defining the fuzzy values of controller inputs and controller outputs are defined off-line, on a common *normalized domain.* This means that the actual, crisp physical values of the controller inputs and controller outputs are mapped onto the same predetermined normalized domain. This mapping, called *normalization,* is done by the so-called *normalization factors.* Input scaling is then the multiplication of a physical, crisp controller input with a normalization factor so that it is mapped onto the normalized domain. Output scaling is the multiplication of a normalized controller output with a *denormalization factor* so that it is mapped back onto the physical domain of the controller outputs.

The advantage of the second case is that fuzzification, rule firing, and defuzzification can be designed independently of the actual physical domains of the controller inputs and controller outputs. For instance, this is the case with SMFLC.

To illustrate the notion of input scaling let us consider, for example the state vector $\mathbf{e} = (e_1, e_2, \ldots, e_n)^T = (e, \dot{e}, \ldots, e^{(n)})^T$, where for each i, $e_i = x_i - x_{d_i}$. This vector of physical controller inputs is normalized with the help of a matrix $\mathbf{N_e}$ containing predetermined normalization factors for each component of $\mathbf{e}$. The normalization is done as

$$\mathbf{e_N} = \mathbf{N_e} \cdot \mathbf{e}, \tag{2.1}$$

with

$$\mathbf{N_e} = \begin{pmatrix} N_{e_1} & 0 & \dots & 0 \\ 0 & N_{e_2} & \dots & 0 \\ \vdots & \vdots & \ddots & \vdots \\ 0 & 0 & \dots & N_{e_k} \end{pmatrix}, \tag{2.2}$$

where N_{e_i} are real numbers and the normalized domain for $\mathbf{e}$ is, say $E_N = [-a, +a]$.

Example 2.1.1. Let $\mathbf{e} = (e_1, e_2)^T = (e, \dot{e})^T$ with

$$e = x - x_d \qquad \text{and} \qquad \dot{e} = \dot{x}_d - \dot{x}_d. \tag{2.3}$$

Then, input scaling of e into e_N and $\dot{e}$ into $\dot{e}_N$ yields

$$e_N = N_e \cdot e \qquad \text{and} \qquad \dot{e}_N = N_{\dot{e}} \cdot \dot{e}, \tag{2.4}$$

where N_e and $N_{\dot{e}}$ are the normalization factors for e and $\dot{e}$ respectively.

In the context of a phase plane representation of the dynamic behavior of the controller inputs, the input scaling affects the angle of the sliding line that divides the phase plane into two semiplanes (see Fig. 2.2).

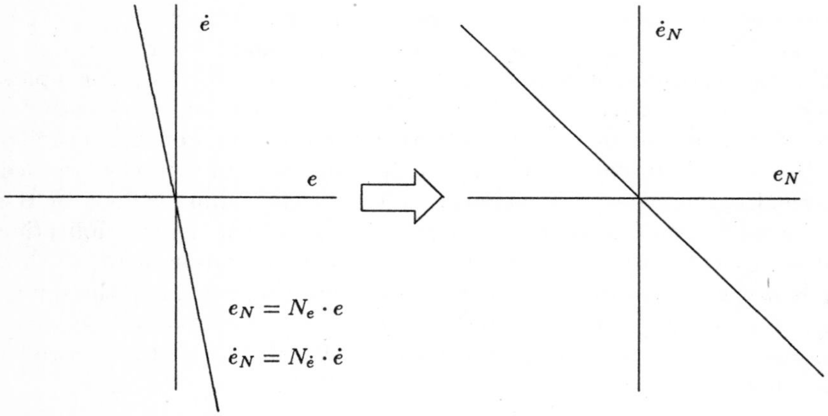

Fig. 2.2. Normalization of the phase plane

In addition to that, we can see how the supports of the membership functions defining the fuzzy values of e and $\dot{e}$ change because of the input scaling of these controller inputs (see Fig. 2.3).

In Sects. 2.1.2–2.1.4, we consider only the case when the fuzzy values of the controller inputs and controller outputs are defined on normalized domains (e.g., E_N and U_N), and in this case we will omit the lower index N from the notation of normalized domains and fuzzy and crisp values. In Sect. 2.1.5 we will use the lower index N to distinguish between normalized and actual fuzzy and crisp values.

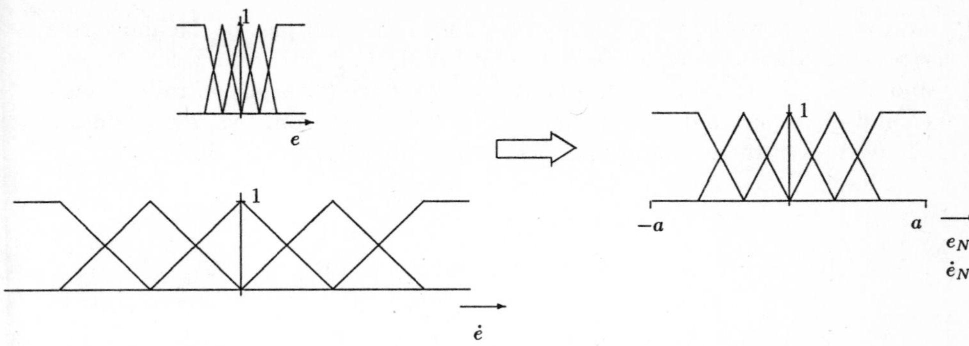

Fig. 2.3. Changing of membership functions supports due to input scaling

2.1.2 Fuzzification

During fuzzification a crisp controller input $\mathbf{x}^*$ is assigned a degree of membership to the fuzzy region from the if-part of a fuzzy rule. Let $LE_1^{\mathbf{i}}, \ldots, LE_n^{\mathbf{i}}$ be some fuzzy values taken by the controller inputs $e_1, \ldots, e_n$ in the if-part of the $\mathbf{i}$-th fuzzy rule $R_C^{\mathbf{i}}$ of an FLC, i.e., these fuzzy values define the fuzzy region $\mathbf{LE^i} = (LE_1^{\mathbf{i}}, \ldots, LE_n^{\mathbf{i}})^T$.

Each of the above fuzzy values $LE_k^{\mathbf{i}}$ is defined by a membership function on the same (normalized) domain of error E. Thus the fuzzy value $LE_k^{\mathbf{i}}$ is given by the membership function $\int_E \mu_{LE_k^{\mathbf{i}}}(e_k)/e_k$.

Let us consider now a particular normalized crisp controller input

$$\mathbf{e}^* = (e_1^*, \ldots, e_n^*)^T, \tag{2.5}$$

from the normalized domain E. Each e_k^* is a normalized crisp value obtained after the input scaling of the current physical controller input. The *fuzzification* of the crisp normalized controller input then consists of finding the membership degree of e_k^* in $\int_E \mu_{LE_k^{\mathbf{i}}}(e_k)/e_k$. This is done for every element of $\mathbf{e}^*$.

Example 2.1.2. Consider the fuzzy rule $R_C^{\mathbf{i}}$ given as

$$R_C^{\mathbf{i}}\text{: } \textit{if } \mathbf{e} = (\mathrm{PS}_e, \mathrm{NM}_{\dot{e}}) \textit{ then } u = \mathrm{PM}_u$$

where PS_e is the fuzzy value POSITIVE SMALL of the controller input e, $\mathrm{NM}_{\dot{e}}$ is the fuzzy value NEGATIVE MEDIUM of the second controller input $\dot{e}$, and PM_u is the fuzzy value NEGATIVE MEDIUM of the single controller output u. The membership functions representing these two fuzzy values are given in Fig. 2.4.

In this example we have $\mathbf{e} = (e, \dot{e})^T$ and thus the if-part of the above rule represents the fuzzy region $\mathbf{LE^i} = (PS_e, NM_{\dot{e}})^T$. Furthermore, let $e^* = a_1$ and $\dot{e}^* = a_2$ be the current normalized values of the physical controller inputs e^* and $\dot{e}^*$ respectively as depicted in Fig. 2.4. Then from Fig. 2.4 we obtain the degrees of membership $\mu_{\mathrm{PS}_e}(a_1) = 0.3$ and $\mu_{\mathrm{NM}_{\dot{e}}}(a_2) = 0.65$.

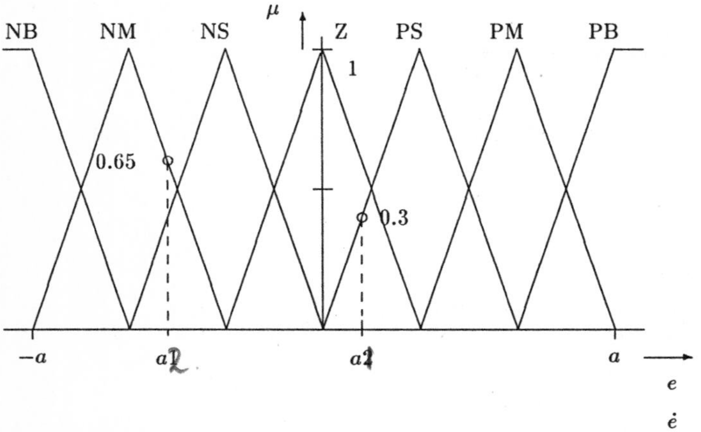

Fig. 2.4. Fuzzification of crisp values e^* and $\dot{e}^*$

2.1.3 Rule Firing

For a multi-input/single-output FLC the **i**-th fuzzy rule of the set of fuzzy rules has the form

R_C^i: *if* $\mathbf{e} = \mathbf{LE^i}$ *then* $u = LU^{\mathbf{i}}$,

where the fuzzy region $\mathbf{LE^i}$ from the if-part of the above fuzzy rule is given as $\mathbf{LE^i} = (LE_1^{\mathbf{i}}, LE_2^{\mathbf{i}}, \ldots, LE_n^{\mathbf{i}})^T$. Also, $LE_k^{\mathbf{i}}$ denotes the fuzzy value of the k-th normalized controller input e_k belonging to the term-set of e_k given as $\mathbf{TE_k} = \{LE_{k1}, LU_{k2}, \ldots, LU_{kn}\}$. Furthermore, $LU^{\mathbf{i}}$ denotes an arbitrary fuzzy value taken by the normalized controller output u and this fuzzy value belongs to the term-set $\mathbf{TU}$ of u, that is $\mathbf{TU} = \{LU_1, LU_2, \ldots, LU_n\}$.

Let the membership functions defining the fuzzy values from $\mathbf{LE^i}$ and $LU_{\mathbf{i}}$ be denoted by $\int_E \mu_{LE_k^{\mathbf{i}}}(e_k)/e_k$ $(k = 1, 2, \ldots, n)$ and $\int_U \mu^{\mathbf{i}}_{LU^{\mathbf{i}}}(u)/u$ respectively. The membership function $\int_U \mu_{LU^{\mathbf{i}}}(u)/u$ is defined on the normalized domain U, and the membership functions $\int_E \mu_{LE_k^{\mathbf{i}}}(e_k)/e_k$ are defined on the normalized domain E.

Given a controller input vector $\mathbf{e}^*$ consisting of the normalized crisp values $e_1^*, \ldots, e_n^*$, first the degree of satisfaction $\mu^{\mathbf{i}}(\mathbf{e}^*)$ of the fuzzy region $\mathbf{LE^i}$ is computed as

$$\mu^{\mathbf{i}}(\mathbf{e}^*) = \min\left(\mu_{LE_1^{\mathbf{i}}}(e_1^*), \mu_{LE_2^{\mathbf{i}}}(e_2^*), \ldots, \mu_{LE_n^{\mathbf{i}}}(e_n^*)\right). \quad (2.6)$$

Second, given the degree of satisfaction $\mu^{\mathbf{i}}(\mathbf{e}^*)$ of the fuzzy region $\mathbf{LE^i}$, the normalized controller output of the $\mathbf{i}$-th fuzzy rule is computed as

$$CLU^{\mathbf{i}} = \int_U \mu_{CLU^{\mathbf{i}}}(u)/u = \min\left(\mu^{\mathbf{i}}(\mathbf{e}^*), \int_U \mu_{LU^{\mathbf{i}}}(u)/u\right). \quad (2.7)$$

Thus the controller output of the $\mathbf{i}$-th fuzzy rule is modified by the degree of satisfaction $\mu^{\mathbf{i}}(\mathbf{e}^*)$ of the fuzzy region $\mathbf{LE^i}$ and hence defined as the fuzzy subset $CLU^{\mathbf{i}} = \int_U \mu_{CLU^{\mathbf{i}}}(u)/u$ of $\int_U \mu_{LU^{\mathbf{i}}}(u)/u$. That is

$$\forall u : \mu_{CLU^{\mathbf{i}}}(u) = \begin{cases} \mu_{LU^{\mathbf{i}}}(u) & \text{if } \mu_{LU^{\mathbf{i}}}(u) \leq \mu^{\mathbf{i}}, \\ \mu_{LU^{\mathbf{i}}}(u) = \mu^{\mathbf{i}}(\mathbf{e}^*) & \text{otherwise.} \end{cases} \quad (2.8)$$

The fuzzy set $CLU^{\mathbf{i}} = \int_U \mu_{CLU^{\mathbf{i}}}(u)/u$ is called the *clipped controller output*. It represents the modified version of the controller output $\int_U \mu_{LU^{\mathbf{i}}}(u)/u$ from the $\mathbf{i}$-th fuzzy rule given certain crisp controller input $e_1^*, \ldots, e_n^*$. The computational step of rule firing is illustrated graphically in Fig. 2.5 for a two-dimensional controller input vector and a single controller output.

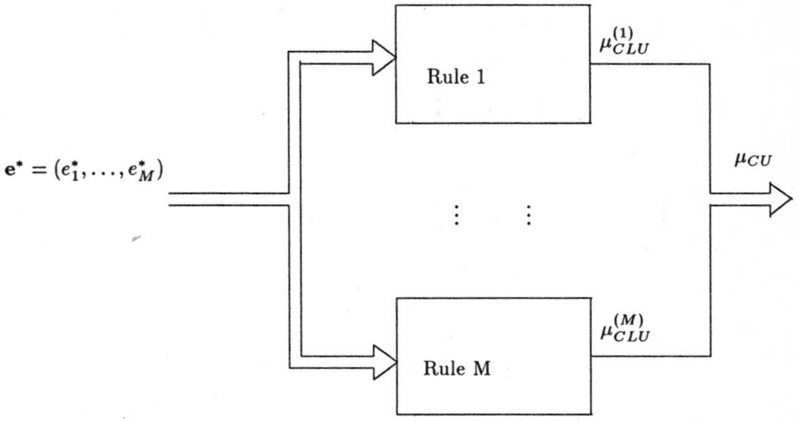

Fig. 2.5. The computational step of rule firing

In the final stage of rule firing, the clipped controller outputs of all fuzzy rules are combined in a *global controller output* via *aggregation*

$$\forall u : \mu_{CU}(u) = \max(\mu_{CLU^1}, \ldots, \mu_{CLU^M}), \quad (2.9)$$

where $CU = \int_U \mu_{CU}(u)/u$ is the fuzzy set defining the fuzzy value of the *global controller output*.

2.1.4 Defuzzification

The result of rule firing is a fuzzy set CU with a membership function $\int_U \mu_{CU}(u)/u$ as defined in (2.9). The purpose of defuzzification is to obtain a scalar value u from μ_{CU}. The scalar value u is called a *defuzzified controller output*. This is done by the *center of gravity method* as follows.

In the continuous case we have

$$u = \frac{\int\limits_U \mu_{CU}(u)/u \cdot u}{\int\limits_U \mu_{CU}(u)/u}, \tag{2.10}$$

and for the discrete case,

$$u = \frac{\sum\limits_U \mu_{CU}(u)/u \cdot u}{\sum\limits_U \mu_{CU}(u)/u}. \tag{2.11}$$

Example 2.1.3. Consider the normalized domain $U = \{1, 2, \ldots, 8\}$ and let the fuzzy set CU be given as

$$CU = \{0.5/3, 0.8/4, 1/5, 0.5/6, 0.2/7\}. \tag{2.12}$$

Then the defuzzified controller output u is computed as (see also Fig. 2.6)

$$u = \frac{0.5 \cdot 3 + 0.8 \cdot 4 + 1 \cdot 5 + 0.5 \cdot 6 + 0.2 \cdot 7}{0.5 + 0.8 + 1 + 0.5 + 0.2} = 4.7. \tag{2.13}$$

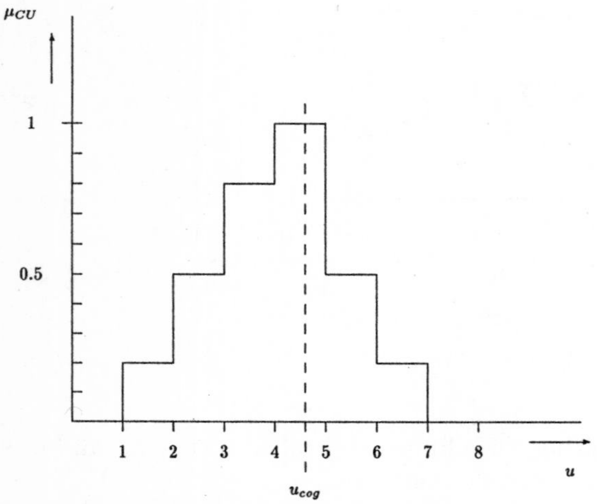

Fig. 2.6. Defuzzification of a fuzzy controller output

2.1.5 Denormalization

In the denormalization procedure the defuzzified normalized controller output u_N is denormalized with the help of an off-line predetermined scalar denormalization factor N_u^{-1} which is the inverse of the normalization factor N_u .

Let the normalization of the controller output be performed as:

$$u_N = N_u \cdot u. \tag{2.14}$$

Then, the denormalization of u_N is simply:

$$u = N_u^{-1} \cdot u_N. \tag{2.15}$$

As we will see in Chap. 3, the choice of N_u essentially determines, together with the rest of the scaling factors, the stability of the system to be controlled. In the case of Takagi–Sugeno FLCs the above computational steps are performed on the actual physical domains of the controller inputs and controller outputs. Thus the computational steps of normalization and denormalization are not involved in the computational structure of a Takagi–Sugeno FLC, which in turn eliminates the need for input and output scaling factors.

2.2 The Nonlinearity of the FLC

In this section we will describe the sources of nonlinearity of the transfer characteristic of an FLC by relating them to particular computational steps.

System theory distinguishes between two basic types of systems: *linear* and *nonlinear*. A system is linear if and only if it has both the *additivity property* and the *scaling property*, otherwise it is a nonlinear system.

The Additivity Property (Superposition Property): Let it be the case that

$$y_1 = f(x) \qquad \text{and} \qquad y_2 = f(z). \tag{2.16}$$

Then for the *additivity property* to hold we require

$$y_1 + y_2 = f(x + z). \tag{2.17}$$

Hence, we obtain

$$f(x) + f(z) = f(x + z). \tag{2.18}$$

Scaling Property (Homogenity Property): Let it be the case that

$$y = f(x). \tag{2.19}$$

Then for the *scaling property* to hold we require

$$\alpha \cdot y = f(\alpha \cdot x) \qquad \text{and} \qquad \alpha \cdot f(x) = f(\alpha \cdot x). \tag{2.20}$$

Because of fuzzification and defuzzification, an FLC is in fact a crisp TE. This crisp TE has a nonlinear transfer characteristic because of the nonlinear character of fuzzification (when performed on nonlinear membership functions), rule firing, and defuzzification. The argument for this is that if one computational step within the computational structure of the TE is nonlinear then the whole TE is nonlinear as well. Using the additivity and scaling properties of a linear system we will now establish the linearity, or nonlinearity, of each computational step in the computational structure of an FLC with respect to these two properties.

In what follows, without any loss of generality, we will use a single MISO fuzzy rule such as

R_C: *if* $e =$ LE *then* $u =$ LU,

where LE and LU are the fuzzy values taken by the normalized, single controller input e and the normalized, single controller output u respectively. These two fuzzy values are determined by the membership functions $\int_E \mu_{LE}(e)/e$ and $\int_U \mu_{LU}(u)/u$ defined on the normalized domains E and U. Here again we only consider normalized domains and fuzzy and crisp values, and thus the lower index N will be omitted from the notation, unless there is a need to distinguish between normalized and actual crisp and fuzzy values used within the same expression.

Furthermore, let e_1^* and e_2^* be two normalized crisp controller inputs and u_1^* and u_2^* be the defuzzified controller outputs corresponding to these normalized controller inputs.

2.2.1 Input Scaling and Output Scaling

Input scaling is linear because it simply multiplies each physical controller input e_1^* and e_2^* with a predetermined scalar N_e (normalization factor) to obtain their normalized counterparts e_{1N}^* and e_{2N}^*. Thus we have

$$N_e \cdot e_1^* + N_e \cdot e_2^* = N_e \cdot (e_1^* + e_2^*). \tag{2.21}$$

Furthermore, for a given scalar α we have

$$\alpha \cdot N_e \cdot e_1^* = N_e \cdot (\alpha \cdot e_1^*). \tag{2.22}$$

Thus input scaling has the properties of additivity and scaling and is thus a linear computational step. The same is valid for output scaling since it uses N_e^{-1} instead of N_e.

2.2.2 Fuzzification

Let the membership function $\int_E \mu_{LE}(e)/e$ defining the normalized fuzzy value LE be, in general, a nonlinear function, e.g., a triangular membership function. The fuzzification of e_1^* and e_2^* results in finding $\mu_{LE}(e_1^*)$ and $\mu_{LE}(e_2^*)$. Linearity requires

$$\mu_{LE}(e_1^*) + \mu_{LE}(e_2^*) = \mu_{LE}(e_1^* + e_2^*). \tag{2.23}$$

The above equality cannot be fulfilled because the membership function $\int_E \mu_{LE}(e)/e$ is nonlinear. Thus fuzzification in the case of nonlinear membership functions is a nonlinear computational step.

2.2.3 Rule Firing

Let the membership function $\int_U \mu_{LU}(u)/u$ defining the normalized fuzzy value LU be, in general, a nonlinear function. Then the result of rule firing given the normalized crisp controller input e_1^* will be:

$$\forall u : \mu'_{CLU}(u) = \min\left(\mu_{LU}(e_1^*), \mu_{LU}(u)\right). \tag{2.24}$$

Similarly, for the normalized crisp controller input e_2^* we obtain

$$\forall u : \mu''_{CLU}(u) = \min\left(\mu_{LE}(e_2^*)\mu_{LU}(u)\right). \tag{2.25}$$

Linearity requires

$$\forall u : \mu'_{CLU}(u) + \mu''_{CLU}(u) = \min\left(\mu_{LE}(e_1^* + e_2^*), \mu_{LU}(u)\right), \tag{2.26}$$

but the above equality does not hold because

- $\int_U \mu_{LU}(u)/u$ is a nonlinear membership function,
- $\int_U \mu'_{CLU}(u)/u$ and $\int_U \mu''_{CLU}(u)/u$ are nonlinear membership functions, (usually defined as piecewise linear functions),
- the function min is a nonlinear function.

Thus rule firing is a nonlinear computational step within the computational structure of an FLC.

2.2.4 Defuzzification

Let defuzzification be performed with the center of gravity method. Let furthermore u_1 and u_2 be the normalized defuzzified controller outputs obtained after defuzzification. That is,

$$u_1 = \frac{\int\limits_U \mu'_{CLU}(u)/u \cdot u}{\int\limits_U \mu'_{CLU}(u)/u}, \tag{2.27}$$

$$u_2 = \frac{\int\limits_U \mu''_{CLU}(u)/u \cdot u}{\int\limits_U \mu''_{CLU}(u)/u}. \tag{2.28}$$

Linearity requires

$$u_1 + u_2 = \frac{\int\limits_U (\mu'_{CLU}(u)/u + \mu''_{CLU}(u)/u) \cdot u}{\int\limits_U (\mu'_{CLU}(u)/u + \mu''_{CLU}(u)/u)}. \tag{2.29}$$

However, the above equality cannot be fulfilled since instead of it we have

$$u_1 + u_2 = \frac{\int\limits_U \mu'_{CLU}(u)/u \cdot u}{\int\limits_U \mu'_{CLU}(u)/u} + \frac{\int\limits_U \mu''_{CLU}(u)/u \cdot u}{\int\limits_U \mu''_{CLU}(u)/u}. \tag{2.30}$$

This shows that the nonlinearity of the computational step of defuzzification comes from the normalization of the products $\int_U \mu'_{CLU}(u)/u \cdot u$ and $\int_U \mu''_{CLU}(u)/u \cdot u$.

From all of the above it is readily seen that an FLC is a nonlinear TE, its sources of nonlinearity being the nonlinearity of membership functions, rule firing, and defuzzification.

However, in the case of a Takagi–Sugeno FLC-1 each single fuzzy rule is a linear TE for all controller inputs (state vectors) belonging to the center of the fuzzy region specified by the if-part of this rule. At the same time, for controller inputs outside the center of a fuzzy region this same fuzzy rule is a nonlinear TE. Because of the latter, the set of all fuzzy rules of a Takagi–Sugeno FLC-1 defines a nonlinear TE (for details see Sect. 3.1.2). In the case of a Takagi–Sugeno FLC-2 we have that each fuzzy rule defines a linear TE everywhere in a given fuzzy region (for details see Sect. 3.2.3).

2.2.5 Discontinuities in the Controller-Output

Certain characteristics of the membership functions defining the fuzzy values of the controller inputs may result in a discontinuous TE which in turn would affect the FLC's performance negatively. A discontinuous TE is mainly due to the presence of points of discontinuity in the membership functions defining the fuzzy values of the controller inputs. This can be illustrated by a SISO FLC with x as the controller input and u as the controller output and consisting of the following fuzzy rules

R_C^1: *if* $x = \mathrm{S}_x^1$ *then* $u = \mathrm{B}_u^1$,

R_C^2: *if* $x = \mathrm{B}_x^2$ *then* $u = \mathrm{S}_u^2$.

Figure 2.7 shows the membership functions assumed for the fuzzy values of x and u. Figure 2.8 shows the corresponding TE from the domain X of x to the domain U of u after defuzzification using an arbitrary defuzzification method. The crisp values x_1^* and x_3^* are discontinuity points of the membership functions for the fuzzy values of x and the u_i^* are the defuzzified controller outputs for the corresponding x_i^*.

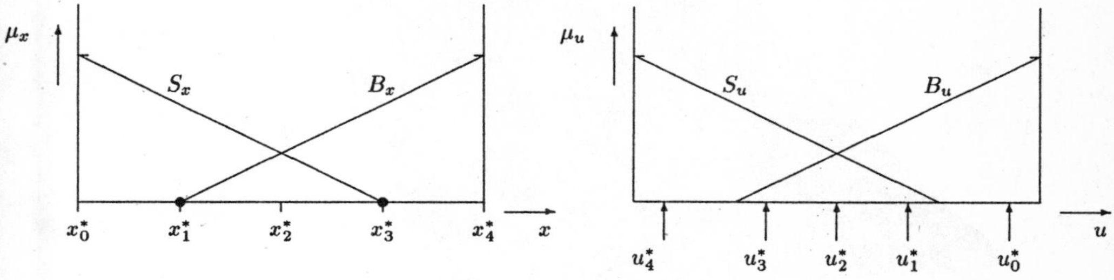

Fig. 2.7. Membership functions for the fuzzy values in R_C^1 and R_C^2

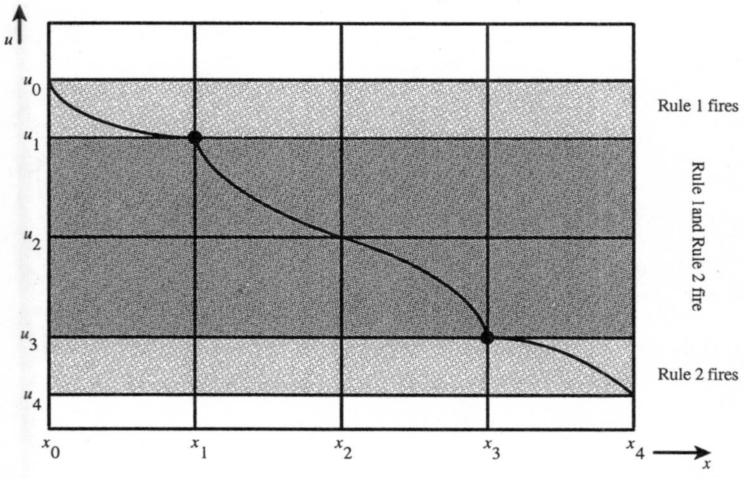

Fig. 2.8. Discontinuities in the transfer characteristic of an FLC

The commonly used triangular and trapezoidal membership functions both exhibit points of discontinuity. Figure 2.9 shows the controller output of an FLC consisting of the above two fuzzy rules where the resulting discontinuous TE can be recognized easily at the marked edges.

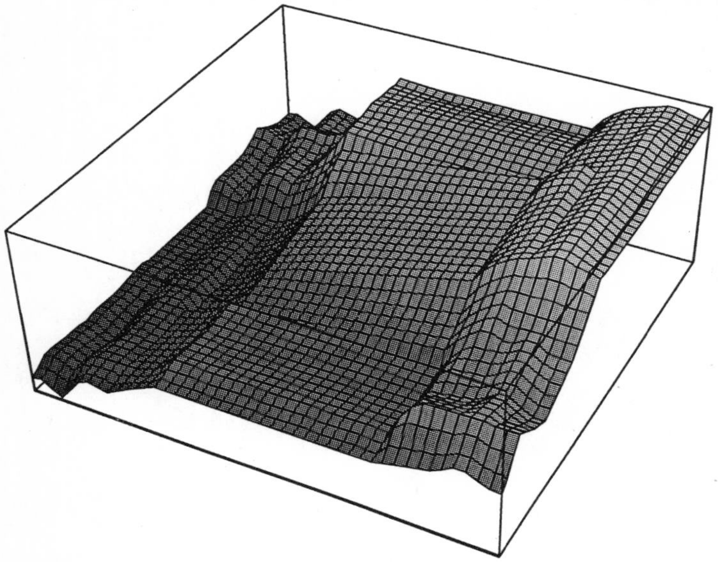

Fig. 2.9. Transfer characteristic of an FLC

However, if a discontinuous TE actually deteriorates the performance of the FLC, this can be avoided by either one of the following two ways:

- smoothing out the membership functions,
- *low-pass filtering* of the controller outputs.

Other characteristics of the membership functions defining the fuzzy values of the controller inputs are presented in detail in [7, Sect. 3.1.1].

2.3 Rule-Based Conventional TE

This section deals with the relationship between conventional TEs and *rule-based TEs*. We show the transition from a conventional TE to a *crisp rule-based TE*, and finally to a *fuzzy rule-based TE*, that is an FLC.

Conventional TEs can be classified into linear and nonlinear and they are dynamical systems in so far that they are represented by an analytic function of the controller-input vector $\mathbf{x} = (x_1, x_2, \ldots, x_n)$. Linear TEs are described as a linear mapping from $\mathbf{x}$ to $\mathbf{u}$ which in the case of a MISO TE corresponds to

$$u = f(\mathbf{x}) = a_1 \cdot x_1 + a_2 \cdot x_2 + \cdots + a_n \cdot x_n. \tag{2.31}$$

A nonlinear TE is obtained when u is given as a nonlinear function of the components of $\mathbf{x}$.

Example 2.3.1. From the equation

$$\frac{1}{u} = \frac{b_1}{x_1} + \frac{b_2}{x_2}, \tag{2.32}$$

we obtain the nonlinear function

$$u = \frac{x_1 \cdot x_2}{b_1 \cdot x_1 + b_2 \cdot x_2}. \tag{2.33}$$

Let the domains of the controller inputs x_i be X_i, $i = 1, \ldots, n$. Furthermore, let each X_i be partitioned into m disjoint intervals as

$$I_{i1}, \ldots, I_{im}, \quad \text{where} \quad \forall j, \ell : I_{ij} \cap I_{i\ell} = \emptyset. \tag{2.34}$$

Thus each x_i takes disjoint *interval values* $I_{i1}, \ldots, I_{im}$ instead of crisp (pointwise) values. An arbitrary interval value of x_i will be denoted as I_i, i.e., $I_i \in I_{i1}, \ldots, I_{im}$ Then the **k**-th *interval rule* describing the relationship between the interval controller inputs and the single crisp controller output is given as

$$R_{\mathrm{C}}^{\mathbf{k}}\text{: } \textit{if } \mathbf{x} \in (I_1^{\mathbf{k}}, \ldots, I_n^{\mathbf{k}})^T \textit{ then } u = u^{\mathbf{k}},$$

or

$$R_{\mathrm{C}}^{\mathbf{k}}\text{: } \textit{if } x_1 \in I_1^{\mathbf{k}} \text{ and } \ldots \text{and } x_n \in I_n^{\mathbf{k}} \textit{ then } u = u^{\mathbf{k}},$$

where $u^{\mathbf{k}} \in U$ is the crisp value of the controller output in the **k**-th interval rule and $I_j^{\mathbf{k}}$ is the interval-value of x_j in this same interval rule.

The latter interval rules can also be rewritten in the form from Sect. 1.2.1 as

$$R_{\mathrm{C}}^{\mathbf{k}}\text{: } \textit{if } \mathbf{x} = \mathbf{I}^{\mathbf{k}} \textit{ then } u = u^{\mathbf{k}},$$

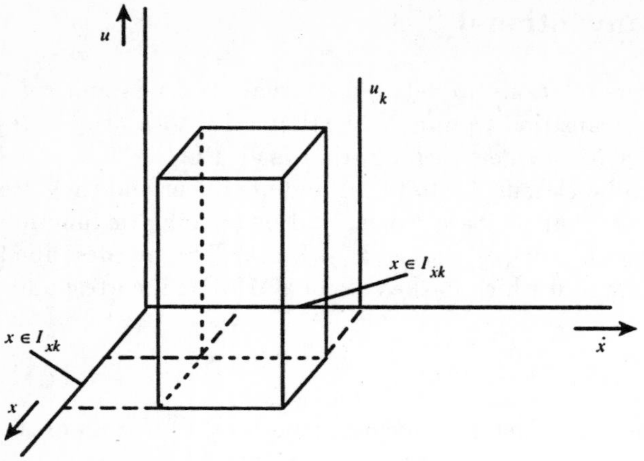

Fig. 2.10. Interval region in the state space

where $\mathbf{I^k} = (I_1^{\mathbf{k}}, \ldots, I_n^{\mathbf{k}})^T$ is the **k**-th interval region.

This means that in the case of m interval values for each element of $\mathbf{x}$ we obtain m^n *interval regions* in the controller-input space (i.e., the state space). Each interval region in turn defines one interval rule $R_{\mathrm{C}}^{\mathbf{k}}$ (for a two-dimensional state-vector see Fig. 2.10).

In terms of membership functions, each interval value $I_j^{\mathbf{k}}$ can be represented as a fuzzy set on the domain X_j where the elements of this fuzzy set have membership degrees equal to either 0 or 1 (see Fig. 2.11).

For the **k**-th interval rule of a second-order TE in which $x_1 = x$ and $x_2 = \dot{x}$ and thus $\mathbf{x} = (x, \dot{x})^T$, we obtain

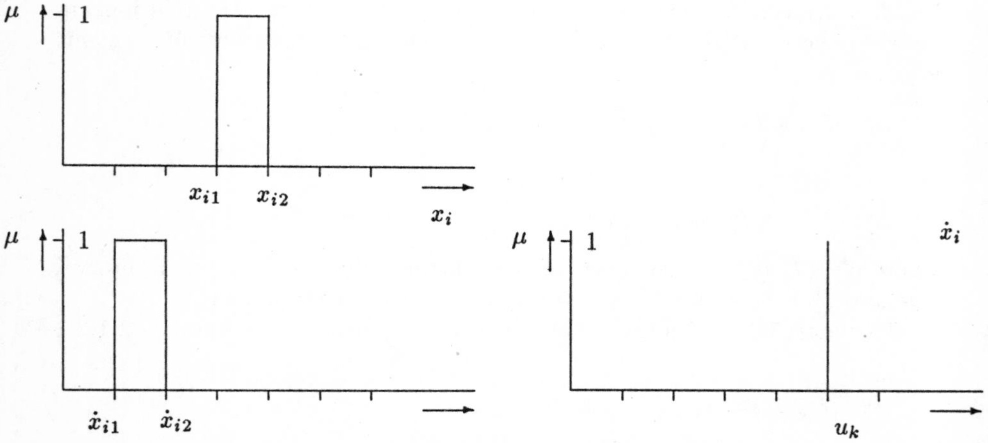

Fig. 2.11. Membership function in the case of interval values

$R_{\mathbf{C}}^{\mathbf{k}}$: *if* $\mathbf{x} = (I_x^{\mathbf{k}}, I_{\dot{x}}^{\mathbf{k}})^T$ *then* $u = u^{\mathbf{k}}$.

The membership functions of $I_x^{\mathbf{k}}$, $I_{\dot{x}}^{\mathbf{k}}$, and $u^{\mathbf{k}}$ are given as

$$\forall x : \mu_{I_x^{\mathbf{k}}}(x) = \begin{cases} 1 & \text{if } x \in I^{\mathbf{k}}{}_x \\ 0 & \text{otherwise,} \end{cases} \tag{2.35}$$

$$\forall \dot{x} : \mu_{I_{\dot{x}}^{\mathbf{k}}}(\dot{x}) = \begin{cases} 1 & \text{if } \dot{x} \in I_{\dot{x}}^{\mathbf{k}} \\ 0 & \text{otherwise,} \end{cases} \tag{2.36}$$

$$\forall u : \mu_{u^{\mathbf{k}}}(u) = \begin{cases} 1 & \text{if } u = u^{\mathbf{k}} \\ 0 & \text{otherwise.} \end{cases} \tag{2.37}$$

Computing the controller output for a given crisp controller input is done by the consecutive application of fuzzification, rule firing, and defuzzification since the controller inputs and controller outputs are defined on their original physical domains rather than on normalized domains.

Let x^* and $\dot{x}^*$ be crisp controller inputs belonging to $I_x^{\mathbf{k}}$ and $I_{\dot{x}}^{\mathbf{k}}$ respectively. As already described in Sect. 2.2, the computational step of fuzzification provides the degrees of satisfaction of different fuzzy regions. In this case we have instead interval regions and thus we obtain the following for the degrees of satisfaction of the different interval regions:

1. From x^* we obtain $\mu_{I_x^{\mathbf{k}}}(x^*) = 1$, and for all $\mathbf{r} \neq \mathbf{k}$, $\mu_{I_x^{\mathbf{r}}}(x^*) = 0$ because $I_x^{\mathbf{k}} \cap I_x^r = \emptyset$.
2. From $\dot{x}^*$ we obtain $\mu_{I_{\dot{x}}^{\mathbf{k}}}(\dot{x}^*) = 1$ and for all $\mathbf{r} \neq \mathbf{k}$, $\mu_{I_{\dot{x}}^{\mathbf{r}}}(\dot{x}^*) = 0$.
3. Finally, we compute $\min(\mu_{I_x^{\mathbf{k}}}(x^*), \mu_{I_{\dot{x}}^{\mathbf{k}}}(\dot{x}^*)) = 1$, and thus obtain that for the given controller input only the interval region $\mathbf{I}^{\mathbf{k}}$ is satisfied to degree 1.

The computational step of rule firing will now provide the clipped controller output in terms of the membership function $\int_U \mu_{Cu^{\mathbf{k}}}(u)/u$. The result is

$$\forall u \in U : \mu_{Cu^{\mathbf{k}}}(u) = \min(1, \mu_{u^{\mathbf{k}}}(u)) = \mu_{u^{\mathbf{k}}}(u^{\mathbf{k}}) = 1, \tag{2.38}$$

since the only u which has degree of membership 1 to $\int_U \mu_{u^{\mathbf{k}}}(u)/u$ is $u^{\mathbf{k}}$. Thus the clipped controller output of rule $R_{\mathbf{C}}^{\mathbf{k}}$ is $u^{\mathbf{k}}$ for all rules $R_{\mathbf{C}}^{\mathbf{k}}$.

Finally, the computational step of defuzzification gives the scalar, global controller output as

$$u = \frac{\int_U \mu_{u^{\mathbf{k}}}(u^{\mathbf{k}})/u^{\mathbf{k}} \cdot u^{\mathbf{k}}}{\int_U \mu_{u^{\mathbf{k}}}(u^{\mathbf{k}})/u^{\mathbf{k}}} = \frac{0 + 0 + \cdots + 1 \cdot u^{\mathbf{k}} + \cdots + 0}{0 + 0 + \cdots + 1 + \cdots + 0} = u^{\mathbf{k}}. \tag{2.39}$$

The change to a set of fuzzy rules employing with fuzzy values rather than interval values can be done in the following two consecutive steps (see also Fig. 2.12):

1. Enlarging the interval values within the domain of each controller-input space so that they overlap instead of being disjoint intervals.
2. Fuzzifying the membership functions representing the overlapping interval values so that the degrees of membership are within the unit interval $[0, 1]$ rather than in the set $\{0, 1\}$.

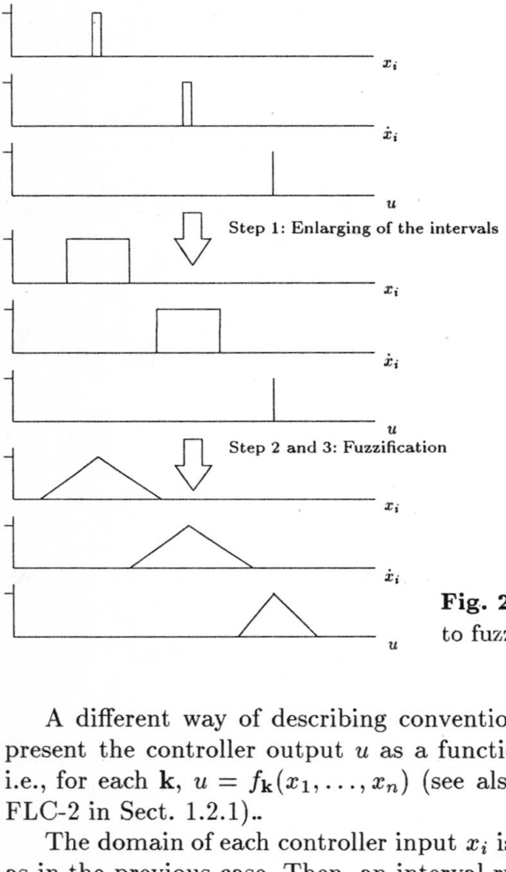

Fig. 2.12. The change from crisp to fuzzy values

A different way of describing conventional TEs by means of rules is to present the controller output u as a function of the crisp controller inputs, i.e., for each $\mathbf{k}$, $u = f_{\mathbf{k}}(x_1, \ldots, x_n)$ (see also the Takagi–Sugeno FLC-1 and FLC-2 in Sect. 1.2.1)..

The domain of each controller input x_i is divided into m disjoint intervals as in the previous case. Then, an interval rule is given as

$$R_{\mathrm{C}}^{\mathbf{k}}\text{: } \textit{if } \mathbf{x} = (I_1^{\mathbf{k}}, \ldots, I_n^{\mathbf{k}})^T \textit{ then } u = f_{\mathbf{k}}(x_1, \ldots, x_n).$$

In this case the degree of satisfaction of each interval region $\mathbf{I}^{\mathbf{k}}$ by a given crisp controller input $\mathbf{x}^*$ is given as

$$\mu^{\mathbf{k}}(\mathbf{x}^*) = \begin{cases} 1 & \text{if } \mathbf{x}^* \in (I_1^{\mathbf{k}}, \ldots, I_n^{\mathbf{k}})^T \\ 0 & \text{otherwise.} \end{cases} \tag{2.40}$$

The equation above implies that given a particular crisp controller input $\mathbf{x}^*$ only **one** interval rule can fire. Furthermore, for each $\mathbf{k} \neq \mathbf{r}$ we have that $f_{\mathbf{k}}(x_1, \ldots, x_n)$ is different from $f_{\mathbf{r}}(x_1, \ldots, x_n)$.

Example 2.3.2. The above type of interval rules for a second-order FLC are

R^1_C: *if* $\mathbf{x} = (I^1_x, I^1_{\dot{x}})^T$ *then* $u = f_1(x, \dot{x})$,

R^2_C: *if* $\mathbf{x} = (I^2_x, I^2_{\dot{x}})^T$ *then* $u = f_2(x, \dot{x})$,

where

$$f_1(x, \dot{x}) = a_{01} + a_{11} \cdot x + a_{21} \cdot \dot{x}; \quad x \in I^1_x, \quad \dot{x} \in I^1_{\dot{x}}, \tag{2.41}$$

$$f_2(x, \dot{x}) = a_{02} + a_{12} \cdot x + a_{22} \cdot \dot{x}; \quad x \in I^2_x, \quad \dot{x} \in I^2_{\dot{x}}. \tag{2.42}$$

See also Fig. 2.13.

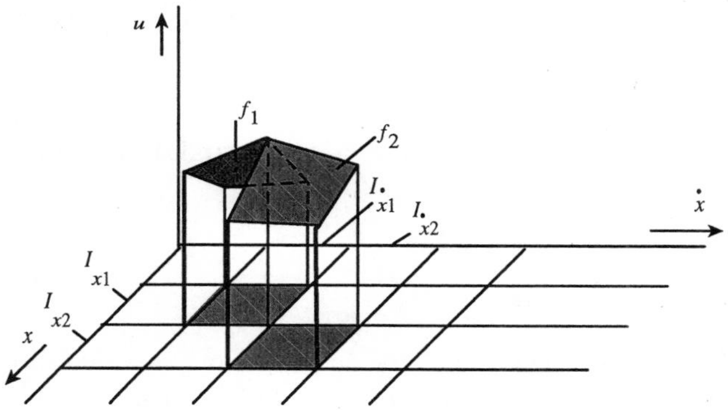

Fig. 2.13. Graphical representation of interval rules with analytical controller output

It is easily seen that making the interval values of the controller inputs overlap and then fuzzifying the membership functions lead to the Takagi–Sugeno FLCs. In this case the fuzzy rules from the present example will be of the form

R^1_C: *if* $\mathbf{x} = \mathbf{LX^1}$ *then* $u = f_1(x, \dot{x})$,

R^2_C: *if* $\mathbf{x} = \mathbf{LX^2}$ *then* $u = f_2(x, \dot{x})$.

In the above fuzzy rules we have, for example,

- $\mathbf{LX^1} = (LX^1_{x1}, L\dot{X}^1_{\dot{x}1})^T$ is a fuzzy region in which LX^1_{x1} and $L\dot{X}^1_{\dot{x}1}$ are particular fuzzy values of the controller inputs x and $\dot{x}$ respectively,
- $\mathbf{LX^2} = (LX^2_{x1}, L\dot{X}^2_{\dot{x}2})^T$ is a fuzzy region in which LX^2_{x1} and $L\dot{X}^2_{\dot{x}2}$ are particular fuzzy values of the controller inputs x and $\dot{x}$ respectively. Thus we have that the two fuzzy regions $\mathbf{LX^1}$ and $\mathbf{LX^2}$ are neighboring fuzzy regions,
- the fuzzy values of the controller-input variables are given by the following membership functions:

1. $\int_X \mu_{LX^1_{x1}}(x)/x = \int_X \mu_{LX^2_{x1}}(x)/x$ for LX^1_{x1} and LX^2_{x1},
2. $\int_{\dot{X}} \mu_{L\dot{X}^1_{\dot{x}1}}(\dot{x})/\dot{x}$ and $\int_{\dot{X}} \mu_{L\dot{X}^2_{\dot{x}2}}(\dot{x})/\dot{x}$ for $L\dot{X}^1_{\dot{x}1}$ and $L\dot{X}^2_{\dot{x}2}$.

In what follows we will illustrate the computational structure for the Takagi–Sugeno fuzzy rules with the help of the above fuzzy rules R^1_C and R^2_C.

Let us first remark here that the computational steps of input and output scaling are omitted since FLCs of this type do not use normalized domains, that is, the domains X of x, $\dot{X}$ of $\dot{x}$, and U of u are not normalized.

Let $\mathbf{x} = (x, \dot{x})^T$ and x^* and $\dot{x}^*$ be the crisp values of the two controller-input variables x and $\dot{x}$ respectively. Thus the degree of satisfaction of the fuzzy regions $\mathbf{LX^1}$ and $\mathbf{LX^2}$ are computed as follows during the computational step of fuzzification

$$\mu^1(\mathbf{x}^*) = \min(\mu_{LX^1_{x1}}(x^*), \mu_{L\dot{X}^1_{\dot{x}1}}(\dot{x}^*)), \tag{2.43}$$

$$\mu^2(\mathbf{x}^*) = \min(\mu_{LX^2_{x1}}(x^*), \mu_{L\dot{X}^2_{\dot{x}2}}(\dot{x}^*)). \tag{2.44}$$

At the computational step of rule firing the crisp controller outputs u^1 and u^2 of R_1 and R_2 are first computed as

$$u^1 = f_1(x^*, \dot{x}^*) = a_{01} + a_{11} \cdot x^* + a_{21} \cdot \dot{x}^*, \tag{2.45}$$

$$u^2 = f_2(x^*, \dot{x}^*) = a_{02} + a_{12} \cdot x^* + a_{22} \cdot \dot{x}^*. \tag{2.46}$$

Since in the case of a Takagi–Sugeno FLC, the controller outputs take only crisp values, we do not have in this case the equivalent of clipped controller outputs.

Finally the global controller output u is obtained by taking the weighted average of u^1 and u^2 where the respective weights are the degrees of satisfaction μ^1 and μ^2 of the fuzzy regions $\mathbf{LX^1}$ and $\mathbf{LX^2}$, that is

$$u = \frac{\mu^1(\mathbf{x}^*) \cdot u^1 + \mu^2(\mathbf{x}^*) \cdot u^2}{\mu^1(\mathbf{x}^*) + \mu^2(\mathbf{x}^*)}. \tag{2.47}$$

In [14] one can find a detailed description of the conditions under which a conventional PID controller is equivalent to an FLC of the PID type.

2.4 Stability in Model Based Fuzzy Control

Despite the fact that we repeatedly used the concept of stability in Chap. 1 we have not yet attempted any detailed discussion of it and its use in model based fuzzy control. We will not aim at an exhaustive description of stability, but will rather present only the concepts and results needed for the design of the particular types of FLCs that are the subject of this book. Since we will limit our discussion of stability to a number of well-known definitions and results, the reader can find the missing details in easily available literature sources such as [28, Chaps. 3–4], [40, Chap. 5], and [6, Chaps. 2–5].

Before we begin our discussion of stability let us first introduce some concepts and notation related to the representation of nonlinear and linear open and closed loop systems, which we will use throughout this section and the rest of the book.

A *nonlinear autonomous (time invariant) open loop system* is represented in the form

$$\dot{\mathbf{x}} = \mathbf{f}(\mathbf{x}, \mathbf{u}), \tag{2.48}$$

where $\mathbf{f}$ is a $n \times 1$ nonlinear vector function, $\mathbf{x}$ is the $n \times 1$ state vector, and $\mathbf{u}$ is the $m \times 1$ input vector. The components of both $\mathbf{x}$ and $\mathbf{u}$ are functions of time.

Let also the *nonlinear control law* for the above nonlinear autonomous open loop system be given as

$$\mathbf{u} = \mathbf{g}(\mathbf{x}), \tag{2.49}$$

and thus the *nonlinear autonomous closed loop system* is given by

$$\dot{\mathbf{x}} = \mathbf{f}(\mathbf{x}, \mathbf{g}(\mathbf{x})) = \mathbf{f}'(\mathbf{x}). \tag{2.50}$$

A *nonlinear nonautonomous (time varying) open loop system* is represented as

$$\dot{\mathbf{x}} = \mathbf{f}(\mathbf{x}, \mathbf{u}, t), \tag{2.51}$$

where the additional time parameter t is added to denote the fact that $\mathbf{f}$ depends *explicitly* on time.

The nonlinear control law for the above nonlinear nonautonomous system is given in the form

$$\mathbf{u} = \mathbf{g}(\mathbf{x}, t), \tag{2.52}$$

and consequently, the *nonlinear nonautonomous closed loop system* is

$$\dot{\mathbf{x}} = \mathbf{f}(\mathbf{x}, \mathbf{g}(\mathbf{x}, t), t) = \mathbf{f}'(\mathbf{x}, t). \tag{2.53}$$

The fundamental difference between autonomous and nonautonomous systems lies in the fact that the state trajectory of an autonomous system is independent of the initial time, while that of a nonautonomous system generally is not. It is this difference that requires us to consider the initial time explicitly when defining stability concepts for nonautonomous systems.

A *linear autonomous open loop system* is usually represented in the form

$$\dot{\mathbf{x}} = \mathbf{A} \cdot \mathbf{x} + \mathbf{B} \cdot \mathbf{u}, \tag{2.54}$$

where $\mathbf{A}$ is an $(n \times n)$ *system matrix*, $\mathbf{B}$ is an $(n \times m)$ *input matrix*, $\mathbf{x}$ is an $(n \times 1)$ state vector, and $\mathbf{u}$ is $(m \times 1)$. The components of $\mathbf{x}$ and $\mathbf{u}$ are functions of time while the two matrices $\mathbf{A}$ and $\mathbf{B}$ are constant and not functions of time. Thus the open loop system is autonomous.

Normally, the above equation is written together with the output equation in the form

$$\mathbf{y} = \mathbf{C} \cdot \mathbf{x}, \tag{2.55}$$

where $\mathbf{C}$ is a $(m \times n)$ matrix, but for the sake of simplicity we will assume throughout the book that $\mathbf{y} = \mathbf{x}$ and and thus omit the output equation from the representation of a linear system.

The control law for the above system is of the form

$$\mathbf{u} = \mathbf{K} \cdot \mathbf{x}, \tag{2.56}$$

where $\mathbf{K}$ is an $(m \times n)$ *gain matrix* representing a *state controller*, and thus the *linear autonomous closed loop system* is of the form

$$\dot{\mathbf{x}} = (\mathbf{A} + \mathbf{B} \cdot \mathbf{K}) \cdot \mathbf{x} = \mathbf{A}' \cdot \mathbf{x}. \tag{2.57}$$

If the matrices $\mathbf{A}$ and $\mathbf{B}$ are explicitly dependent on time then we have a *linear nonautonomous open loop system* represented as

$$\dot{\mathbf{x}} = \mathbf{A}(t) \cdot \mathbf{x} + \mathbf{B}(t) \cdot \mathbf{u}, \tag{2.58}$$

and the control law for the above system is then of the form

$$\mathbf{u} = \mathbf{K}(t) \cdot \mathbf{x}, \tag{2.59}$$

and consequently, the *linear nonautonomous closed loop system* is represented as

$$\dot{\mathbf{x}} = (\mathbf{A}(t) + \mathbf{B}(t) \cdot \mathbf{K}(t)) \cdot \mathbf{x} = \mathbf{A}'(t) \cdot \mathbf{x}, \tag{2.60}$$

where $\mathbf{A}'(t) = \mathbf{A}(t) + \mathbf{B}(t) \cdot \mathbf{K}(t)$.

Finally, we impose some constraints on the permissible form of the vector function $\mathbf{f}'$ for any particular input $\mathbf{u}$. Namely, the function $\mathbf{f}'$ is such that the equation

$$\dot{\mathbf{x}} = \mathbf{f}'(\mathbf{x}, t), \tag{2.61}$$

has a unique solution over $[t_0, \infty)$ which depends continuously on the initial conditions $\mathbf{x}_0$ and t_0, and $\mathbf{f}(\mathbf{0}, t) = 0$ for each $t \geq 0$. Here we have that $\mathbf{x}_0 = \mathbf{x}(t_0)$ where t_0 denotes the initial time.

In what follows we will use $\mathbf{x}(t)$ to denote any solution of the closed/open loop equations corresponding to an initial condition $\mathbf{x}_0 = \mathbf{x}(0)$. When the time t varies from zero to infinity, the solution $\mathbf{x}(t)$ can be represented as a curve in the state space. Such a curve is called a *state trajectory*, or *system trajectory.*

The above constraints on the permissible form of $\mathbf{f}'$ imply that there will be one and only one trajectory passing through any given point in the state space. Another constraint on $\mathbf{f}'$ is the requirement that it should be *continuously differentiable.* These constraints on the permissible form of $\mathbf{f}'$ will be assumed throughout the rest of the book.

2.4.1 Equilibrium Points

For nonlinear autonomous systems of the form

$$\dot{\mathbf{x}} = \mathbf{f}'(\mathbf{x}), \tag{2.62}$$

equilibrium points (states) $\mathbf{x}^\star$ are defined as:

$$\mathbf{0} = \mathbf{f}'(\mathbf{x}^\star), \tag{2.63}$$

which means that if $\mathbf{x}(t)$ is once equal to $\mathbf{x}^\star$, it remains equal to it for all future times. The above definition also applies to linear autonomous systems.

For nonlinear nonautonomous systems of the form

$$\dot{\mathbf{x}} = \mathbf{f}'(\mathbf{x}, t), \tag{2.64}$$

equilibrium points (states) $\mathbf{x}^\star$ are defined as

$$\mathbf{0} = \mathbf{f}'(\mathbf{x}^\star, t) \quad \forall t \geq t_0. \tag{2.65}$$

The above definition applies to linear nonautonomous systems as well. A nonlinear system can have several (or infinitely many) equilibrium points. A linear autonomous system of the form

$$\dot{\mathbf{x}} = \mathbf{A}' \cdot \mathbf{x}, \tag{2.66}$$

has a single equilibrium point (the origin $\mathbf{0}$) if $\mathbf{A}'$ is not singular, and infinitely many equilibrium points if $\mathbf{A}'$ is singular. In the latter case the equilibrium points are all confined in the subspace defined by $\mathbf{A}' \cdot \mathbf{x} = \mathbf{0}$. The linear nonautonomous system

$$\dot{\mathbf{x}} = \mathbf{A}'(t) \cdot \mathbf{x}, \tag{2.67}$$

also has a unique equilibrium point at the origin unless $\mathbf{A}'(t)$ is always singular.

In the literature on linear and nonlinear control, for notational and analytical simplicity, the equilibrium point normally considered is the origin of the state space. However, if a specific equilibrium point $\mathbf{x}^\star$, different from the origin, is to be considered then one can transform the equations defining the open/closed loop system in such a way that the equilibrium point becomes again the origin of the state space [28, Sect. 3.1].

Let us assume that the equilibrium point to be considered is $\mathbf{x}^\star \neq \mathbf{0}$. Then we can introduce the new state vector

$$\mathbf{e} = \mathbf{x} - \mathbf{x}^\star, \tag{2.68}$$

and substituting $\mathbf{x} = \mathbf{e} + \mathbf{x}^\star$ into say

$$\dot{\mathbf{x}} = \mathbf{f}'(\mathbf{x}, t), \tag{2.69}$$

we obtain a new equation involving the state vector $\mathbf{e}$,

$$\dot{\mathbf{e}} = \mathbf{f}'(\mathbf{e} + \mathbf{x}^\star, t). \tag{2.70}$$

The one-to-one correspondence between the solutions of the above two equations is easily verified, and also that $\mathbf{e} = \mathbf{0}$, the solution corresponding to $\mathbf{x} = \mathbf{x}^\star$, is an equilibrium point of the latter equation. Thus the study of the behavior of (2.69) in the neighborhood of $\mathbf{x}^\star$ will produce results equivalent to studying the behavior of (2.70) in the neighborhood of the origin.

Very often one is also interested in the so-called *stability of motion* rather than just stability around an equilibrium point, i.e., whether a system will remain close to an original trajectory it has been following, when perturbed slightly away from it. However, the motion stability problem can be easily transformed into an equivalent stability problem around an equilibrium point, though the transformed system becomes a nonautonomous one if it was autonomous before the transformation [28, Sect. 3.1].

Let $\mathbf{x}^*(t)$ be the solution corresponding to an initial condition $\mathbf{x}^*(0) = \mathbf{x}_0$ of the autonomous system

$$\dot{\mathbf{x}} = \mathbf{f}'(\mathbf{x}). \tag{2.71}$$

Let us now perturb the initial condition $\mathbf{x}^*(0)$ so that it becomes $\mathbf{x}(0) = \mathbf{x}_0 + \delta\mathbf{x}_0$, and study the associated variation of the motion error

$$\mathbf{e}(t) = \mathbf{x}(t) - \mathbf{x}^*(t), \tag{2.72}$$

as illustrated in Fig. 2.14.

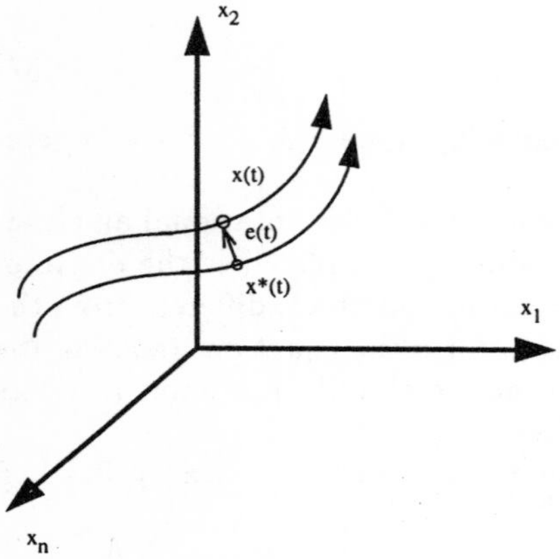

Fig. 2.14. Nominal and perturbed motions

Since both $\mathbf{x}^*(t)$ and $\mathbf{x}(t)$ are solutions of (2.71), we have

$$\dot{\mathbf{x}}^* = \mathbf{f}'(\mathbf{x}^*) \qquad \mathbf{x}(0) = \mathbf{x}_0, \tag{2.73}$$

and

$$\dot{\mathbf{x}} = \mathbf{f}'(\mathbf{x}) \qquad \mathbf{x}(0) = \mathbf{x}_0 + \delta\mathbf{x}_0, \tag{2.74}$$

and thus, $\mathbf{e}(t)$ satisfies the following nonautonomous differential equation

$$\dot{\mathbf{e}} = \mathbf{f}'(\mathbf{x}^* + \mathbf{e}, t) - \mathbf{f}'(\mathbf{x}^*, t) = \mathbf{h}'(\mathbf{e}, t). \tag{2.75}$$

with initial condition $\mathbf{e}(0) = \delta\mathbf{x}(0)$. Since $\mathbf{h}'(\mathbf{0}, t) = \mathbf{0}$, the new system, with $\mathbf{e}$ as state vector and $\mathbf{h}'$ instead of $\mathbf{f}'$, has an equilibrium point at the origin of the state space. Therefore, instead of studying the deviation of $\mathbf{x}(t)$ from $\mathbf{x}^*(t)$ for the original system (2.71), one may simply study the stability of (2.75) with respect to the equilibrium point $\mathbf{0}$. However, the dynamics of (2.75) is nonautonomous, due to the presence of the trajectory $\mathbf{x}^*(t)$ on the right hand side of (2.75). Thus, the study of (2.75) requires design and analysis techniques for nonautonomous systems.

For nonlinear nonautonomous systems, the stability of the motion problem can also be transformed to a stability problem around the origin for an equivalent nonautonomous system. If the original system is a linear autonomous one, then the equivalent system is still autonomous since we have

$$\dot{\mathbf{e}} = \mathbf{A}' \cdot \mathbf{e}. \tag{2.76}$$

In the next two sections we will consider the different stability properties of an equilibrium point. When presenting these properties we consider an equilibrium point identical with the origin of the state space since we have already seen that: (i) the study of stability for an arbitrary equilibrium point can be reduced to the study of stability of the origin, and (ii) the study of stability of motion again can be reduced to a study of stability of the origin, though the resulting system is in this case a nonautonomous one.

2.4.2 Stability Concepts for Autonomous Systems

Consider the autonomous system from (2.50). Let $\mathbf{B}_R$ denote a spherical region (*ball*) in the state space defined by $\| \mathbf{x} \| \leq R$, for some $R > 0$, and $\mathbf{S}_R$ denotes the sphere itself defined by $\| \mathbf{x} \| = R$. Here, $\| \bullet \|$ denotes an arbitrary norm, e.g., a Euclidian norm.

Stable Equilibrium

The equilibrium point $\mathbf{x}^\star = \mathbf{0}$ of (2.50) is *a stable equilibrium* if for any $R > 0$, there exists $r > 0$, such that if $\| \mathbf{x}(0) \| < r$, then $\| \mathbf{x}(t) \| < R$. Otherwise the equilibrium point is *unstable.*

The above definition means that a trajectory can be made to remain within an arbitrary small distance from $\mathbf{x}^\star$ by starting sufficiently close to it. The geometrical interpretation of a stable equilibrium point is illustrated in Fig. 2.15.

More formally, the definition states that the origin is stable, if, given that we do not want the state trajectory to leave a ball of arbitrarily specified radius $\mathbf{B}_R$, a value r can be found such that a trajectory starting within $\mathbf{B}_r$ at time 0 is guaranteed to stay within $\mathbf{B}_R$. Conversely, an equilibrium point is unstable if there exists at least one ball $\mathbf{B}_R$, such that for every $r > 0$, no matter how small, it is always possible for the trajectory to start somewhere within $\mathbf{B}_r$ and eventually leave $\mathbf{B}_R$ (see Fig. 2.15).

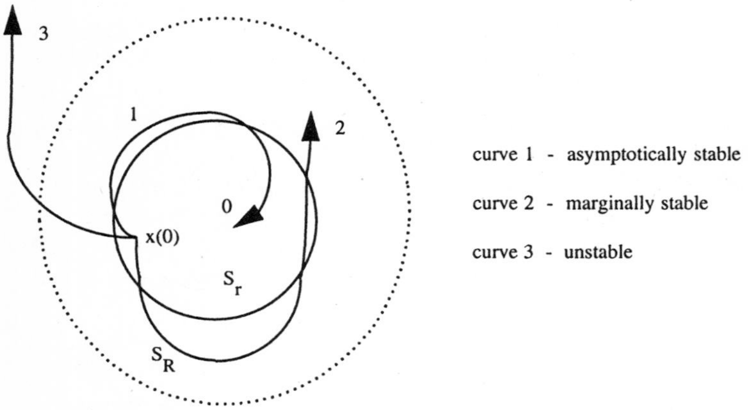

Fig. 2.15. A stable equilibrium

In the context of a fuzzy state space we first have that it is a closed set since all state variables take their values in the closed interval $X = [a, b] \subset \mathbb{R}$. Thus the fuzzy state space is $X^n \subset \mathbb{R}^n$ and cannot be identified with the whole state space. The spaces of the the input and output variables are also closed sets since they take their values also in closed intervals of reals. Second, since the fuzzy state space cannot extend beyond X^n this means that the radius R of the larger ball $\mathbf{B}_R$ cannot be extended to infinity, but there is instead one largest ball $\mathbf{B}_{R_{\max}}$ (its center at the origin of X^n) with the maximum radius $R_{\max}$.

However, in many applications, it is not enough that a trajectory, having started sufficiently close to the equilibrium point, remains close to it. In addition one wants this trajectory to converge to (approach) the equilibrium point as t goes to infinity. This additional requirement is captured by the notion of asymptotic stability.

Asymptotic Stability

An equilibrium point $\mathbf{0}$ is *asymptotically stable* if it is stable and if in addition there exists some $r > 0$ such that $\| \mathbf{x}(0) \| < r$ implies that $\| \mathbf{x}(t) \| \rightarrow \mathbf{0}$ as $t \rightarrow \infty$.

The above notion of stability means that the origin is stable and, in addition, trajectories that start close to the origin converge to it as time goes to infinity (see Fig. 2.15). The ball $\mathbf{B}_r$ is called *a domain of attraction* of the equilibrium point, while *the* domain of attraction of the equilibrium point refers to the largest such region, i.e., to the set of all points such that trajectories initiated at these points eventually converge to the origin. In the context of the fuzzy state space, it is obvious that *the* domain of attraction is the largest ball $\mathbf{B}_{R_{\max}}$ contained in X^n.

Again, in many applications, it is still not enough to know that the system converges to the equilibrium point after an infinite period of time. In addition, one needs an estimate for how fast the system converges to the equilibrium point. In this case, the concept of exponential stability is used.

Exponential Stability

An equilibrium point $\mathbf{0}$ is *exponentially stable* if there exist two strictly positive numbers α and λ such that

$$\| \mathbf{x}(t) \| \ \leq \alpha \cdot \| \mathbf{x}(0) \| \cdot e^{-\lambda t} \qquad \forall t > 0 \tag{2.77}$$

in some ball $\mathbf{B}_r$ around the origin.

In other words, the above definition means that the trajectory of an exponentially stable system approaches the origin faster than an exponential function. The positive number λ is called the *exponential convergence rate.*

None of the above properties of the equilibrium point are based on infinitesimal deviations from the equilibrium, but they still do not allow such deviations to be arbitrarily large. In this sense they are properties of the *local* behavior of the system, i.e., how does it evolve in time after having started *near* the equilibrium point. They do not say much about how the system will behave when its initial state is at a larger distance away from the equilibrium point. To cover this possibility one needs the concept of an equilibrium point that is globally assympotically stable.

Global Asymptotic Stability

The equilibrium point $\mathbf{0}$ is said to be *globally asymptotically* (or *exponentially) stable* if it is asymptotically (or exponentially) stable for any initial state.

In the context of a fuzzy state space, the above definition obviously does not apply since all possible initial states are located within X^n which is a strict subset of the whole state space. Thus the initial states in the fuzzy state space are a strict subset of the set of all possible initial states, that is, the set of initial states to which the above definition of global stability refers. That is why the notion of global stability, whenever used in the literature on fuzzy control, actually refers to local stability within the largest ball $\mathbf{B}_{R_{\max}}$ contained in X^n.

The definition of global stability implies that that the system cannot have any other equilibrium points, and also that every trajectory remains bounded for any $t \geq 0$. Linear autonomous systems that are asymptotically stable are always globally exponentially stable.

On the other hand, if an equilibrium point is asymptotically stable, but not globally asymptotically stable, it is desirable to quantify the extent of its convergence to the origin in some way. For this purpose, the concept of an *invariant set* of a dynamic system is utilized. An invariant set is defined as any set of points in the state space, such that each trajectory starting within it remains there for all subsequent times. For example, any equilibrium point is an invariant set and a trivial invariant set is the whole state space. The union of all domains of attraction of the origin (or the union of all points from which trajectories converge to the origin) is called the *maximum domain of attraction.*

Then it can be shown that the maximum domain of attraction of the asymptotically stable equilibrium point $\mathbf{0}$ is an *open*, *connected*, and *invariant* set containing $\mathbf{0}$ [40, Lemma 45]. An open set is a set such that every point in it has a neighborhood entirely contained in this set. A set is connected if for every two points in it there is a path connecting these points and lying entirely in this set. A *maximum domain of attraction* of the asymptotically stable equilibrium point $\mathbf{0}$ is the union of all domains of attraction of this equilibrium point, or equivalently, the set of all points from which trajectories converge to the equilibrium point. It follows trivially that, if the equilibrium point $\mathbf{0}$ is globally asymptotically stable, then the maximum domain of attraction is the whole state space.

In fuzzy control, heuristic and model based, the design goal is an FLC such that the closed loop system (2.50) incorporating this FLC is asymptotically/exponentially stable at the origin and the maximum domain of attraction of the origin is the whole fuzzy state space. However, as already said, the fuzzy state space is a closed set, that is, there are points in it that do not have a neighborhood entirely contained in the fuzzy state space. For example, the point $(a, a, \ldots, a)^T$ is in the fuzzy state space, but for an arbitrary $0 < d < r$ the point $(a+d, a+d, \ldots, a+d)^T$ while in the neighborhood of $(a, a, \ldots, a)^T$ is not in the fuzzy state space since it is not in $X^n = [a, b]^n$. The fact that the fuzzy state space is a closed set implies that it cannot be the maximum domain of attraction of the equilibrium point $\mathbf{0}$ since the maximum domain of attraction of the origin is, amongst other things, an open set.

To make the fuzzy state space an open set, and thus to be able to use all available conventional concepts of stability in the design and analysis of an FLC, one needs to consider an open subset of the fuzzy state space X^n which does not contain points like $(a, a, \ldots, a)^T$. To achieve this one can redefine X as $X = (a, b)$, which makes the fuzzy state space an open set, but still a strict subset of the state space. Thus, from now on, when we refer to the fuzzy state space we mean the set $X^n = (a, b)^n$.

To conclude this section, we will present some results concerning the local stability of nonlinear systems based on the idea that a nonlinear system should behave similarly to its linearized approximation for small range motions. In this context we will present the *Lyapunov linearization method* which serves as a fundamental justification of using linear control techniques in practice. That is, it shows that asymptotically stable design of the Lyapunov-linearized closed loop system guarantees the asymptotic stability of the original nonlinear system locally.

Lyapunov Linearization

Consider the nonlinear autonomous open loop system (2.48). Recall here that $\mathbf{f}$ is assumed continuously differentiable and let $\mathbf{f}(\mathbf{0},\mathbf{0}) = \mathbf{0}$. Now we can write

$$\dot{\mathbf{x}} = \left(\frac{\partial \mathbf{f}(\mathbf{x},\mathbf{u})}{\partial \mathbf{x}}\right)_{\mathbf{x}=\mathbf{0},\mathbf{u}=\mathbf{0}} \cdot \mathbf{x} + \left(\frac{\partial \mathbf{f}(\mathbf{x},\mathbf{u})}{\partial \mathbf{u}}\right)_{\mathbf{x}=\mathbf{0},\mathbf{u}=\mathbf{0}} \cdot \mathbf{u} + \mathbf{f}_{\mathrm{hot}}(\mathbf{x},\mathbf{u}), \quad (2.78)$$

where $\mathbf{f}_{\mathrm{hot}}$ stands for higher-order terms in $\mathbf{x}$ and $\mathbf{u}$. Denoting the *Jacobian matrix* of $\mathbf{f}$ with respect to $\mathbf{x}$ at $(\mathbf{x} = 0, \mathbf{u} = 0)$ with $\mathbf{A}$, and denoting by $\mathbf{B}$ the Jacobian matrix of $\mathbf{f}$ with respect to $\mathbf{u}$ at the same point (an $n \times m$ matrix of elements $\partial f_i/\partial u_j$, where m is the number of inputs),

$$\mathbf{A} = \left(\frac{\partial \mathbf{f}}{\partial \mathbf{x}}\right)_{\mathbf{x}=\mathbf{0},\mathbf{u}=\mathbf{0}}, \quad (2.79)$$

$$\mathbf{B} = \left(\frac{\partial \mathbf{f}}{\partial \mathbf{u}}\right)_{\mathbf{x}=\mathbf{0},\mathbf{u}=\mathbf{0}}, \quad (2.80)$$

and neglecting the higher order terms we obtain

$$\dot{\mathbf{x}} = \mathbf{A} \cdot \mathbf{x} + \mathbf{B} \cdot \mathbf{u}, \quad (2.81)$$

which is called the Lyapunov-linearization of (2.48) (or the Lyapunov-linearized version of (2.48)).

Now let the design objective be to find a control law of the form $\mathbf{u} = \mathbf{g}(\mathbf{x})$ such that the equilibrium point $\mathbf{0}$ of the resulting nonlinear closed loop system $\dot{\mathbf{x}} = \mathbf{f}(\mathbf{x}, \mathbf{g}(\mathbf{x}))$ is asymptotically stable. A solution to this problem exists if there exists an $m \times n$ matrix $\mathbf{K}$ such that all *eigenvalues* of $\mathbf{A} - \mathbf{B} \cdot \mathbf{K}$ have negative real parts, i.e., $\mathbf{A} - \mathbf{B} \cdot \mathbf{K}$ is a *Hurwitz matrix* [40, Theorem 53]. Under this condition, if we apply the control law

$$\mathbf{u} = -\mathbf{K} \cdot \mathbf{x}, \quad (2.82)$$

to (2.48), then $\mathbf{0}$ is an asymptotically stable equilibrium of the resulting nonlinear closed loop system.

In other words, if the closed loop linearized approximation is asymptotically stable so is the original nonlinear closed loop system. However, this result is valid only in a small region around $(\mathbf{x} = \mathbf{0}, \mathbf{u} = \mathbf{0})$ within which the original nonlinear system retains its linear behavior and thus the asymptotic stability of the original closed loop nonlinear system is only local.

Because of the above limitation of Lyapunov-linearization we will present some known results that give sufficient conditions for asymptotic and exponential stability of a nonlinear autonomous system without recourse to the Lyapunov-linearized version of this same system. These conditions are formulated using the so-called *direct Lyapunov method* and are expressed in terms of *Lyapunov functions* usually denoted as $V(\mathbf{x})$. These functions are simply continuous scalar functions of the state variables, with continuous partial derivatives, so that the time-derivative $\dot{V}(\mathbf{x})$ of $V(\mathbf{x})$ along a trajectory, given by

$$\dot{V}(\mathbf{x}) = \sum_{i=1}^{n} \frac{\partial V}{\partial x_i} \cdot \dot{x}_i = \sum_{i=1}^{n} \frac{\partial V}{\partial x_i} \cdot f_i(\mathbf{x}), \tag{2.83}$$

is itself a continuous function of $\mathbf{x}$.

In the next paragraph we will present the properties which a Lyapunov function has and from which properties information about the stability of an equilibrium point can be deduced.

Lyapunov Direct Method

Let S be an open, connected, and invariant set containing the equilibrium point $\mathbf{0}$.

The first property of $V(\mathbf{x})$ is a property of the function itself: it is strictly positive unless the state vector is zero. Thus for all $\mathbf{x} \in S$ we have

$$\text{(i)} \quad V(\mathbf{x}) > V(\mathbf{0}) \text{ whenever } \mathbf{x} \neq \mathbf{0}. \tag{2.84}$$

If $V(\mathbf{x})$ has the above property it is called *locally positive definite* since we can always make $V(\mathbf{x}) = 0$ by adding an appropriate constant to it. Of course, a function shifted by a constant has the same time-derivative as the original function. Furthermore, $V(\mathbf{x})$ is *negative definite* if $-V(\mathbf{x})$ is positive definite. Also, $V(\mathbf{x})$ is *positive semi-definite* if $V(\mathbf{0}) = 0$ and $V(\mathbf{x}) \geq 0$ for $\mathbf{x} \neq \mathbf{0}$, and $V(\mathbf{x})$ is *negative semi-definite* if $-V(\mathbf{x})$ is positive semi-definite. The prefix "semi" is used to reflect the possibility of V being equal to zero for $\mathbf{x} \neq \mathbf{0}$.

The positive-definiteness property implies that the function V has a unique minimum at the origin.

The geometrical meaning of locally positive definite functions can be illustrated as follows [28, Sect. 3.4.1]. Consider a positive definite function $V(\mathbf{x})$ of the two state variables x_1 and x_2. Plotted in a 3-dimensional space, $V(\mathbf{x})$ typically corresponds to a surface looking like an upward cup (see Fig. 2.16). The lowest point of the cup is located at the origin.

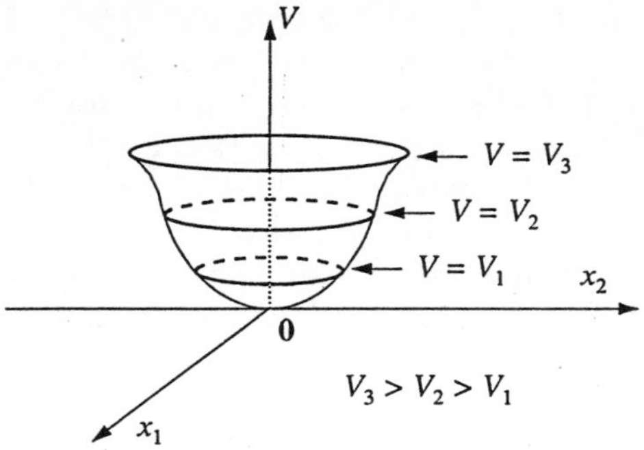

Fig. 2.16. The typical shape of a locally positive definite function

The second property (ii) of $V(\mathbf{x})$ is called *radial unboundness* and is only required if, for example, S is the whole state space, but it is not necessary if S is bounded, which is the case of a fuzzy state space.

We will now consider the implications, with respect to stability, of the properties of $\dot{V}(\mathbf{x})$.

The first property of $\dot{V}(\mathbf{x})$ is that it is locally negative semi-definite. Formally, this property is expressed as

$$\text{(iii)} \quad \dot{V}(\mathbf{x}) \leq 0 \quad \forall \mathbf{x} \in S. \tag{2.85}$$

The above property of $\dot{V}(\mathbf{x})$ implies that the equilibrium point $\mathbf{0}$ is stable. A further property is imposed on $\dot{V}(\mathbf{x})$, namely (iv): $\dot{V}(\mathbf{x})$ does not vanish identically along any trajectory in S other than $\mathbf{x}(t) \equiv \mathbf{0}$.

The above two properties, taken together, imply that the equilibrium point $\mathbf{0}$ is asymptotically stable. In order for $\dot{V}(\mathbf{x})$ to have both of the above properties, it is sufficient that $\dot{V}(\mathbf{x}) < 0$ for all $\mathbf{x}$ that are different from $\mathbf{0}$.

One of the main uses of Lyapunov functions is in estimation of domains of attraction (see [6, Sect. 5.1] and [40, Lemma 40]). Let S be an open set, containing the origin, and consisting of points where $V(\mathbf{x}) < c$, for some constant c, with the boundary of S given by $V(\mathbf{x}) = c$. If property (iii) holds, then trajectories starting in S cannot leave it. If property (iv) also holds, then all such trajectories converge to the equilibrium point $\mathbf{0}$, so that S is *a* domain of attraction of the origin. One would clearly wish to choose c as large as possible, and in some, though not all, cases this can be done by setting c equal to the minimum value of $V(\mathbf{x})$ over all points (apart from $\mathbf{0}$) where $\dot{V}(\mathbf{x}) = 0$. For this to work, it is necessary that $\dot{V}(\mathbf{x}) < 0$ for all $\mathbf{x}$ sufficiently near $\mathbf{0}$. Further, the procedure can be generalized to a wider context by taking S to consist of points satisfying $b < V(\mathbf{x}) < c$, where b and c are constants, so that the boundary of S has two distinct components given by $V(\mathbf{x}) = b$

and $V(\mathbf{x}) = c$. Then, if conditions (iii) and (iv) hold, with the reference to $\mathbf{0}$ removed from (iv), it can be shown that all trajectories that start in a certain region are eventually confined within a smaller region, which is a subset of the first. Moreover, if the stronger condition $\dot{V}(\mathbf{x}) \leq K \cdot \{b - V(\mathbf{x})\}$ is satisfied everywhere in S, for some positive constant K, then one can estimate the rate of convergence, since $\{b - V(\mathbf{x})\} \cdot e^{Kt}$ remains finite as $t \to \infty$.

A precise statement summarizing the above discussion is as follows [28, Theorem 3.4]. Consider the autonomous system of the form (2.50), and let $V(\mathbf{x})$ be a scalar function with continuous partial derivatives. Assume that

- for some $l > 0$, the region Ω_l defined by $V(\mathbf{x}) < l$ is bounded (the bound being $V(\mathbf{x}) = l$),
- $\dot{V}(\mathbf{x}) < 0$ for all $\mathbf{x} \in \Omega_l$, and
- let $\mathbf{R}$ be the set of all points within Ω_l where $\dot{V}(\mathbf{x}) = 0$, and $\mathbf{M}$ be the union of all invariant sets in $\mathbf{R}$, i.e., the maximum domain of attraction.

Then, every trajectory originating in Ω_l tends to $\mathbf{M}$ as $t \to \infty$. In particular, if the set $\mathbf{R}$ is invariant, then $\mathbf{M} = \mathbf{R}$. The geometrical meaning of this result is illustrated in Fig. 2.17. For more details on the estimation of regions of attraction the reader is referred to [28, Sect. 3.4.3], [6, Chap. 5], and [40, Sect. 5.3.2].

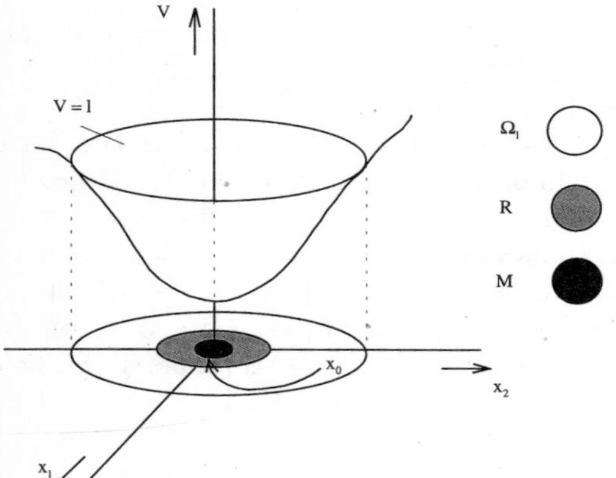

Fig. 2.17. Convergence to the maximum domain of attraction

Lyapunov functions can also be used to describe the stability of autonomous linear systems. Given a linear autonomous system of the form (2.57) let us use the *quadratic function*

$$V(\mathbf{x}) = \mathbf{x}^T \cdot \mathbf{P} \cdot \mathbf{x}, \tag{2.86}$$

as a candidate for a Lyapunov function. In the above equation, $\mathbf{P}$ is a given *symmetric positive definite matrix*. A square symmetric $n \times n$ matrix is positive definite if $\mathbf{x}^T \cdot \mathbf{P} \cdot \mathbf{x} > 0$ whenever $\mathbf{x} \neq \mathbf{0}$. In other words, a matrix $\mathbf{P}$ is positive definite if the quadratic function $\mathbf{x}^T \cdot \mathbf{P} \cdot \mathbf{x}$ is positive definite. The definition thus implies that every positive definite matrix is associated with a positive definite function. However, the converse is not true. A necessary condition for a square matrix to be positive definite is that its diagonal elements be strictly positive. The *Sylvester's theorem* from matrix algebra shows that if $\mathbf{P}$ is symmetric, a necessary and sufficient condition for $\mathbf{P}$ to be positive definite is that its principal minors all are strictly positive; or, equivalently, that all its eigenvalues are strictly positive. In particular, a positive definite matrix is always invertible.

Differentiating the positive definite function V along the system trajectory yields another quadratic function

$$\dot{V}(\mathbf{x}) = \dot{\mathbf{x}}^T \cdot \mathbf{P} \cdot \mathbf{x} + \mathbf{x}^T \cdot \mathbf{P} \cdot \dot{\mathbf{x}} = -\mathbf{x}^T \cdot \mathbf{Q} \cdot \mathbf{x} \tag{2.87}$$

where

$$\mathbf{A}'^{\mathrm{T}} \cdot \mathbf{P} + \mathbf{P} \cdot \mathbf{A}' = -\mathbf{Q}, \tag{2.88}$$

is called a *Lyapunov equation*. The question thus is, to determine whether the symmetric matrix $\mathbf{Q}$ from the Lyapunov equation is itself positive definite. If this is the case, then V and $\dot{V}$ have the properties (i), (iii), and (iv), and the origin is an asymptotically stable equilibrium of (2.57). However, this approach may lead to inconclusive results, i.e., $\mathbf{Q}$ may be not positive definite even for stable systems.

A more useful approach to studying a given linear autonomous system using scalar quadratic functions is, instead, to derive a positive definite matrix $\mathbf{P}$ from a given positive definite matrix $\mathbf{Q}$. This is done as follows.

1. Choose a positive definite matrix $\mathbf{Q}$.
2. Solve for $\mathbf{P}$ from the Lyapunov equation (2.88).
3. Check whether $\mathbf{P}$ is positive definite.

If $\mathbf{P}$ is positive definite, then $1/2 \cdot (\mathbf{x}^{\mathrm{T}} \cdot \mathbf{P} \cdot \mathbf{x})$ is a Lyapunov function for (2.57) and asymptotic stability is guaranteed. This technique always leads to conclusive results as illustrated by the following result [28, Theorem 3.6].

A necessary and sufficient condition for (2.57) to be asymptotically stable is that, for any symmetric positive definite matrix $\mathbf{Q}$, the unique matrix $\mathbf{P}$ solution of the Lyapunov equation be symmetric positive definite.

The above result shows that any positive definite matrix $\mathbf{Q}$ can be used to determine the stability of a linear autonomous system. A simple choice for $\mathbf{Q}$ is the identity matrix $\mathbf{I}$. When $\mathbf{Q} = \mathbf{I}$ this provides the best convergence rate estimate. For details see [28, Sect. 3.5.5].

The connection between the stability of (2.57) in terms of quadratic Lyapunov functions and in terms of $\mathbf{A}'$ being a Hurwitz matrix is established by a result in [40, Theorem 42], showing the equivalence of the following two statements:

1. $\mathbf{A}'$ is a Hurwitz matrix.
2. For every positive definite matrix $\mathbf{Q}$ the Lyapunov equation has a unique solution for $\mathbf{P}$, and this solution is positive definite.

2.4.3 Stability Concepts for Nonautonomous Systems

As discussed in Sect. 2.4.2, determining the stability of motion for an autonomous system requires the stability analysis of an equivalent nonautonomous system around the origin. Therefore, we will now briefly present the stability analysis concepts relevant for model based fuzzy control. For details the reader is referred to [28, Sect. 4.1–4.5] and [40, Sect. 5.4.3].

Equilibrium Points

For a nonautonomous system of the form (2.53) an equilibrium point $\mathbf{x}^\star$ is defined by

$$\mathbf{f}'(\mathbf{x}^\star, t) = 0 \qquad \forall t \geq t_0. \tag{2.89}$$

Note here that the above equation has to be satisfied for all t greater than or equal to t_0, implying that the system is able to stay at the equilibrium point all the time. Through the rest of this section we will have that $\mathbf{x}^\star = \mathbf{0}$.

Stable Equilibrium

The equilibrium point $\mathbf{0}$ of (2.53) is a *stable equilibrium* at t_0 if for any $R > 0$, there exists $r(t_0) > 0$, such that if $\| \mathbf{x}(t_0) \| < r(t_0)$, then $\| \mathbf{x}(t) \| < R, \forall t > t_0$. Otherwise the equilibrium point is *unstable.*

Again this definition means that we can keep a trajectory in a ball of arbitrary small radius R by starting this trajectory in a ball of sufficiently small radius r. Observe here that the radius r of the initial ball depends on the initial time t_0.

Asymptotic Stability

An equilibrium point $\mathbf{0}$ is *asymptotically stable* at t_0 if it is stable and if in addition there exists some $r(t_0) > 0$ such that $\| \mathbf{x}(t_0) \| < r(t_0)$ implies that $\| \mathbf{x}(t) \| \to \mathbf{0}$ as $t \to \infty$.

Here the definition of asymptotic stability requires that there exists a domain of attraction for every initial time t_0. The size of this domain and rate of convergence depend on the initial time t_0.

Exponential Stability

The equilibrium point **0** is *exponentially stable* at t_0 if there exist two positive numbers, α and λ, such that for sufficiently small $\mathbf{x}(t_0)$,

$$\| \mathbf{x}(t) \| \leq \alpha \cdot \| \mathbf{x}(t_0) \| \cdot e^{-\lambda(t-t_0)} \qquad \forall t > t_0. \tag{2.90}$$

We do not present the global stability counterparts of the above definitions since these use the whole state space while the fuzzy state space is only a strict subset of it.

Uniform Stability

The above definitions of stability for nonautonomous systems all indicate the importance of initial time. However, in practice, it is desired that the nonautonomous system has a certain uniformity in its behavior regardless of when the operation of a control system starts. This is the motivation for introducing the concepts of uniform stability. Observe here that because the behavior of autonomous systems is independent of the initial time, all of the stability properties of autonomous systems are uniform.

The equilibrium point **0** is locally *uniformly stable* if the scalar r can be chosen independently of the initial time t_0. The intuition behind the concept of uniform stability is to rule out nonautonomous systems that are "less and less stable" for larger values of t_0. In a similar manner, the definition of asymptotic uniform stability also intends to restrict the effect of initial time on the trajectory convergence pattern.

Uniform Asymptotic Stability

The equilibrium point **0** is locally *uniformly asymptotically stable* if

- it is uniformly stable,
- there exists a domain (or a ball) of attraction $\mathbf{B}_{R_0}$, whose radius is independent of t_0, such that any system trajectory with initial states in $\mathbf{B}_{R_0}$ converges to **0** uniformly in t_0.

By uniform convergence in terms of t_0, one means that for all R_1 and R_2 satisfying $0 < R_2 < R_1 < R_0$, there exists $T(R_1, R_2)$, such that, for each $t_0 \geq 0$,

$$\| \mathbf{x}(t_0) \| < R_1 \quad \text{implies} \| \mathbf{x}(t) \| < R_2 \quad \forall t \geq t_0 + T(R_1, R_2). \tag{2.91}$$

i.e., the trajectory, starting from within the ball $\mathbf{B}_{R_1}$, will converge into a smaller ball $\mathbf{B}_{R_2}$ after a period of time T that is independent of $t + 0$.

By definition, uniform asymptotic stability always implies asymptotic stability, but the converse is generally not true.

Lyapunov-Linearization of Nonautonomous Systems

The Lyapunov-linearization method can also be developed for nonlinear nonautonomous systems of the form (2.51). Suppose that $(\mathbf{0}, \mathbf{0})$ is an equilibrium point, that is, $\mathbf{f}(\mathbf{0}, \mathbf{0}, t) = \mathbf{0}$, $\forall t \geq 0$ [28, Sect. 4.2.3]. Define

$$\mathbf{A}(t) = \left(\frac{\partial \mathbf{f}(\mathbf{x}, \mathbf{u}, t)}{\partial \mathbf{x}} \right)_{\mathbf{x}=\mathbf{0}, \mathbf{u}=\mathbf{0}}, \tag{2.92}$$

$$\mathbf{B}(t) = \left(\frac{\partial \mathbf{f}(\mathbf{x}, \mathbf{u}, t)}{\partial \mathbf{u}} \right)_{\mathbf{x}=\mathbf{0}, \mathbf{u}=\mathbf{0}}. \tag{2.93}$$

Then, for any fixed t, i.e., regarding t as a parameter, a Taylor expansion of $\mathbf{f}$ leads to

$$\dot{\mathbf{x}} = \mathbf{A}(t) \cdot \dot{\mathbf{x}} + \mathbf{B}(t) \cdot \mathbf{u} + \mathbf{f}_{\mathrm{hot}}(\mathbf{x}, \mathbf{u}, t). \tag{2.94}$$

If the following condition holds

$$\limsup_{\|\mathbf{x}\| \to 0} \frac{\| \mathbf{f}_{\mathrm{hot}}(\mathbf{x}, \mathbf{u}, t) \|}{\| \mathbf{x} \|} = 0 \qquad \forall t \geq 0, \tag{2.95}$$

then the system

$$\dot{\mathbf{x}} = \mathbf{A}(t) \cdot \dot{\mathbf{x}} + \mathbf{B}(t) \cdot \mathbf{u}, \tag{2.96}$$

is called the Lyapunov-linearization, or the Lyapunov-linearized version of (2.51).

The following result relates the stability of the linear nonautonomous system (2.96) to the stability of the original nonlinear nonautonomous system (2.53) in a region around the origin [40, Theorem 15].

> If the Lyapunov-linearized version (2.96) of (2.53), with condition (2.95) satisfied and the matrices $\mathbf{A}$ and $\mathbf{B}$ bounded, is uniformly exponentially stable, then the equilibrium point $\mathbf{0}$ of the original nonlinear autonomous system (2.53) is also uniformly exponentially stable.

Observe that the Lyapunov-linearized version (2.96) of (2.53) must be uniformly exponentially stable. If it is only exponentially stable no conclusion can be drawn as to the stability of the original nonlinear autonomous system. Furthermore, unlike the Lyapunov-linearization of autonomous systems, the above result does not relate the instability of the Lyapunov-linearized version of (2.53) to the instability of the original system. Finally, this result guarantees only the local stability of (2.53).

However, it remains to be seen when the Lyapunov-linearized version of (2.53) is uniformly exponentially stable. Thus, in the next section, we will consider the stability of linear nonautonomous systems, in particular, the stability of *slowly varying* linear nonautonomous systems.

2.4.4 Slowly Varying Nonautonomous Systems

Consider the linear nonautonomous closed loop system system from (2.53), that is (2.58), or

$$\dot{\mathbf{x}} = \mathbf{A}'(\mathbf{x}, t). \tag{2.97}$$

If τ is any fixed positive real number, then one can think of the autonomous system

$$\dot{\mathbf{x}} = \mathbf{A}'(\mathbf{x}, \tau), \tag{2.98}$$

as a particular case of (2.53), with its time dependence *frozen* at time τ. However, even if each of the frozen systems is asymptotically stable, the overall system can be unstable. Nevertheless, one can show that if each frozen system is exponentially stable, and the system (2.53) is slowly varying, then it is also uniformly exponentially stable.

The following result is from [40, Theorem 15].

Consider the linear nonautonomous system (2.53) and let $\mathbf{A}'$ be a Hurwitz matrix for each τ, $\lambda < \infty$ be the maximum of $\| \mathbf{A}'(t) \|$ with respect to t, $-\delta$ be the largest (i.e., the least negative) of the real parts of the eigenvalues of $\mathbf{A}'(t)$ as t varies, and μ be the maximum of the condition number of $\mathbf{A}'(t)$ as t varies. Then the linear nonautonomous system is uniformly exponentially stable if

$$\epsilon < \frac{\delta \cdot [(p-1) \cdot \delta - \lambda]}{p \cdot \mu^p}, \tag{2.99}$$

where ϵ is a constant strictly greater than zero and $p > 1$ is any number such that $(p-1) \cdot \delta > \lambda$.

3. Model Based Design of Sliding Mode FLC

For a large class of second-order nonlinear systems, FLCs are designed by using the fuzzy phase plane determined by the fuzzy values of error e and change of error $\dot{e}$ [22, 23, 37, 41]. The fuzzy rules of these FLCs determine a fuzzy value for the control input u for each pair of fuzzy values of error and change of error, that is, for each fuzzy state vector. The usual heuristic approach to the design of these fuzzy rules is the partitioning of the phase plane into two semi-planes by means of a *sliding line*. This means that the FLC has the so-called *diagonal form*.

Each semi-plane is used to define only negative or positive fuzzy values of the control input u. The magnitude of a specific positive/negative fuzzy value of the control input u is determined on the basis of the distance between its corresponding state vector and the sliding line. This is normally done in such a way that the absolute value of the control input u required increases/decreases with the increasing/decreasing distance between the state vector and the sliding line.

It is easily observed that this design method is very similar to sliding mode control (SMC) with a *boundary layer* (BL), which is a robust control method [38], [28, Sect. 7.2]. Sliding mode control is applied especially to control of nonlinear systems in the presence of model uncertainties, parameter fluctuations, and disturbances. The similarity between the diagonal form FLC and SMC is used in this chapter to redefine a diagonal form FLC in terms of an SMC with BL and then to verify its stability, robustness, and performance properties in a manner corresponding to the analysis of an SMC with BL.

In Sect. 3.1 we describe the control law of an SMC for an n-th-order SISO nonlinear nonautonomous system and its design for a tracking control problem, with and without integrator term.

In Sect. 3.2 we describe in detail the *diagonal form FLC* for a second-order SISO nonlinear autonomous system and derive the similarities between the control law of a diagonal form SMFLC and the control law of an SMC with BL [16, 11, 18, 10].

In Sect. 3.3 we describe the design of the control law of an SMFLC f
n-th order SISO system for the tracking control problem, w
integrator term.

In Sect. 3.4 the tuning of input scaling factors of an SMF

In Sect. 3.5 we give an example of a force adapting manipulator arm for the design of an SMFLC.

In Sect. 3.6 we extend the SMFLC design method to MIMO systems.

3.1 A Brief Introduction to Sliding Mode Control

Consider the nonlinear nonautonomous open loop system of the form

$$x^{(n)}(t) = f(\mathbf{x}, t) + b(\mathbf{x}, t) \cdot u + \tilde{d} \tag{3.1}$$

where $\mathbf{x}(t) = (x, \dot{x}, ..., x^{(n-1)})^T$ is the state vector, $\tilde{d}(t)$ are time-dependent disturbances with known upper bounds, u is the control input, and $f(\mathbf{x}, t)$ and $b(\mathbf{x}, t)$ are nonlinear nonautonomous functions of the state vector $\mathbf{x}$ and the time t. Finally, let ν_u be unmodeled frequencies which have to be taken into account for design. The tracking control problem is to find a control law such that given a desired trajectory $\mathbf{x^d}(t)$ the tracking error $\mathbf{x}(t) - \mathbf{x^d}(t)$ tends to $\mathbf{0}$ despite the presence of model uncertainties, unmodeled frequencies, and disturbances.

With the tracking error defined as

$$\mathbf{e}(t) = \mathbf{x}(t) - \mathbf{x^d}(t) = (e, \dot{e}, ..., e^{(n-1)})^T, \tag{3.2}$$

a *sliding surface* (*sliding line* for second-order systems)

$$s(\mathbf{x}, t) = 0, \tag{3.3}$$

is determined by

$$s(\mathbf{x}, t) = (\mathrm{d}/\mathrm{d}t + \lambda)^{n-1} e = \sum_{k=0}^{n-1} \binom{n-1}{k} \lambda^k \cdot e^{(n-1-k)}. \tag{3.4}$$

In order to make (3.3) a stable surface, λ is chosen to be a positive constant scalar. Starting from the initial condition

$$\mathbf{e}(0) = \mathbf{0}, \tag{3.5}$$

the tracking control problem requires the design of a control law such that the state vector $\mathbf{e}(t)$ remains on the sliding surface $s(\mathbf{x}, t) = 0$ for all $t \geq 0$. For simplicity of notation we omit the arguments t and $\mathbf{x}$ of s in the following. In order to derive such a control law we define a Lyapunov-like function

$$V = \frac{1}{2} s^2, \tag{3.6}$$

with $V(0) = 0$ and $V > 0$ for $s > 0$.

So, a sufficient condition for the stability of the system (3.1) is

$$\dot{V} = \frac{1}{2} \frac{\mathrm{d}}{\mathrm{d}t} (s^2) \leq -\eta |s|. \tag{3.7}$$

From the above expression we obtain the so-called reaching condition

$$\dot{s} \cdot \operatorname{sgn}(s) \leq -\eta, \tag{3.8}$$

where $\eta > 0$, and which, if satisfied, drives the system (3.1) into the so-called sliding mode.

Sliding mode means that once the state trajectory $\mathbf{e}$ has reached the *sliding surface* $s = 0$ the system trajectory remains on it while sliding into the origin $\mathbf{e} = \mathbf{0}$, independently of model uncertainties, unmodeled frequencies, and disturbances.

Reaching the sliding mode means a system trajectory $\mathbf{e}$ is outside the sliding surface but follows the reaching condition (3.8). Figure 3.1 illustrates graphically the principle of SMC for a second-order system. In order to reach the sliding mode, the sliding surface has to become a domain of attraction. This is always the case if the vector $\dot{\mathbf{e}}$ associated with the state vector $\mathbf{e}$ points to the sliding surface $s = 0$. In this case, the system (3.1) is uniformly asymptotically stable because once the state $\mathbf{e}$ is on the sliding surface, the error e decreases asymptotically with time.

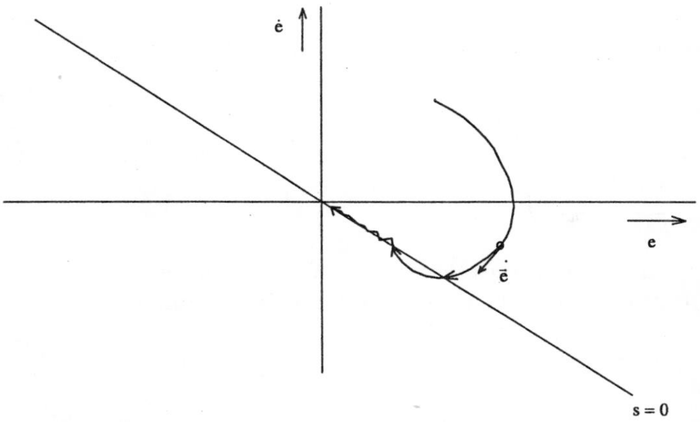

Fig. 3.1. Sliding mode principle

The first step in the design of the control law u is to derive the parameter λ. If (3.1) is a second-order system then λ determines the slope of the sliding line $s = 0$.

The linear differential equation (3.4) can be considered as a chain of $n-1$ filters of first order with the scalar s as input and the tracking error e as output (see Fig. 3.2). The parameter λ plays the role of a break frequency.

λ has to be designed in such a way that unmodeled frequencies ν_u are filtered out. Let $\nu_{u\min}$ be a lower bound of ν_u. Then λ has to be designed such that

$$\lambda \ll \nu_{u\min}. \tag{3.9}$$

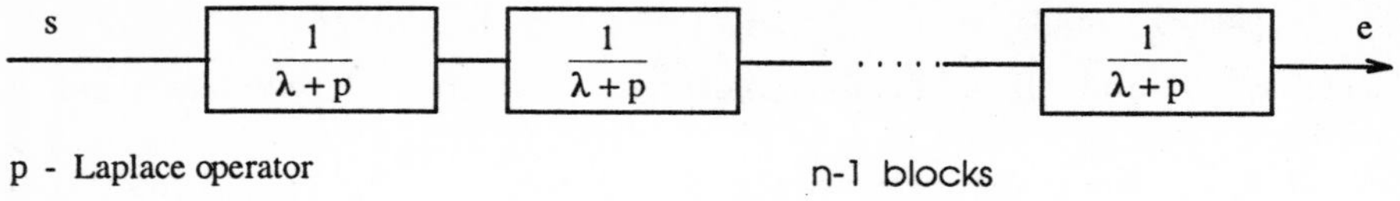

Fig. 3.2. The filter $s(\mathbf{x},t) = (\mathrm{d}/\mathrm{d}t + \lambda)^{n-1} e$

The next design step is to derive a control law that is able to drive system (3.1) into the sliding mode. Thus, we first compute the time derivative $\dot{s}$ from (3.4),

$$\dot{s} = x^{(n)} - x^{d(n)} + \sum_{k=1}^{n-1} \binom{n-1}{k} \lambda^k \cdot e^{(n-k)} \tag{3.10}$$

Substituting $\dot{s}$ and (3.1) into (3.8) we obtain

$$\mathrm{sgn}(s)(f + b \cdot u + \tilde{d} - x^{d(n)} + \sum_{k=1}^{n-1} \binom{n-1}{k} \lambda^k \cdot e^{(n-k)}) \leq -\eta. \tag{3.11}$$

Now we define the sliding mode control law as follows

$$\begin{aligned} u &= \hat{b}^{-1}(\tilde{u} - \hat{f}), \\ \tilde{u} &= G \cdot (\hat{u} - K(\mathbf{x},t) \cdot \mathrm{sgn}(s)), \\ \hat{u} &= x^{d(n)} - \sum_{k=1}^{n-1} \binom{n-1}{k} \lambda^k \cdot e^{(n-k)}, \end{aligned} \tag{3.12}$$

where $K(\mathbf{x},t) > 0$, and $\hat{f}$ and $\hat{b}$ are estimates of f and b, respectively. To determine the multiplier term G we define the following bounds

$$0 \leq \beta^{\min} \leq b \cdot \hat{b}^{-1} \leq \beta^{\max}. \tag{3.13}$$

Then we define G as

$$G = \left(\beta^{\min} \cdot \beta^{\max}\right)^{-1/2}. \tag{3.14}$$

Finally, let the gain margins be defined as

$$\beta = \left(\frac{\beta^{\max}}{\beta^{\min}}\right)^{1/2}. \tag{3.15}$$

The design goal is to find a $K(\mathbf{x}, t)$ such that the reaching condition (3.8) is satisfied. By substituting (3.12) into (3.11) we obtain

$$\operatorname{sgn}(s)(\Delta f + (b\hat{b}^{-1}G - 1) \cdot \hat{u} + \tilde{d} - b\hat{b}^{-1}G \cdot K(\mathbf{x}, t) \cdot \operatorname{sgn}(s)) \leq -\eta, \tag{3.16}$$

and with $\Delta f = f - b\hat{b}^{-1}\hat{f}$, we obtain

$$(\Delta f + (b\hat{b}^{-1}G - 1) \cdot \hat{u} + \tilde{d}) \cdot \operatorname{sgn}(s) - b\hat{b}^{-1}G \cdot K(\mathbf{x}, t) \leq -\eta. \tag{3.17}$$

The above inequality is always true if

$$b\hat{b}^{-1}G \cdot K(\mathbf{x}, t) \geq \left| \Delta f + (b\hat{b}^{-1}G - 1) \cdot \hat{u} + \tilde{d} \right| + \eta. \tag{3.18}$$

By taking the individual absolute values of the terms on the right hand side of the above inequality we obtain the stronger inequality

$$b\hat{b}^{-1}G \cdot K(\mathbf{x}, t) \geq |\Delta f| + |(b\hat{b}^{-1}G - 1)| \cdot |\hat{u}| + |\tilde{d}| + \eta. \tag{3.19}$$

Substituting the lower bound $b\hat{b}^{-1} = \beta^{\min}$ into (3.19) and using the fact that $\beta^{\min}G = \beta^{-1}$ we obtain

$$K(\mathbf{x}, t) \geq \beta(|\Delta f| + (1 - \beta^{-1}) \cdot |\hat{u}| + |\tilde{d}| + \eta). \tag{3.20}$$

Assigning the upper bounds

$$|\Delta f| < \tilde{F},$$
$$|\tilde{d}| < D,$$
$$|\hat{u}| < \hat{U},$$

which we assume to know from the analysis of the system (3.1), we finally obtain a sufficient condition for the sliding surface $s = 0$ to be a domain of attraction

$$K(\mathbf{x}, t) \geq \beta(\tilde{F} + (1 - \beta^{-1}) \cdot \hat{U} + D + \eta). \tag{3.21}$$

To summarize, the design of an SMC involves the following steps

1. Derive λ from the lowest bound on the unmodeled frequencies $\nu_{u\min}$.
2. Derive $\hat{u}$ and its upper bound $\hat{U}$.
3. Find estimates $\hat{f}$ and $\hat{b}$ for f and b.
4. Derive G.
5. Determine η and the upper bounds F for $|\Delta f|$ and D for $|\tilde{d}|$.
6. Compute $K(\mathbf{x}, t)$.

A *major feature* of SMC versus other nonlinear control methods is that once the sliding mode is reached, the closed loop system (3.1) has the dynamics of the linear differential equation (3.3) regardless of model uncertainties, and disturbances. A *drawback* of SMC is the drastic changes of the control input u which may be of disadvantage for the plant to be controlled. However, this can be avoided by the introduction of a boundary layer (BL) near the sliding surface $s = 0$ which smoothes out the dynamics of the control input u and ensures that the system states remain within the layer. The width of the BL is denoted as $2 \cdot \Phi$. Let $|s|$ be the distance between the state $\mathbf{e}$ and the sliding line $s = 0$. Then a state $\mathbf{e}$ is located inside the BL if $|s| \leq \Phi$, and it is located outside if $|s| > \Phi$.

We insert the BL in the control law (3.12) by replacing $\mathrm{sgn}(s)$ by $\mathrm{sat}(s/\Phi)$

$$\begin{aligned} u &:= \hat{b}^{-1}(\tilde{u} - \hat{f}), \\ \tilde{u} &= G \cdot (\hat{u} - K(\mathbf{x}, t) \cdot \mathrm{sat}(s/\Phi)), \end{aligned} \tag{3.22}$$

where the saturation function *sat* is defined as

$$\mathrm{sat}(z) = \begin{cases} z & \text{if } |z| < 1 \\ \mathrm{sgn}(z) & \text{if } |z| \geq 1. \end{cases} \tag{3.23}$$

Figure 3.3 shows graphically the BL around the sliding line of a second-order system and the corresponding part $K \cdot \mathrm{sat}(s/\Phi)$ of control law (3.22).

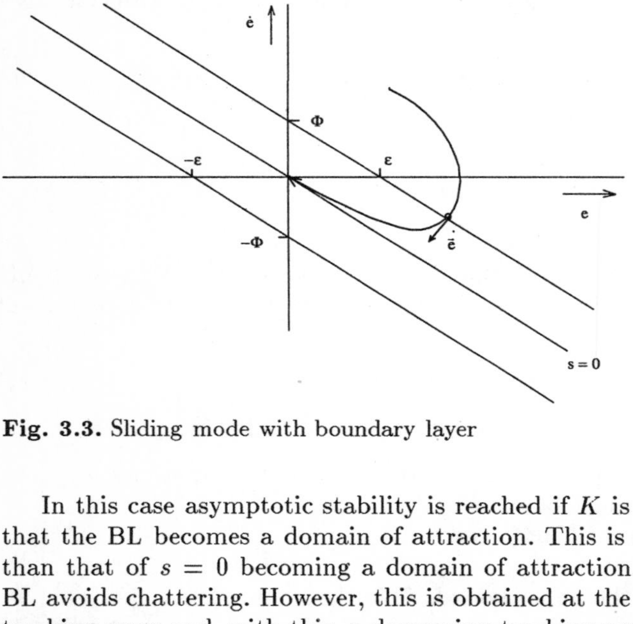

Fig. 3.3. Sliding mode with boundary layer

In this case asymptotic stability is reached if K is designed by (3.20) so that the BL becomes a domain of attraction. This is a weaker requirement than that of $s = 0$ becoming a domain of attraction. The result is that a BL avoids chattering. However, this is obtained at the price of an increasing tracking error and, with this, a decreasing tracking performance.

The width Φ of the BL is designed in the following way. Inside the BL we have the control law

$$\begin{aligned} u &= \hat{b}^{-1}(\tilde{u} - \hat{f}), \\ \tilde{u} &= G \cdot \left(\hat{u} - K(\mathbf{x}, t) \cdot \frac{s}{\Phi}\right). \end{aligned} \tag{3.24}$$

Substituting (3.1) and $\hat{u} = x^{d^{(n)}} - \sum_{k=1}^{n-1} \binom{n-1}{k} \lambda^k \cdot e^{(n-k)}$ into (3.10) we obtain

$$\dot{s} = f + b \cdot u + \tilde{d} - \hat{u}. \tag{3.25}$$

Substituting u with $\hat{b}^{-1}(\tilde{u} - \hat{f})$ we have

$$\dot{s} = b\hat{b}^{-1}\tilde{u} + \Delta f + \tilde{d} - \hat{u}, \tag{3.26}$$

or

$$\dot{s} = b\hat{b}^{-1}G(\hat{u} - K \cdot \frac{s}{\Phi}) + \Delta f + \tilde{d} - \hat{u}. \tag{3.27}$$

Finally we obtain

$$\dot{s} + \frac{b\hat{b}^{-1}GK}{\Phi} \cdot s = \hat{u} \cdot (b\hat{b}^{-1}G - 1) + \Delta f + \tilde{d}. \tag{3.28}$$

The above expression can be considered a lowpass filter with the input $\hat{u} \cdot (b\hat{b}^{-1}G - 1) + \Delta f + \tilde{d}$ and the output s (see Fig. 3.4). The dynamics of the system (3.28) describes the state $\mathbf{e}$ approaching the sliding surface.

Once the term $b\hat{b}^{-1}GK$ is derived, it remains to determine the BL width Φ. Here, there are two main options. The first option is to choose Φ on the basis of a required tracking precision ϵ. According to [28] the guaranteed tracking precision is

$$\epsilon = \Phi/\lambda^{n-1}. \tag{3.29}$$

The second option is to choose the bandwidth $b\hat{b}^{-1}GK/\Phi$ identical to the bandwidth λ, which is referred to as the *balance condition*

$$\frac{b\hat{b}^{-1}GK}{\Phi} = \lambda. \tag{3.30}$$

Φ can be obtained from either (3.29) or (3.29).

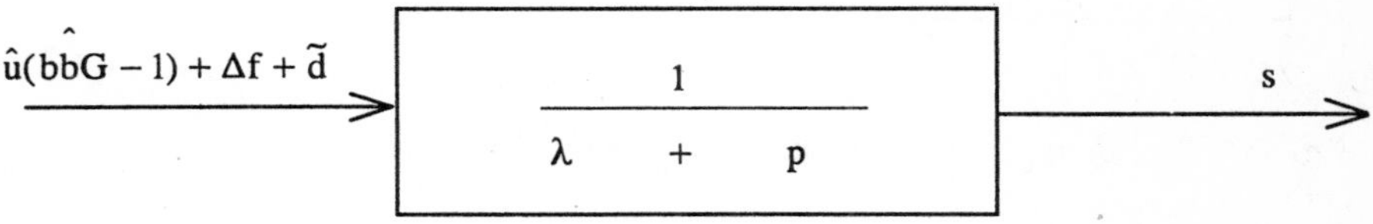

Fig. 3.4. First-order lowpass filter for approaching the sliding surface

The design steps for an SMC with BL are the same as for the pure SMC with the additional step of determining the width Φ of the BL with the help either of the tracking precision ϵ or the balance condition (3.30).

3.2 The Similarity Between FLC and SMC

In Sect. 3.2.1 we start with the description of the so-called diagonal form FLC. In order to show the similarity between the diagonal form FLC and SMC we discuss the SMC with BL for a second-order system in Sect. 3.2.2. In Sect. 3.2.3 follows an analytical description of the diagonal form FLC, and in Sect. 3.2.4 we compare the SMC with BL with the diagonal form FLC. Finally, in Sect. 3.2.5 the SMFLC principle is introduced.

3.2.1 The Diagonal Form FLC

In the case of a diagonal form FLC for a second-order SISO nonlinear autonomous system, the controller inputs are error e and change of error $\dot{e}$, and the controller output is u. The physical domains of e, $\dot{e}$, and u are E, $\dot{E}$, and U respectively, and are defined as intervals around zero. Thus the crisp physical values of e, $\dot{e}$, and u are negative, positive, or equal to zero (see Fig. 3.5).

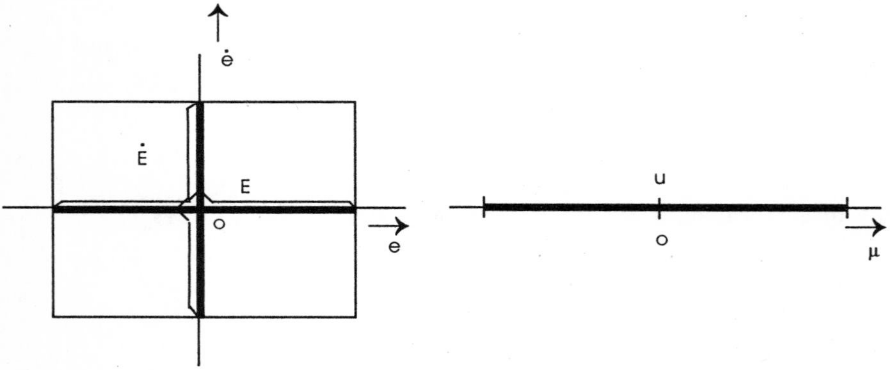

Fig. 3.5. The domains of the controller inputs and controller output

The fuzzy values of e, $\dot{e}$, and u belong to the term-sets **TE**, $\dot{\mathbf{TE}}$, and **TU** respectively. These term-sets are defined as follows

TE $= \{NLE_1, NLE_2, \ldots, NLE_m, ZLE_{m+1}, PLE_{m+2}, \ldots, PLE_n\}$, where $n = 2m + 1$ is an odd integer, and an arbitrary fuzzy value from **TE** is denoted as LE.

$\mathbf{T\dot{E}} = \{NL\dot{E}_1, NL\dot{E}_2, \ldots, NL\dot{E}_m, ZL\dot{E}_{m+1}, PL\dot{E}_{m+2} \ldots, PL\dot{E}_n\}$ and an arbitrary fuzzy value from $\mathbf{T\dot{E}}$ is denoted as $L\dot{E}$.

TU $= \{NLU_1, NLU_2, \ldots, NLU_m, ZLU_{m+1}, PLU_{m+2}, \ldots, PLU_n\}$ and an arbitrary fuzzy value from **TU** is denoted as LU.

Since the domains of the controller inputs and controller outputs are intervals around the zero, the fuzzy values of the two state variables are also classified as positive, negative, and zero. A fuzzy value of error is a positive fuzzy value, PLE_i, if its membership function is defined on the positive crisp values in E; it is a negative fuzzy value, NLE_i, if its membership function is defined on the negative crisp values in E; a fuzzy value is a fuzzy zero, ZLE_{m+1}, if it is defined on the crisp negative and positive values around zero and the degree of membership of zero is equal to one. In the same manner, one obtains the fuzzy values $NL\dot{E}_j$, $PL\dot{E}_j$, and $Z\dot{E}_{m+1}$ of change of error, and the fuzzy values NLU_k, PLU_k, and ZLU_{m+1} of the controller output u (see Figs. 3.6–3.8).

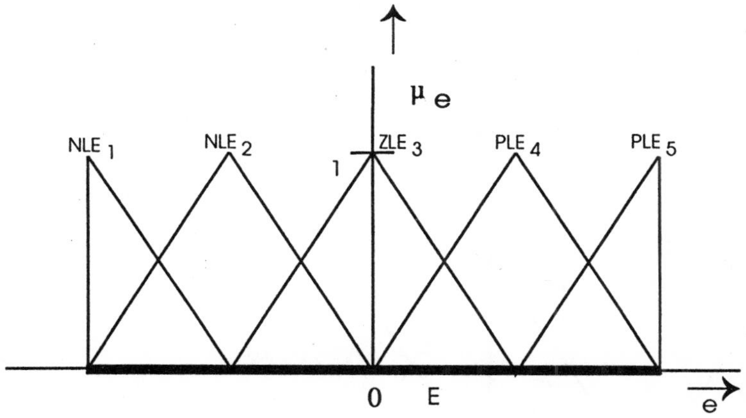

Fig. 3.6. The fuzzy values of error

The fuzzy phase plane is then the set of all fuzzy state vectors (or fuzzy regions) $(LE^{\mathbf{i}}, L\dot{E}^{\mathbf{i}})$, $(\mathbf{i} = \mathbf{1}, \mathbf{2}, \ldots, \mathbf{n} \times \mathbf{n})$, where $LE^{\mathbf{i}} \in \mathbf{TE}$ and $L\dot{E}^{\mathbf{i}} \in \mathbf{T\dot{E}}$ (see Fig. 3.9).

The fuzzy rules of the diagonal form FLC are then designed in the following manner.

For the fuzzy region $(ZLE_{m+1}, ZL\dot{E}_{m+1})$ the controller output is zero, i.e., a steady state at the origin of the fuzzy phase plane. The whole set of regions for which ZLU_{m+1} is the corresponding controller output is

$$\{(PLE_n, NL\dot{E}_1), (PLE_{n-1}, NL\dot{E}_2), \ldots, (ZLE_{m+1}, ZL\dot{E}_{m+1}),$$
$$\ldots, (NLE_2, PL\dot{E}_{n-1}), (NLE_1, PL\dot{E}_n)\}.$$

When illustrated graphically, the set of the zero-regions for which the controller output is ZLU represents a "diagonal" that divides the fuzzy phase plane into two semi-planes (see Fig. 3.10) follows.

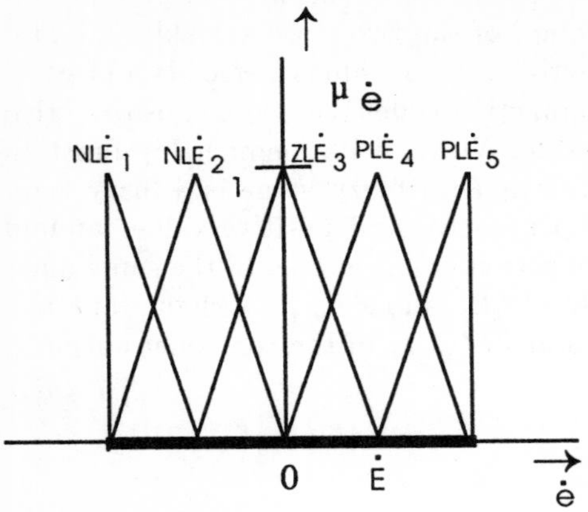

Fig. 3.7. The fuzzy values of change of error

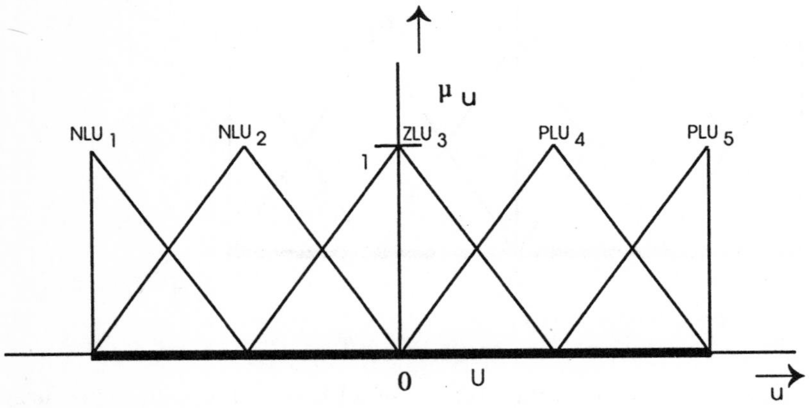

Fig. 3.8. The fuzzy values of the controller output u

For all fuzzy regions below the "diagonal" the controller output is assigned a positive fuzzy value with a magnitude depending on the "distance" between a given fuzzy region and a particular zero-region on the "diagonal" below which the given fuzzy region is located. The set of all fuzzy regions below the "diagonal" is given as (see Fig. 3.11) follows

$(NLE_1, PL\dot{E}_{n-1}), \ldots, (NLE_1, NL\dot{E}_1)$ are the fuzzy regions below the zero-region $(NLE_1, PL\dot{E}_n)$,
$(NLE_2, NL\dot{E}_{n-2}), \ldots (NLE_2, NL\dot{E}_1)$ are the fuzzy regions below the zero-region $(NLE_2, PL\dot{E}_{n-1})$, ...,
$(PLE_{n-1}, NL\dot{E}_1)$ is the fuzzy region below the zero-region $(PLE_{n-1}, PL\dot{E}_2)$.

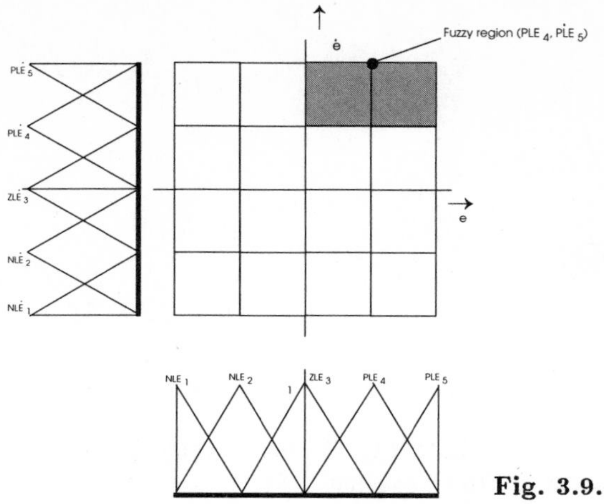

Fig. 3.9. The fuzzy phase plane

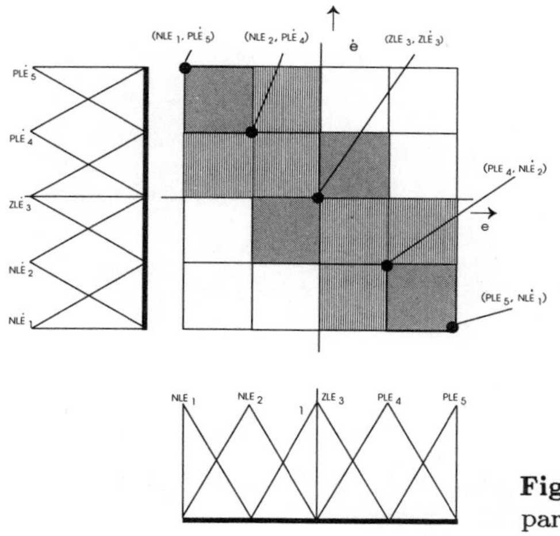

Fig. 3.10. The diagonal fuzzy regions partioning the fuzzy phase plane

There are no fuzzy regions below the zero region $(PLE_n, NL\dot{E}_1)$.

We define the "distance" between a given fuzzy region below the "diagonal" and the "diagonal" as the distance between the center of that fuzzy region and the center of the fuzzy region below which the given fuzzy region is located. Figure 3.12 shows the controller outputs below the "diagonal".

For all fuzzy regions above the "diagonal" the controller output is assigned a negative fuzzy value with a magnitude again depending on the "distance" of the fuzzy region from the "diagonal". The set of all fuzzy regions above the "diagonal" is given as (see Fig. 3.13) follows.

$(PLE_n, NL\dot{E}_2), \ldots, (PLE_n, PL\dot{E}_n)$ are the fuzzy regions above the zero-region $(PLE_n, NL\dot{E}_1)$,

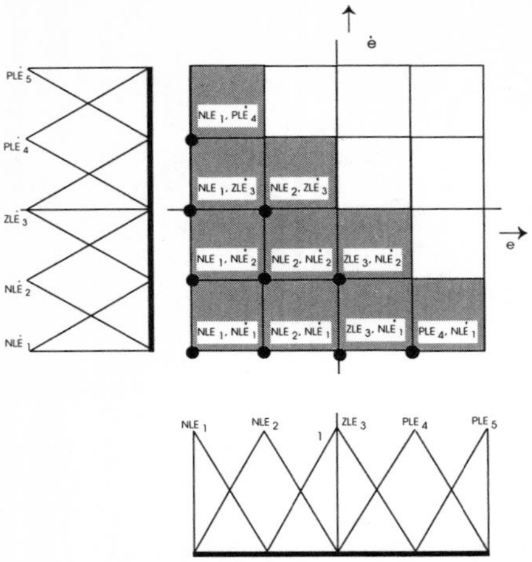

Fig. 3.11. The fuzzy regions below the "diagonal"

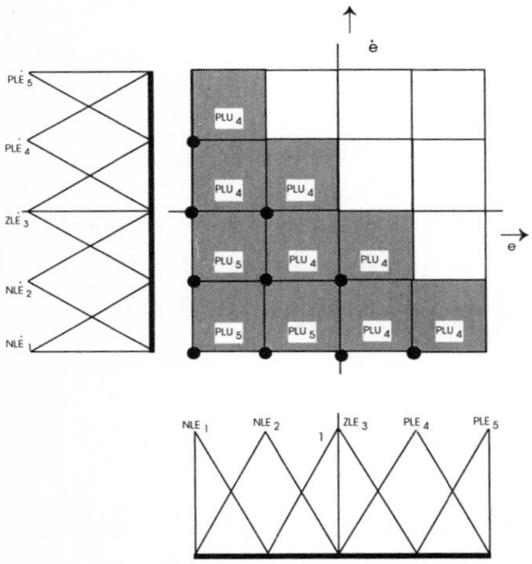

Fig. 3.12. The controller outputs below the "diagonal"

$(PLE_{n-1}, NL\dot{E}_3), \ldots (PLE_{n-1}, PL\dot{E}_n)$ are the fuzzy regions above the zero-region $(PLE_{n-1}, NL\dot{E}_2), \ldots,$
$(NLE_2, PL\dot{E}_n)$ is the fuzzy region above the zero-region $(NLE_2, PL\dot{E}_{n-1})$. There are no fuzzy regions above the zero region $(NLE_1, PL\dot{E}_n)$.

We define the "distance" between a given fuzzy region above the "diagonal" and the "diagonal" as the distance between the center of that fuzzy region and the center of the fuzzy region above which the given fuzzy region is located. Figure 3.14 shows the controller outputs below the "diagonal".

The following Fig. 3.15 illustrates the fuzzy values of the controller outputs associated both below and above the "diagonal" and at the "diagonal" as well.

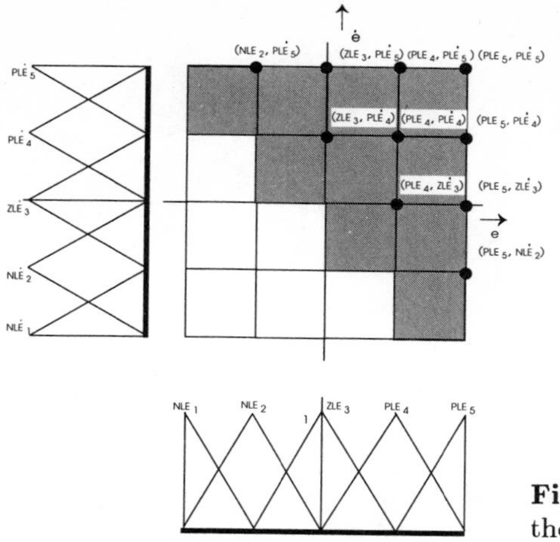

Fig. 3.13. The fuzzy regions above the "diagonal"

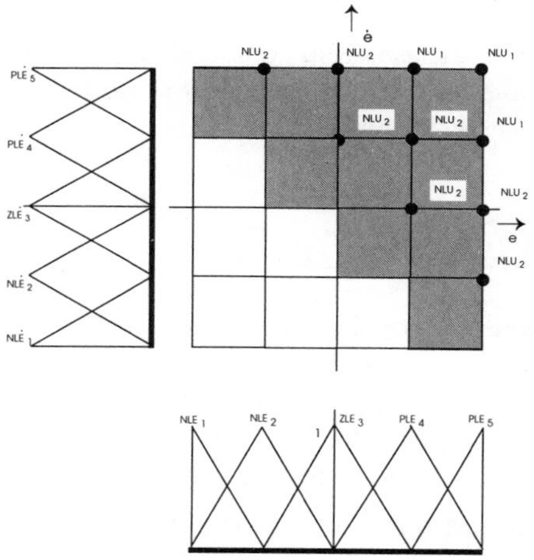

Fig. 3.14. The controller outputs above the "diagonal"

The above *table form* of a diagonal form FLC is translated in fuzzy rules of the form

$$R_C^{\mathbf{i}}: \textit{if } \mathbf{e} = (LE^{\mathbf{i}}, L\dot{E}^{\mathbf{i}})^T \textit{ then } u = LU^{\mathbf{i}}. \tag{3.31}$$

For example, if $LE^{\mathbf{i}} = PLE_4$ and $L\dot{E}^{\mathbf{i}} = NL\dot{E}_1$ then according to Fig. 3.15 $LU^{\mathbf{i}}$ is PLU_4 and thus the corresponding fuzzy rule is

$$R_C^{\mathbf{i}}: \textit{if } \mathbf{e} = (PLE_4, NL\dot{E}_1) \textit{ then } u = PLU_4.$$

Computation with the above type of fuzzy rules was already described in Sect. 2.1.3. We will only briefly repeat here the computational steps we use later on in this chapter.

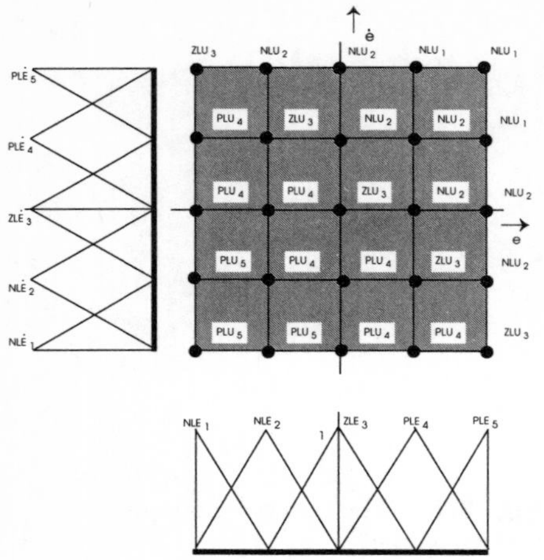

Fig. 3.15. The controller outputs below, above, and at the "diagonal"

Let e^* and $\dot{e}^*$ be given crisp controller inputs, that is, the controller input is the crisp state vector $\mathbf{e}^* = (e^*, \dot{e}^*)^T$. First, these crisp controller inputs are normalized by the use of the input scaling (normalization) factors and their normalized counterparts are obtained (see (2.1), Sect. 2.1.1):

$$
\begin{aligned}
e_N^* &= e^* \cdot N_e, \\
\dot{e}_N^* &= \dot{e}^* \cdot N_{\dot{e}}.
\end{aligned}
\tag{3.32}
$$

Second, the normalized values e_N^* and $\dot{e}_N^*$ are fuzzified, that is, the degrees of satisfaction of each fuzzy region by the crisp state vector $\mathbf{e}^*$ are computed (see Sect. 2.1.2). Let the degree of satisfaction of the $\mathbf{i}$-th fuzzy region $(LE^{\mathbf{i}}, \dot{LE}^{\mathbf{i}})$ by $\mathbf{e}^*$ be $\mu^{\mathbf{i}}(\mathbf{e}^*)$, $(\mathbf{i} = \mathbf{1}, \mathbf{2}, \ldots, \mathbf{n} \times \mathbf{n})$.

Third, the membership functions $\int_{U_N} \mu_{CLU^{\mathbf{i}}}(u_N)/u_N$ for the clipped controller outputs $CLU^{\mathbf{i}}$ for each fuzzy rule are obtained via the use of $\mu^{\mathbf{i}}(\mathbf{e}^*)$ (see (2.10), Sect. 2.1.3).

Fourth, the clipped controller outputs are combined in a global controller output CU whose membership function is $\int_{U_N} \mu_{CU}(u)/u$ and was obtained according to (2.11) in Sect. 2.1.3.

Fifth, the global controller output CU is defuzzified by the center of gravity method (see (2.12), Sect. 2.1.4) as follows:

$$
u_N = \frac{\int\limits_{U_N} \mu_{CU}(u_N)/u_N \cdot u_N}{\int\limits_{U_N} \mu_{CU}(u_N)/u_N},
\tag{3.33}
$$

where u_N is a crisp value in the normalized domain U_N.

Finally, the crisp controller output u_N is denormalized via the use of a denormalization factor (see (2.17), Sect. 2.1.5) as

$$u = N_u^{-1} \cdot u_N. \tag{3.34}$$

Since the fuzzy state space is bounded, the so computed u_N and u have maximum and a minimum crisp bounds denoted as $-u_{\max} \le u \le +u_{\max}$, and $-u_{N\max} \le u_N \le +u_{N\max}$, respectively.

To conclude this section we point out some properties of the transfer characteristic of the diagonal form FLC.

The transfer characteristic, or control surface, of a diagonal form FLC is, in general, a nonlinear mapping $u = h(e, \dot{e})$ which is mainly determined by its operating points and the interpolation between them. An operating point $P^{\mathbf{i}}(\mathbf{e}^{\mathbf{i}}, u^{\mathbf{i}})$ is defined as follows.

Let $\mathbf{e}^{\mathbf{i}} = (e^{\mathbf{i}}, \dot{e}^{\mathbf{i}})^T$ be a particular input and $u^{\mathbf{i}}$ the corresponding output of the FLC. Furthermore, let the center of the fuzzy region $\mathbf{LE}^{\mathbf{i}}$ be defined as $\mathbf{e}^{\mathbf{i}} \in E^2$, where $\mathbf{e}^{\mathbf{i}} = (e^{\mathbf{i}}, \dot{e}^{\mathbf{i}})^T$ are crisp values such that $\mu_{LE^{\mathbf{i}}}(e^{\mathbf{i}}) = 1$ and $\mu_{L\dot{E}^{\mathbf{i}}}(\dot{e}^{\mathbf{i}}) = 1$. Then an operating point $P^{\mathbf{i}}(\mathbf{e}^{\mathbf{i}}, u^{\mathbf{i}})$ is a point for which $\mathbf{e}$ is located at the center of the fuzzy region $\mathbf{LE}^{\mathbf{i}}$ and $u^{\mathbf{i}}$ is the corresponding crisp output of the FLC. The quality of the interpolation between operating points depend on the inference method and the defuzzification method used. Particular features of the control surface $u = h(e, \dot{e})$ are the lines determined by constant controller outputs u, especially the diagonal $u = h(e, \dot{e}) = 0$, where u changes its sign. A diagonal form FLC is designed in such a way that for an increasing Euclidean distance $|s|$ between the state vector $\mathbf{e}$ and the diagonal $u = 0$ the absolute value $|u|$ of the controller output increases monotonically:

$$|u(s_2)| > |u(s_1)| \qquad \text{for} \qquad |s_2| > |s_1|. \tag{3.35}$$

3.2.2 SMC with BL for a Second-Order System

In order to illustrate the similarity of a diagonal form FLC to an SMC with BL we reduce the order of system (3.1) to the second-order system

$$\ddot{x} = f(\mathbf{x}, t) + b(\mathbf{x}, t) \cdot u + \tilde{d}. \tag{3.36}$$

The $(n-1)$-st order sliding surface (3.4) becomes a first-order sliding line

$$s = \lambda e + \dot{e}, \tag{3.37}$$

and the control term $\hat{u}$ in (3.12) becomes

$$\hat{u} = \ddot{x}^d - \lambda \dot{e}. \tag{3.38}$$

Then the control law (3.22) becomes

$$u = \hat{b}^{-1}(-\hat{f} + G \cdot (\ddot{x}^d - \lambda \dot{e}) - G \cdot K(\mathbf{x}, t) \cdot \mathrm{sat}(s/\Phi)). \tag{3.39}$$

Basically, control law (3.39) consists of the following terms:

1. Compensation term: $u_{\text{comp}} = -\hat{b}^{-1}\hat{f}$.
2. Filter term: $u_{\text{filt}} = -\hat{b}^{-1}G\lambda\dot{e}$.

3. Feedforward term: $u_{\rm ff} = \hat{b}^{-1} G \ddot{x}^d$.
4. Control term: $u_c = -\hat{b}^{-1} G K(\mathbf{x}, t) \cdot \text{sat}(s/\Phi)$.

Let us have a closer look at the control term u_c, especially its part $-K(\mathbf{x}, t) \cdot \text{sat}(s/\Phi)$. Obviously, this part is of diagonal form with the "diagonal" $s = 0$. That is why we denote it as

$$u_{\rm diag} = -K(\mathbf{x}, t) \cdot \text{sat}(s/\Phi)). \tag{3.40}$$

where $u_{\rm diag}$ has the following properties

$$\begin{array}{lll} u_{\rm diag} > 0 & \text{for} & s < 0, \\ u_{\rm diag} = 0 & \text{for} & s = 0, \\ u_{\rm diag} < 0 & \text{for} & s > 0. \end{array}$$

If we assume $K(\mathbf{x}, t) = const$ and the state vector $\mathbf{e}$ to be located inside the BL we have

$$u_{\rm diag} = -\frac{K}{\Phi} \cdot s = \frac{K \cdot |s|}{\Phi} \cdot \text{sgn}(s). \tag{3.41}$$

Equation (3.41) shows that $|u_{\rm diag}|$ is proportional to $|s|$, which means that the magnitude of $|u_{\rm diag}|$ increases with increasing distance $|s|$ from the sliding line $s = 0$ and decreases with decreasing distance $|s|$ from the sliding line.

3.2.3 Analytical Description of a Diagonal Form FLC

As already described in Sect. 3.2.1, the magnitude of the fuzzy value of the controller output u depends on the distance of the fuzzy region from the diagonal. On the other hand, the diagonal form FLC provides a mapping from crisp states e and $\dot{e}$ to crisp controller outputs u. The states located on a diagonal play an important role, since there the controller output u changes its sign. This diagonal can be denoted as

$$s = \lambda e + \dot{e} = 0, \tag{3.42}$$

where λ is a design parameter representing the slope of the diagonal. Recall that the rules of the diagonal form FLC have been designed such that

1. The states e and $\dot{e}$ are bounded by $-e_{\rm max} \leq e \leq +e_{\rm max}$, and $-\dot{e}_{\rm max} \leq \dot{e} \leq +\dot{e}_{\rm max}$.
2. The control values u are bounded by $-u_{\rm max} \leq u \leq +u_{\rm max}$.
3. States e and $\dot{e}$ which are located on the diagonal $s = 0$ are mapped to control values $u = 0$.
4. States e and $\dot{e}$ which are located below $s = 0$ are mapped to control values $u > 0$.
5. States e and $\dot{e}$ which are located above $s = 0$ are mapped to control values $u < 0$.

6. The magnitude of $|u|$ increases for increasing values of the distance $|s|$ between state vector $\mathbf{e}$ and $s = 0$ and decreases for decreasing values of $|s|$.

The analytical formulation of the control law u_{fuzz} for the diagonal form FLC is now

$$u_{\text{fuzz}} = -K_{\text{fuzz}}(e, \dot{e}, \lambda) \cdot \text{sgn}(s), \tag{3.43}$$

with the following conditions:

1. $-e_{\max} \leq e \leq +e_{\max}$.
2. $-\dot{e}_{\max} \leq \dot{e} \leq +\dot{e}_{\max}$.
3. $\lambda > 0$.
4. $0 \leq K_{\text{fuzz}} \leq +u_{\max} = K_{\text{fuzz}}|_{\max}$.
5. $K_{\text{fuzz}}(e_1, \dot{e}_1, \lambda) \leq K_{\text{fuzz}}(e_2, \dot{e}_2 . \lambda)$ for $|\lambda e_1 + \dot{e}_1| \leq |\lambda e_2 + \dot{e}_2|$.

3.2.4 Comparison of an SMC with BL with a Diagonal Form FLC

A comparison of (3.41) and (3.43) shows the close relationship between an SMC with BL and a diagonal form FLC. In addition, the layer in the neighborhood of the diagonal form FLC can be interpreted as a BL. The major differences between the two controllers are:

1. The transfer characteristic $u_{\text{fuzz}} = f(s)$ of the diagonal form FLC is nonlinear in contrast to that of the SMC with BL (see Fig. 3.16).

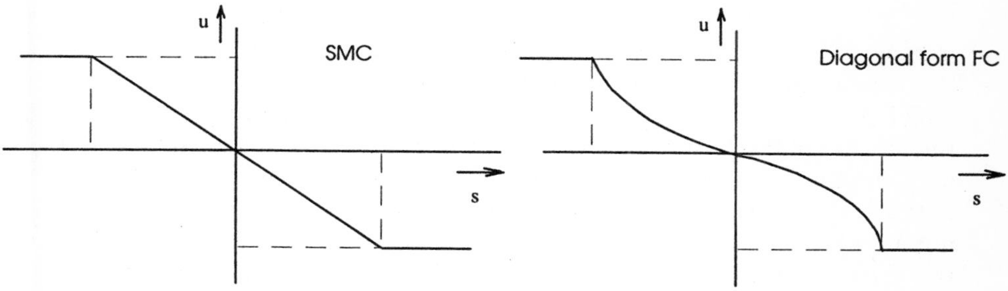

Fig. 3.16. Transfer characteristics of an SMC with BL, and a diagonal form FL

2. For the diagonal form FLC, the state vector $\mathbf{e}$ is, in contrast to the SMC with BL, restricted by bounds on the fuzzy state space (see Fig. 3.17).

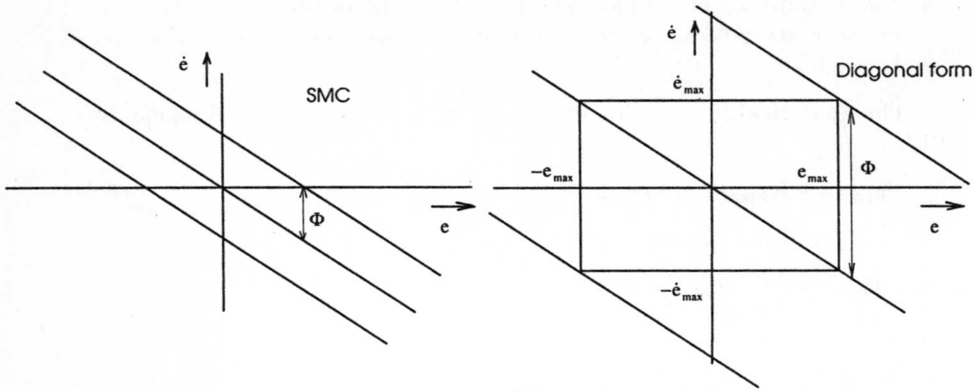

Fig. 3.17. Boundary layer for an SMC with BL, and for a diagonal form FLC

3.2.5 Introduction of the SMFLC

As already discussed, the diagonal form FLC changes the magnitude of u depending on the distance $|s|$ between the state vector $\mathbf{e}$ and the diagonal $s = 0$.

Therefore, we reformulate the control rules (3.31) as follows

$$R_C^i: \textit{ if } s = LS^i \textit{ then } u = LU^i. \tag{3.44}$$

Then, the corresponding control law is

$$u_{\text{fuzz}} = -K_{\text{fuzz}}(|s|) \cdot \text{sgn}(s). \tag{3.45}$$

Because of the similarity of the controller (3.45) and an SMC with BL we call this type of controller a *Sliding Mode FLC* (SMFLC). The advantage of an SMFLC over a common diagonal form FLC is that using an SMFLC reduces the number of fuzzy rules considerably. This is because a diagonal form FLC uses the state variables e and $\dot{e}$ as inputs. Therefore, the number of inputs for a diagonal form FLC is equal to the number of states. In contrast, the only input for an SMFLC is the "signed distance" s, which has to be derived from (3.37) for a second-order system, and from (3.4) for an n-th-order system.

It is now only a small step to the design of SMFLCs, to be discussed in the next section.

3.3 Design of an SMFLC

Before we discuss the design of an SMFLC let us recall the control law (3.22)

$$u = \hat{b}^{-1}G \cdot \hat{u} - \hat{b}^{-1}\hat{f} - \hat{b}^{-1}G \cdot K(\mathbf{x}, t) \cdot \mathrm{sat}(s/\Phi),$$
$$\hat{u} = x^{d(n)} - \sum_{k=1}^{n-1} \binom{n-1}{k} \lambda^k \cdot e^{(n-k)}. \tag{3.46}$$

Instead of an SMC with BL we now consider an SMFLC. The above control law is to be changed into

$$u = \hat{b}^{-1}G \cdot \hat{u} - \hat{b}^{-1}\hat{f} + \hat{b}^{-1}G \cdot u_{\mathbf{fuzz}},$$
$$u_{\mathbf{fuzz}} = -K(|s|) \cdot \mathrm{sgn}(s). \tag{3.47}$$

The design procedure for the SMFLC concentrates on the fuzzy part

$$u_{\mathbf{fuzz}} = -K(|s|) \cdot \mathrm{sgn}(s), \tag{3.48}$$

whereas the design of the "rest" of (3.47) can be adopted from the design of an SMC discussed in Sect. 3.1.

In the following we start with the design of the transfer characteristic. Then we discuss the design of the normalization and denormalization factors of an SMFLC for a second-order system. Next, the design is extended to n-th-order systems. Then, by introducing an additional distance in the state space, the SMFLC is extended to a two-input single-output controller (TISO). Finally, an integrator term is introduced and several control schemes with integrator are discussed.

3.3.1 Design of the Transfer Characteristic

A crucial point in designing an SMFLC is the choice of the number of fuzzy values for the controller inputs and controller outputs of the SMFLC, and the form and location of the corresponding membership functions.

The number of fuzzy values

First, an operating point $P(s^{\mathrm{i}}, u^{\mathrm{i}})$ of the transfer characteristic of an SMFLC is defined as follows.

Let s^{i} be a particular input and u^{i} the corresponding output of the SMFLC. Furthermore, let the center of the fuzzy region LS^{i} be defined as $s^{\mathrm{i}} \in S$, where s^{i} are crisp values such that $\mu_{LS^{\mathrm{i}}}(s^{\mathrm{i}}) = 1$. Then, an operating point $P(s^{\mathrm{i}}, u^{\mathrm{i}})$ is a point for which s is located in the center of the fuzzy region LS^{i} and u^{i} is the corresponding crisp output of the SMFLC. This means that for an operating point $P(s^{\mathrm{i}}, u^{\mathrm{i}})$ only one rule $R_{\mathrm{C}}^{\mathrm{i}}$ in (3.44) fires.

Further, for a SISO SMFLC we assume the same odd number for the fuzzy values of controller inputs and controller outputs. Thus, the number of input fuzzy values is equal to the number of operating points. Depending on the type of fuzzy inference, and on the defuzzification method, the SMFLC provides a linear or nonlinear interpolation between two operating points.

The number of operating points determines the number of discontinuities of the transfer characteristic. Normally, the number of operating points can be $3, 5, 7, 9, \ldots$ depending on how many discontinuity points are allowed.

Shape and location of the membership functions

One of the simplest forms for membership functions is the triangular form. That is why the triangular form is used in most applications, and throughout this chapter.

The problem of the location of a membership function μ_{LS^i} in the domain S can be reduced to the problem of where the operating points should be located. As we will see in Sect. 3.3.3, this is also connected to the choice of the gain $\mathrm{d}u/\mathrm{d}s$ of the SMFLC in different parts of the domain S, since for a given domain S the locations of the operating points determine the slopes of the transfer characteristic in different parts of the domain S.

Thus, the location of the operating points and the membership functions, respectively, can be chosen as follows:

- For a flat slope in the middle of the domain S and increasing slopes towards increasing $|s|$ values, choose larger distances between operating points in the middle of the domain (see Fig. 3.18a). This means

$$\text{For} \quad |s_2| > |s_1| \quad \text{choose} \quad |\mathrm{d}u/\mathrm{d}s|_{s_2} > |\mathrm{d}u/\mathrm{d}s|_{s_1}. \tag{3.49}$$

- For a steep slope in the middle of the domains S and decreasing slopes towards increasing $|s|$ values, choose smaller distances between operating points in the middle of the domains (see Fig. 3.18b). This means

$$\text{For} \quad |s_2| > |s_1| \quad \text{choose} \quad |\mathrm{d}u/\mathrm{d}s|_{s_2} < |\mathrm{d}u/\mathrm{d}s|_{s_1}. \tag{3.50}$$

The first option should be chosen if for small errors a slow reaction to disturbances of the system under control is required. The second option should be chosen if for small errors the system is supposed to be sensitive with respect to disturbances.

3.3.2 Input Normalization and Output Denormalization for a Second-Order System

This section deals with the design of λ and K_{fuzz}, and its maximum value $K_{\mathrm{fuzz}}|_{\mathrm{max}}$, respectively, via normalization and denormalization of controller inputs and controller outputs.

Normalization of the controller inputs is a mapping from a physical domain into a normalized domain. Denormalization of the controller output is a mapping of values of the normalized domain into a corresponding physical domain. The quality of the control depends on these two operations. Normalization influences the sensitivity of the controller and the gain around the setpoint. Denormalization influences the overall gain and, with this, the stability of the closed loop. In the following, the two features are discussed separately.

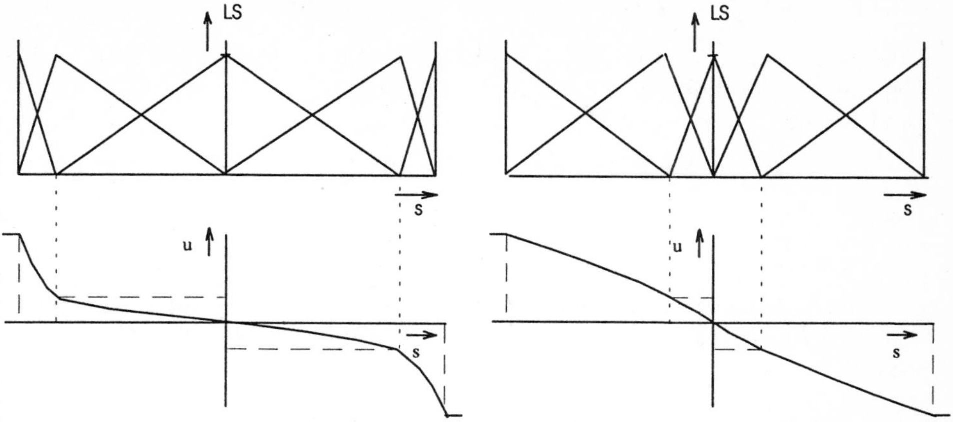

Fig. 3.18. Connection between the location of the input membership functions and the operating points

Input normalization

As discussed in Sect. 2.2.1, normalization is a linear transformation. The actual processing of the fuzzy rules takes place within the normalized phase plane. The sliding line $s = 0$ has to be transformed as follows. Within the non-normalized phase plane we have $\lambda \cdot e + \dot{e} = 0$. In the normalized plane we obtain $\lambda_N \cdot e_N + \dot{e}_N = 0$. By means of the relationship

$$e_N = e \cdot N_e; \quad \dot{e}_N = \dot{e} \cdot N_{\dot{e}}, \tag{3.51}$$

we obtain

$$\lambda = \lambda_N \cdot \frac{N_e}{N_{\dot{e}}}. \tag{3.52}$$

The physical meaning of λ is the following. Once the state $\mathbf{e}$ has reached the sliding line, the system (3.1) behaves as the linear filter function $s = \lambda \cdot e + \dot{e} = 0$. In this filter, the design parameter λ plays the role of the break frequency. λ has to be chosen in such a way that all unmodeled frequencies ν_{su} are filtered out. The corresponding design rule $\lambda \ll \nu_{su}$ leads to

$$\frac{N_e}{N_{\dot{e}}} \ll \frac{\nu_{su}}{\lambda_N}. \tag{3.53}$$

However, this only results in a quotient of the normalization factors $N_e/N_{\dot{e}}$. To determine N_e or $N_{\dot{e}}$ separately, different methods can be used. One method is described in in [19, Sect. 3.4].

Output denormalization

Normalized control values u_N are mapped into a non-normalized control value u by

$$u_N = N_u \cdot u. \tag{3.54}$$

The choice of N_u is of importance for the stability of the system (3.1) and depends on the choice of the maximum value of K_{fuzz}.

If we now return to (3.21), we obtain

$$K_{\text{fuzz}}|_{\text{max}} \geq \beta(\tilde{F} + (1 - \beta^{-1}) \cdot \hat{U} + D + \eta), \tag{3.55}$$

where

$$K_{\text{fuzz}}|_{\text{max}} = \max(K_{\text{fuzz}}(|s|)). \tag{3.56}$$

This is the sufficient condition that the BL is a domain of attraction. From this and $K_{\text{fuzz}N}|_{\text{max}} = N_u \cdot K_{\text{fuzz}}|_{\text{max}}$, the denormalization factor N_u is obtained as

$$N_u = \frac{K_{\text{fuzz}N}|_{\text{max}}}{K_{\text{fuzz}}|_{\text{max}}}. \tag{3.57}$$

3.3.3 The Sliding Mode FLC (SMFLC) as a State Dependent Filter

This section deals with the SMFLC as a filter and provides an insight into the behavior of the system (3.1) under control when approaching the sliding line.

Generally, in contrast to the SMC with BL, the SMFLC generates a nonlinear function $u = f(s)$. Yet with an increasing number of membership functions $u = f(s)$ becomes linear [37]. Corresponding to the SMC with BL we consider the SMFLC as a filter function. If we consider the transfer characteristic between two operating points i and $i+1$ to be an (approximately) linear segment we can attach to the i-th segment a specific gain k_i/ϕ_i representing the characteristic filter parameter for this segment (see Fig. 3.19). Since the gain changes from segment to segment we obtain a "state dependent" filter function. Similar to (3.28) we obtain a filter function for the i-th segment

$$\dot{s} + b\hat{b}^{-1}G \cdot \frac{k_i}{\phi_i} \cdot s = b\hat{b}^{-1}G \cdot u_i \cdot \text{sgn}(s) + \hat{u} \cdot (b\hat{b}^{-1}G - 1) + \Delta f + \tilde{d}, \tag{3.58}$$

with

$$u_i = \begin{cases} -\sum_{\nu=1}^{i-1} k_\nu + \frac{k_i \cdot \sum_{\nu=1}^{i-1} \phi_\nu}{\phi_i} & \text{if } i \geq 2 \\ 0 & \text{if } i = 1 \end{cases}, \tag{3.59}$$

$$k_\nu, \phi_\nu > 0; \quad i = 1, \ldots n \quad (n = \text{number of segments}).$$

Equation (3.58) is a state dependent filter with different break frequencies $b\hat{b}^{-1}G \cdot k_i/\phi_i$. This can be used to choose different approach velocities for the state $\mathbf{e}$ depending on the distance $|s|$ between the state and the sliding line. For a large distance $|s|$ between the state vector $\mathbf{e}$ and the sliding line

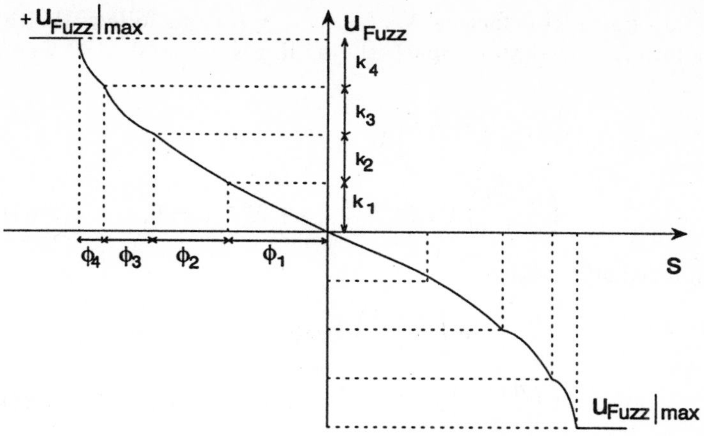

Fig. 3.19. Nonlinear transfer characteristic

$s = 0$ any unmodeled frequencies are unable to cause a change of sign of the controller-output variable. Therefore, for a large $|s|$ we may choose a bigger control gain than for a small $|s|$. In contrast to this, in order to provide smooth behavior in the vicinity of the sliding line, we choose smaller control gain.

To produce such a transfer function the inequalities

$$\frac{k_1}{\phi_1} \leq \frac{k_2}{\phi_2} \leq \ldots \leq \frac{k_n}{\phi_n}, \tag{3.60}$$

must hold.

It has to be emphasized that different slopes of the nonlinear transfer characteristic can be influenced by the form and location of both the controller input and the controller output membership functions.

Regarding the pure SMC the balance condition

$$b\hat{b}^{-1}G \cdot \frac{k_i}{\phi_i} \leq \lambda, \tag{3.61}$$

has to be fulfilled only in the vicinity of the origin of the phase plane.

The tracking quality is guaranteed by the maximum values $K_{\text{fuzz}}|_{\max} = \sum_{\nu=1}^{i-1} k_\nu$ and $\Phi_{\max} = \sum_{\nu=1}^{i-1} \phi_\nu$ as long as

$$b\hat{b}^{-1}G \cdot \frac{K_{\text{fuzz}}|_{\max}}{\Phi_{\max}} \leq \lambda. \tag{3.62}$$

3.3.4 SMFLC for a System of n-th Order

An SMFLC for an n-th-order system is, analogous to the second-order case, a SISO controller. The crucial point here is to derive appropriate normalization factors $N_e, N_{\dot{e}}, \ldots, N_{e^{(n-1)}}$ for the states $e, \dot{e}, \ldots, e^{(n-1)}$.

We obtain the normalization factors $N_e, N_{\dot{e}}, \ldots, N_{e^{(n-1)}}$ as follows. With respect to the non-normalized state space the sliding surface $s = 0$ is described by

$$\begin{aligned}(\frac{\mathrm{d}}{\mathrm{d}t} + \lambda)^{(n-1)} e &= e^{(n-1)} + \binom{n-1}{1} \lambda e^{(n-2)} \\ &+ \binom{n-1}{2} \lambda^2 e^{(n-3)} + \cdots + \lambda^{n-1} e = 0, \end{aligned} \quad (3.63)$$

and for the normalized state space

$$\begin{aligned}(\frac{\mathrm{d}}{\mathrm{d}t} + \lambda_N)^{(n-1)} e_N &= e_N^{(n-1)} + \binom{n-1}{1} \lambda_N e_N^{(n-2)} \\ &+ \binom{n-1}{2} \lambda_N{}^2 e_N^{(n-3)} + \cdots + \lambda_N^{n-1} e_N = 0. \end{aligned} \quad (3.64)$$

With the normalization factors, $N_e, N_{\dot{e}}, \ldots, N_{e^{(n-1)}}$, (3.64) can be rewritten as

$$e^{(n-1)} + \binom{n-1}{1} \lambda_N \cdot \frac{N_{e^{(n-2)}}}{N_{e^{(n-1)}}} e^{(n-2)} + \cdots + \lambda_N^{n-1} \frac{N_e}{N_{e^{(n-1)}}} e = 0. \quad (3.65)$$

The comparison of the coefficients of (3.64) and (3.65) leads to

$$\lambda = \lambda_N \cdot \frac{N_{e^{(n-2)}}}{N_{e^{(n-1)}}}; \lambda^2 = \lambda_N^2 \cdot \frac{N_{e^{(n-3)}}}{N_{e^{(n-1)}}}; \ldots; \lambda^{n-1} = \lambda_N^{n-1} \cdot \frac{N_e}{N_{e^{(n-1)}}}. \quad (3.66)$$

From this we obtain the design rule for the normalization factors.

$$\frac{N_{e^{(n-2)}}}{N_{e^{(n-1)}}} = \ldots = \frac{N_e}{N_{\dot{e}}} = \frac{\lambda}{\lambda_N}. \quad (3.67)$$

This means that once the parameters λ, λ_N, and N_e are derived, all normalization factors from $N_{\dot{e}}$ to $N_{e^{(n-1)}}$ are fixed.

3.3.5 The TISO SMFLC

For an SMFLC with a controller input $\mathbf{e}$ and a scalar controller output u a general design rule is that the absolute value of u should monotonically increase with increasing distance $|s|$. This rule evaluates large errors $\mathbf{e}$ in the same way as small errors if they only represent the same distance $|s|$ to the sliding surface $s = 0$. To improve the behavior of the system it might be of advantage to introduce an additional degree of freedom for the state vector $\mathbf{e}$ in the fuzzy rules. One particular option is to introduce the change $\dot{s}$ in the rules ([10]). Another option is to introduce an additional distance d so that the region near the origin of the state space can be arrived at faster than before (see Fig. 3.20) [16]. This option is described in the following. With respect to the distances $|s|$ and d, two general design rules can be formulated:

R1: $|u|$ should increase as the distance $|s|$ between the actual state and the sliding surface $s = 0$ increases.

R2: $|u|$ should increase as the distance d between the actual state and the line perpendicular to the sliding surface $s = 0$ increases.

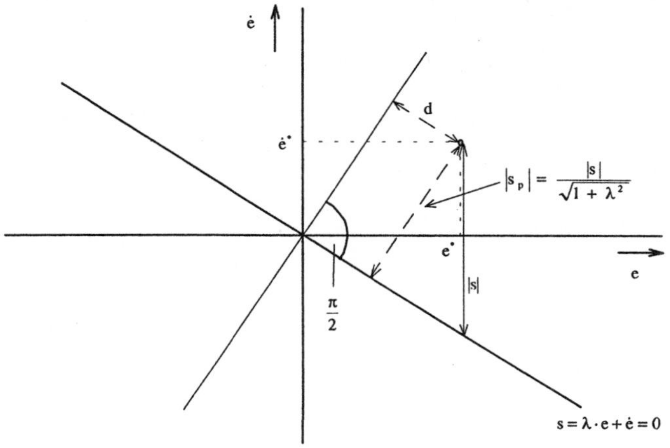

Fig. 3.20. Distances $|s|$ and d of an SMFLC

For the $(n-1)$-dimensional sliding surface the distance d is derived as follows. Let

$$\mathbf{n} = \frac{\left(1, \binom{n-1}{1}\lambda, \binom{n-1}{2}\lambda^2, \ldots, \lambda^{n-1}\right)^T}{\left|\left(1, \binom{n-1}{1}\lambda, \binom{n-1}{2}\lambda^2, \ldots, \lambda^{n-1}\right)^T\right|}, \tag{3.68}$$

be the normal vector of the $(n-1)$-dimensional sliding surface within the n-dimensional state space. Furthermore, let $s_p = \mathbf{e}^T \cdot \mathbf{n}$ be the projection of the state vector $\mathbf{e}$ onto the direction of the normal vector $\mathbf{n}$ (the signed distance from $\mathbf{e}$ to the sliding surface $s = 0$). Hence one obtains the shortest Euclidean distance d (the perpendicular) between $\mathbf{e}$ and the direction of $\mathbf{n}$,

$$d = \sqrt{|\mathbf{e}|^2 - s_p{}^2}. \tag{3.69}$$

Now the distance $|s_p|$ between $\mathbf{e}$ and the sliding surface, and the distance d between the direction of the normal vector and the sliding surface are evaluated by fuzzy rules. We assign a fuzzy set to each of the variables s_p, d, and u and obtain from this the s_p-d diagram (see Fig. 3.21).

The fuzzy values in the cells of this diagram describe the magnitude of the controller output. They are filled in according to the above design rules R1 and R2. For the second-order case this diagram corresponds uniquely to the phase plane of the system. For higher-order systems the diagram is an aggregation of the phase space so that the correspondence between s_p and d on the one hand, and the vector $\mathbf{e}$ on the other hand, is not unique any more.

The **i**-th rule of a set of fuzzy rules can be stated as

d \ s_p	NB	NM	NS	NZ	PZ	PS	PM	PB
B	PB	PB	PB	PB	NB	NB	NB	NB
M	PB	PB	PB	PM	NM	NB	NB	NB
S	PB	PB	PM	PS	NS	NM	NB	NB
Z	PB	PM	PS	PZ	NZ	NS	NM	NB

Fig. 3.21. s_p-d diagram

$$R_C^{\mathbf{i}}: \textit{if } s_p = LS_p^{\mathbf{i}} \textit{ and } d = LD^{\mathbf{i}} \textit{ then } u = LU^{\mathbf{i}}.$$

The analytical function of such an SMFLC can be defined as

$$u_{\mathbf{fuzz}} = -K_{\mathbf{fuzz}}(|s_p|, d) \cdot \mathrm{sgn}(s). \tag{3.70}$$

The result is that all design rules postulated in the previous sections are also applicable to this SMFLC.

3.3.6 SMFLC with Integrator

In contrast to the previously used error variable e, let the integral of the error be the variable of interest:

$$\delta(t) = \int_0^t e \cdot \mathrm{d}t'. \tag{3.71}$$

With respect to $\delta(t)$, the system

$$x^{(n)} = f(\mathbf{x}, t) + b(\mathbf{x}, t) \cdot u + \tilde{d} \tag{3.72}$$

is of $(n+1)$-th order. For the sake of simplicity we omit the argument t in the following. For the sliding surface we obtain

$$\begin{aligned} s = \left(\frac{\mathrm{d}}{\mathrm{d}t} + \lambda\right)^{(n)} \delta \quad &= \quad \delta^{(n)} + \binom{n}{1} \cdot \lambda \delta^{(n-1)} \\ &+ \ldots + \binom{n}{n-1} \cdot \lambda^{n-1} \dot{\delta} + \binom{n}{n} \cdot \lambda^n \delta, \end{aligned} \tag{3.73}$$

and finally

$$s = \sum_{k=1}^{n} \binom{n}{k} \cdot \lambda^k \cdot \delta^{(n-k)} + \delta^{(n)}. \tag{3.74}$$

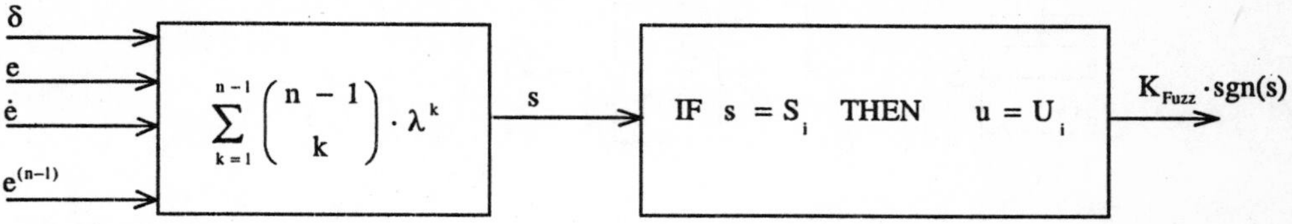

Fig. 3.22. Control structure with additional integrator input term δ

Differentiating (3.74) with respect to time we obtain

$$\dot{s} = \sum_{k=1}^{n} \binom{n}{k} \cdot \lambda^k \cdot e^{(n-k)} + e^{(n)}. \tag{3.75}$$

With the reaching condition stated as

$$s \cdot \dot{s} < -\eta |s|, \tag{3.76}$$

we have

$$s \cdot (f - x^{d(n)} + \sum_{k=1}^{n} \binom{n}{k} \cdot \lambda^k \cdot e^{(n-k)} + b \cdot u) < -\eta |s|. \tag{3.77}$$

Similar to (3.12) we choose the control law

$$\begin{aligned} u &= \hat{b}^{-1}(\tilde{u} - \hat{f}), \\ \tilde{u} &= G \cdot (\hat{u} - K_{\text{fuzz}}(\mathbf{e}, \delta) \cdot \text{sgn}(s)), \\ \hat{u} &= x^{d(n)} - \sum_{k=1}^{n} \binom{n}{k} \lambda^k \cdot e^{(n-k)}. \end{aligned} \tag{3.78}$$

The only differences between (3.78) and (3.12) appear in the term $\hat{u}$ and the FLC itself

$$u_{\text{fuzz}} = -K_{\text{fuzz}}(\mathbf{e}, \delta) \cdot \text{sgn}(s). \tag{3.79}$$

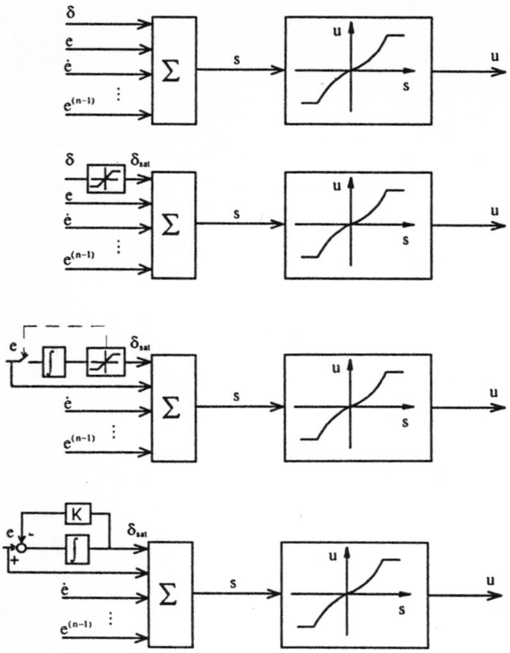

Fig. 3.23. Treatment of integral action within an SMFLC

Here we have an FLC with an additional integral controller input δ. If we focus on a SISO SMFLC with the "distance" s as the only controller input we obtain the same fuzzy rule structure as before.

The control scheme, however, turns out to incorporate a certain drawback. Because of the saturation of the controller output the integral term δ may reach undesirable high values compared with the other terms $e, \dot{e}, \ldots, e^{(n-1)}$, so that they are dominated by δ.

Therefore, the magnitude of the integral term should be restricted in the case when the state $\mathbf{e}$ is far from the sliding surface. This can be done in any one of the following ways.

1. Restriction by the domain of s itself (see Fig. 3.23a).
2. Restriction by a saturation element before computing s (see (3.23) and Fig. 3.23b).
3. Switching off the integral term when it has reached a predefined value (see Fig. 3.23c).
4. Changing the integrator into a first-order filter by means of a constant feedback (see Fig. 3.23d).

From the four ways of restricting the integral action, options 3 or 4 should be preferred since the first two options do restrict the integral action, but the integrator remains active. Thus, one has to take into account the time period

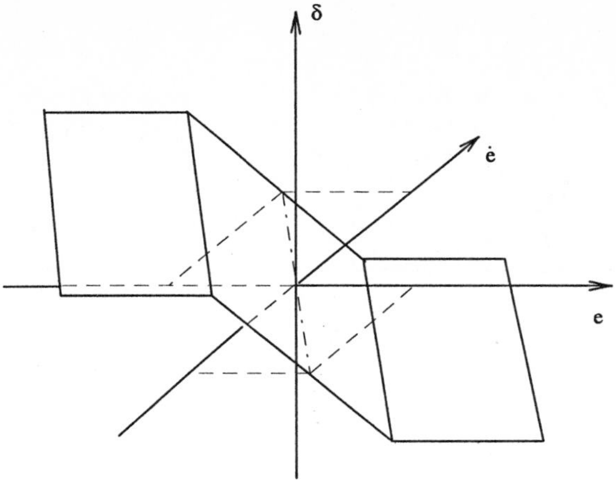

Fig. 3.24. Control surface for an SMFLC with saturated control action

for "charging" and "discharging" the integrator beyond its saturation bounds. Option 4 is likely the best one since it does not need any discontinuously switching function. It works as an integrator in the vicinity of $e = 0$ and as a first-order filter far from $e = 0$. Figure 3.24 shows a corresponding view of the control surface of a third-order controller.

3.4 Tuning of Input Scaling Factors

Fuzzy controllers with crisp inputs and outputs are, in general, multidimensional nonlinear transfer elements with upper and lower bounds (see Fig. 3.25).

Before fuzzification, the corresponding controller inputs have to be scaled to fit their normalized domains. In chap. 3, section 3.3.2 input scaling (normalization) has already been described. However, only the quotients of input scaling factors were determined. In this section a method is described that shows how the domain of the controller inputs can be appropriately utilized.

Let the controller inputs for the FLC over a large period of time have as behavior a stationary process with Gaussian distribution. Our assumption is that for a stationary controller input a certain signal amplitude around the origin of the FLC should be linearly transferred by the FLC.

A measure for linear input-output dependence of an arbitrary transfer element is the input-output cross-correlation function. If a specific linearity between input and output is required, the standard deviation of the input signal should be chosen such that a corresponding cross-correlation is met. For a given FLC with a fixed set of fuzzy rules and their corresponding membership functions, the only parameter to influence the input-output cross-correlation is the scaling factor. From nonlinear control theory we know the "describing

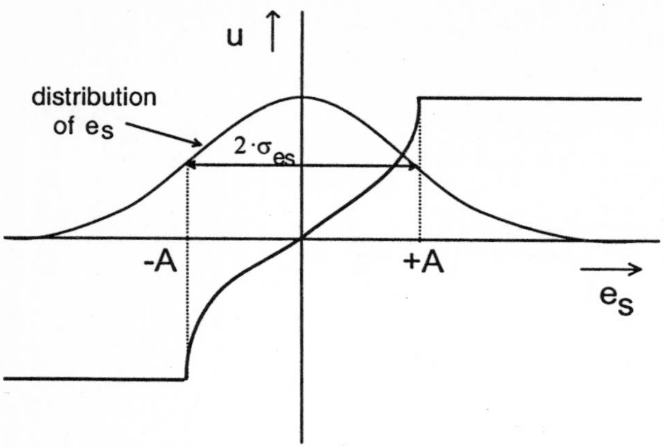

Fig. 3.25. Symmetrical nonlinear transfer characteristic of an FLC with limits

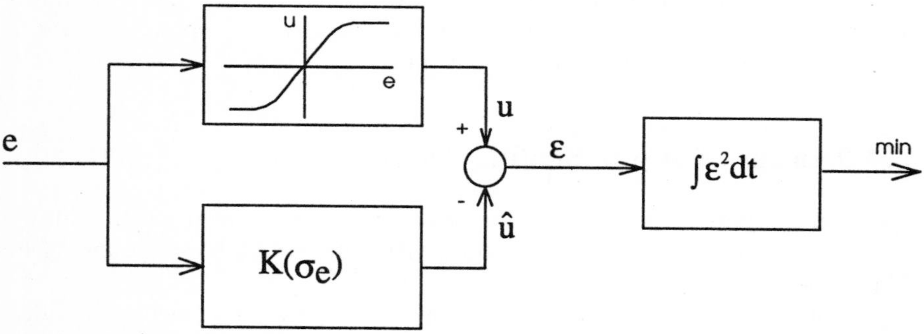

Fig. 3.26. Equivalent gain $K(\sigma_e)$

function" for sinusoidal input signals, and the "equivalent gain" for signals with noise. In order to develop the idea of partial linear transfer of Gaussian distributed signal amplitudes we construct a linear connection of controller input and controller output represented by a gain which is variable with respect to the standard deviation σ_e of the input signal.

Let e be the centered controller input (with zero mean) and u the controller output, which is also centered because of the symmetry property of the nonlinear transfer function with respect to the origin. Hence, we have the transfer function $u = h(e)$. On the other hand we construct a linear model of the nonlinear transfer function $u_l = K(\sigma_e) \cdot e$. The gain $K(\sigma_e)$ is then determined by the comparison of u and u_l (see Fig. 3.26). We now have

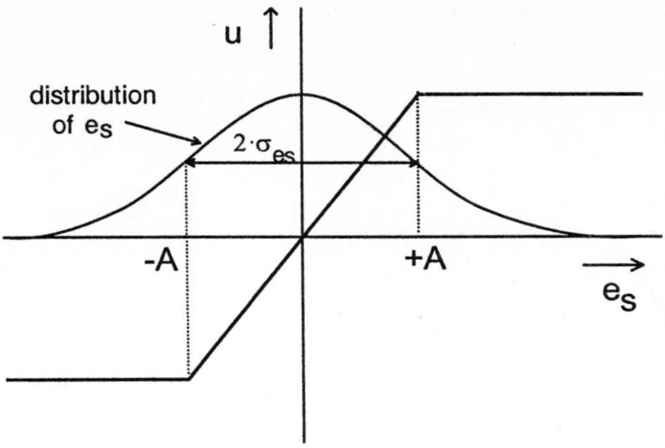

Fig. 3.27. Linear transfer characteristic with limits

$$\varepsilon = u - u_l = u - K(\sigma_e) \cdot e. \tag{3.80}$$

In the following we seek a K for which the expected value of ε^2 is a minimum

$$E[\varepsilon^2] = E[(u - K(\sigma_e) \cdot e)^2] \rightarrow \min. \tag{3.81}$$

Differentiation with respect to K yields

$$\begin{aligned} \frac{\mathrm{d}}{\mathrm{d}K} E[(u - K(\sigma_e) \cdot e)^2] &= E[\frac{\mathrm{d}}{\mathrm{d}K}(u - K(\sigma_e) \cdot e)^2] \\ &= -2 \cdot E[u \cdot e - K(\sigma_e) \cdot e^2] = 0. \end{aligned} \tag{3.82}$$

From this we obtain the equivalent gain

$$K(\sigma_e) = \frac{E[u \cdot e]}{E[e^2]}. \tag{3.83}$$

Since $E[e \cdot u] = R_{e,u}|_{\tau=0}$ and $E[e^2] = \sigma_e^2 = R_{e^2}|_{\tau=0}$ we obtain

$$K(\sigma_e) = \frac{R_{e,u}(\sigma_e)}{\sigma_e^2}. \tag{3.84}$$

Here, $R_{e,u}|_{\tau=0}$ is the linear cross-correlation between controller input e and controller output u for $\tau = 0$, and $R_{e^2}|_{\tau=0}$ the linear auto-correlation for $\tau = 0$. σ_e is the standard deviation of e.

The controller input e is now scaled by

$$e_N = N_e \cdot e. \tag{3.85}$$

The standard deviations σ_e and σ_{e_N} of the unscaled and scaled controller inputs are connected in the same way as the controller inputs themselves

$$\sigma_{e_N} = N_e \cdot \sigma_e. \tag{3.86}$$

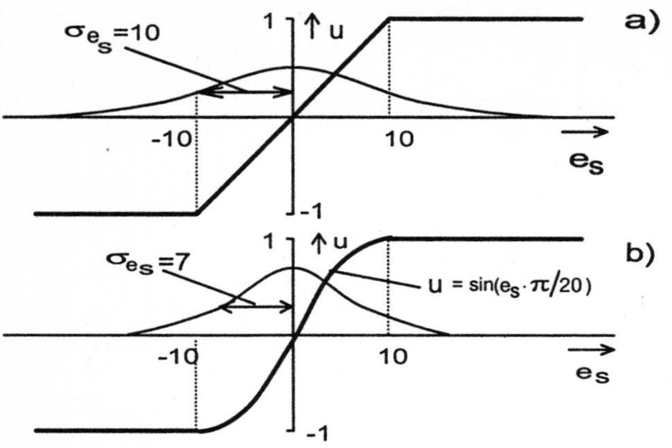

Fig. 3.28. FLCs with linear (a) and nonlinear (b) characteristics between the lower and upper limits

From (3.84) and (3.86) we obtain the equivalent gain for the scaled variables

$$K(\sigma_{e_N}) = \frac{\tilde{R}_{e,u} \cdot \sigma_u}{\sigma_{e_N}}, \tag{3.87}$$

where

σ_u is the standard deviation of u,
$\tilde{R}_{e,u} = R_{e,u}/(\sigma_{e_N} \cdot \sigma_u)$ is the normalized cross-correlation coefficient.

The controller input e is now scaled such that

$$\sigma_{e_N} = A, \tag{3.88}$$

where A is the half-width of the controller input domain of the FLC (see Fig. 3.27).

For a linear curve between the bounds of the controller output (see Fig. 3.28a) we have for $\sigma_{e_N} = A$ a controller input probability $P = 0.68$ for the linear region of the SMFLC. If, however, the characteristic of the SMFLC between the bounds is nonlinear and monotone (see Fig. 3.28b) then, by keeping the same $\tilde{R}_{e,u}$, we are on the safe side because one obtains automatically a scaling factor N_e such that $\sigma_{e_N} < A$.

3.5 Numerical Example

The following example shows the SMFLC compared with an SMC with BL for a second-order system.

3.5.1 The Model

The task is to follow a contour by means of a force-adaptive manipulator which is used for robot guided grinding of castings, welding tasks, and related industrial applications. Suppose that the a priori knowledge about the stiffness of the contour is incomplete. The robot effector (tool, gripper) has to follow the surface keeping a constant desired force. The actual force between effector and surface is measured with the help of a force sensor. The force error between desired force and actual force is given as a controller input to the SMFLC, The controller output of the SMFLC is a position correction of the robot arm. Assume for simplicity that the whole dynamics of the system is determined by the the robot effector and the surface. A further simplification is the restriction to one degree of freedom, which means that we only have one coordinate in our model. Furthermore, let the effector be modeled as a mass-spring-damper system and the surface as a spring. The corresponding differential equation is

$$m\cdot\ddot{y}+c\cdot(\dot{y}-\dot{y}_O)-m\cdot g+K_1\cdot(y-y_O-\tilde{D})+K_2\cdot(y-y_c+r+A)=0. \quad (3.89)$$

Equation (3.89) is a force balance equation (see Fig. 3.29):

$$F_T+F_D-F_G+F_F+F_O=0, \quad (3.90)$$

with

F_T = inertial force,
F_D = damping force,
F_G = weighting force,
F_F = spring force,
F_O = reaction force within the surface.

Let the sensor force be represented by the spring force F_F. Then

$$F_F=K_1(y-y_O-\tilde{D}); \quad \dot{F}_F=K_1(\dot{y}-\dot{y}_O); \quad \ddot{F}_F=K_1(\ddot{y}-\ddot{y}_O), \quad (3.91)$$

we obtain the equation for the spring (sensor) force F_F:

$$\ddot{F}_F=-\frac{c}{m}\cdot\dot{F}_F+K_1\cdot g-\frac{K_1}{m}\cdot F_F-\frac{K_1}{m}\cdot F_O-K_1\cdot\ddot{y}_O. \quad (3.92)$$

In this equation we have that

$$u=-K_1\cdot\ddot{y}_O, \quad (3.93)$$

is the controller output (the control input) to be produced by the SMFLC. The model-specific parameters are:

c = 50 kg s^{-1}
m = 0.05 kg
K_1 = 5 000 kg s^{-2}
K_2 = 10 000 kg s^{-2}

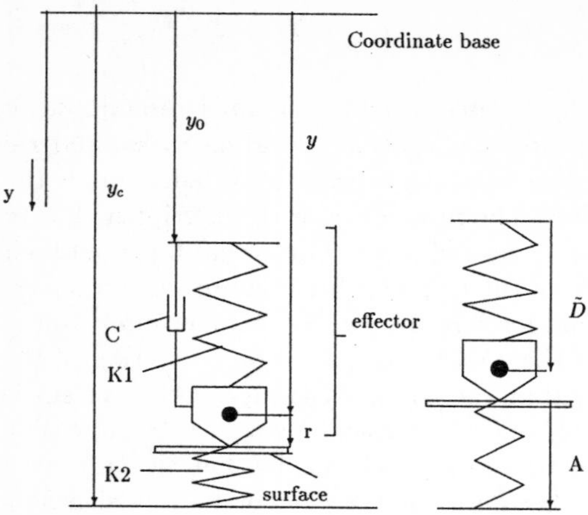

Fig. 3.29. Simplified model of the robot effector acting upon a surface

$$\begin{aligned} \tau_{\text{sample}} &= 0.01 \text{ s} \\ F^d &= 10 \text{ N} \quad \text{(desired force)} \\ v &= 0.2 \text{ m s}^{-1} \quad \text{(feed rate)} \end{aligned}$$

3.5.2 Design of the TISO SMFLC

In order to apply the previous results for the design of an SMFLC for system (3.1) we compare system (3.1) and (3.92) and derive the corresponding terms for $x(t)$, $x^{(n)}(t)$, and $f(\mathbf{x}, t)$. A comparison between (3.1) and (3.92) yields:

$x(t)$ becomes $F_F(t)$,
$x^{(n)}(t)$ becomes $\ddot{F}_F$,
$f(\mathbf{x}, t)$ becomes $-\frac{c}{m} \cdot \dot{F}_F + K_1 \cdot g - \frac{K_1}{m} \cdot F_F - \frac{K_1}{m} \cdot F_O$,
$b(\mathbf{x}, t)$ becomes 1.

In the following we refer to the TISO SMFLC described in Sect. 3.3.5. The corresponding design steps are:

1. Introduction of the overall control law.
2. Choice of the fuzzy values for the normalized controller inputs s_{p_N} and d_N, and the controller output u_N.
3. Design of the fuzzy rules.
4. Choice of the slope λ of the sliding line $s = 0$.
5. Choice of the normalization factors N_e, and $N_{\dot{e}}$.
6. Choice of the upper bound:

$$\tilde{F} = \left| -\frac{c}{m} \cdot \dot{F}_F + K_1 \cdot g - \frac{K_1}{m} \cdot F_F - \frac{K_1}{m} \cdot F_O \right|_{\max} . \tag{3.94}$$

7. Design $K_{\text{fuzz}}|_{\max}$, and N_u, respectively, such that

$$K_{\text{fuzz}}|_{\max} > \left| -\frac{c}{m} \cdot \dot{F}_F + K_1 \cdot g - \frac{K_1}{m} \cdot F_F - \frac{K_1}{m} \cdot F_O \right|_{\max} . \tag{3.95}$$

In the above upper bound we assume the disturbances $\tilde{d}$ to be taken into account.

The design steps are then as follows.

1. **Introduction of the overall control law**
With the sliding line

$$s = \lambda e + \dot{e}; \qquad e = F_F - {F_F}^d, \tag{3.96}$$

we introduce the overall control law according to (3.39) and (3.70):

$$u = -\lambda \cdot \dot{e} - K_{\text{fuzz}}(|s_p|, d) \cdot \text{sgn}(s); \qquad s_p = \frac{s}{\sqrt{1+\lambda^2}}. \tag{3.97}$$

2. **Choice of the fuzzy values**
Within the normalized phase plane the "distance" s_{p_N} and distance d_N are

$$s_{p_N} = (e_N + \dot{e}_N)/\sqrt{2}, \tag{3.98}$$

and

$$d_N = \left| (-e_N + \dot{e}_N)/\sqrt{2} \right| . \tag{3.99}$$

For the normalized values s_{p_N}, d_N and the normalized control variable u_N the following fuzzy sets are defined:

PSS – s_{p_N} is positive small.
PSB – s_{p_N} is positive big.
NSS – s_{p_N} is negative small.
NSB – s_{p_N} is negative big.
DS – d_N is small.
DB – d_N is big.
PUS – u_N is positive small.
PUB – u_N is positive big.
NUS – u_N is negative small.
NUB – u_N is negative big.

Figure 3.30 shows the corresponding membership functions. The respective s_{p_N}-d_N diagram is shown in Fig. 3.31.

3. **Design of the fuzzy rules**
From Fig. 3.31 we obtain the fuzzy rules for the calculation of the normalized controller output u_N. To obtain as few fuzzy rules as possible we summarize fuzzy rules with the same consequent. This is the reason why the "or" operator appears in two of the following rules.

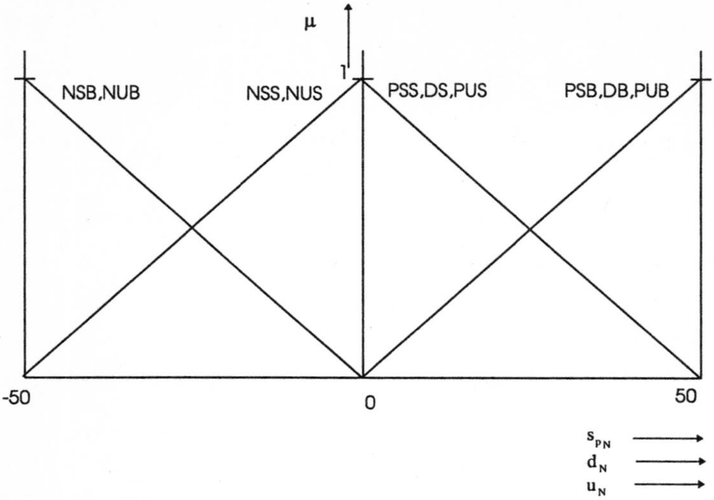

Fig. 3.30. Membership functions for s_{pN}, d_N, and u_N

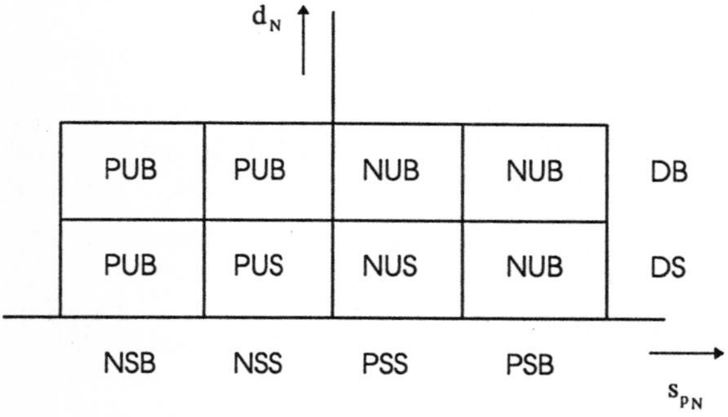

Fig. 3.31. s_{p_N}-d_N diagram for the contour tracking problem

For $s_{p_N} > 0$,
if PSS *and* DS *then* NUS,
if (PSS *and* DB) *or* PSB *then* NUB.
For $s_{p_N} \leq 0$,
if NSS *and* DS *then* PUS,
if (NSS *and* DB) *or* NSB *then* PUB.

4. **Choice of λ**
   The design rule for λ is $\lambda \ll \nu_{su}$, where ν_{su} are unmodeled frequencies. If we assume that unmodeled frequencies occur above the eigenfrequency ω of the system (3.92) we only have to choose $\lambda \leq \omega$.
   We obtain the eigenfrequency of (3.92) from the homogeneous equation

$$\ddot{F}_F + \frac{c}{m} \cdot \dot{F}_F + \frac{K_1}{m} \cdot F_F = 0, \tag{3.100}$$

which can be rewritten as

$$\ddot{F}_F + 2\zeta\omega \cdot \dot{F}_F + \omega^2 \cdot F_F = 0, \tag{3.101}$$

where ζ denotes the damping.
Hence, we obtain

$$\omega = \sqrt{\frac{K_1}{m}} = \sqrt{\frac{5000}{0.05}} = 316 \text{ s}^{-1}. \tag{3.102}$$

Since λ has to be less than ω we choose $\lambda = 50 \text{ s}^{-1}$.

5. **Choice of the normalization factors N_e and $N_{\dot{e}}$**
From correlation tests we choose $N_{\dot{e}} = 0.4 \text{ s}^3 \text{ kg}^{-1} \text{ m}^{-1}$. Hence

$$N_e = \lambda \cdot N_{\dot{e}} = 50 \text{ s}^{-1} \cdot 0.4 \text{ s}^3 \text{ kg}^{-1} \text{ m}^{-1} = 20 \text{ s}^2 \text{ kg}^{-1} \text{ m}^{-1}. \tag{3.103}$$

6. **Choice of the upper bounds**
Since we do not compensate for f, the $\tilde{F}$ in (3.55) is chosen to be

$$\tilde{F} = \left| -\frac{c}{m} \cdot \dot{F}_F + K_1 \cdot g - \frac{K_1}{m} \cdot F_F - \frac{K_1}{m} \cdot F_O \right|_{\max}. \tag{3.104}$$

Since we expect small values for $\ddot{F}_F$, the upper bound $\tilde{F}$ is chosen to be relatively small

$$\tilde{F} = 2500 \text{ kg m s}^{-4}. \tag{3.105}$$

7. **Choice of $K_{\text{fuzz}}|_{\max}$ and N_u**
From the upper bound obtained in the last step we choose

$$K_{\text{fuzz}}|_{\max} = 3900 \text{ kg m s}^{-4}. \tag{3.106}$$

Since our normalized domain is $(-39, 39)$, this corresponds to a normalization factor

$$N_u = 0.01 \text{ kg m s}^{-4}. \tag{3.107}$$

3.5.3 Design of the Sliding Mode Controller with BL

The design steps for the SMC with BL are similar to the design steps 1,4,6, and 7 for the SMFLC.

1. Introduction of the overall control law.
2. Choice of the slope λ of the sliding line $s = 0$.
3. Choice of the width Φ of the BL.
4. Choice of the upper bound:

$$\tilde{F} = \left| -\frac{c}{m} \cdot \dot{F}_F + K_1 \cdot g - \frac{K_1}{m} \cdot F_F - \frac{K_1}{m} \cdot F_O \right|_{\max}. \tag{3.108}$$

5. Design $K_{\max}$ such that

$$K_{\max} > \left| -\frac{c}{m} \cdot \dot{F}_F + K_1 \cdot g - \frac{K_1}{m} \cdot F_F - \frac{K_1}{m} \cdot F_O \right|_{\max} . \qquad (3.109)$$

The SMC with BL evaluates only the sign of s. The maximum controller output and the denormalization factor are the same as those with the SM-FLC.

The design steps for the SMC with BL are performed as follows.

1. **Introduction of the overall control law**
   The overall control law is

$$u = -\lambda \cdot \dot{e} - K \cdot \mathrm{sat}(s/\Phi). \qquad (3.110)$$

2. **Choice of the slope λ**
   Here, we choose the same slope as for the SCMFLC: $\lambda = 50 \;\; \mathrm{s}^{-}1$.
3. **Choice of the width Φ of the BL**
   In order to obtain a good tracking performance we choose the width of the BL comparatively small.

$$\Phi = 2.5 \text{ kg m s}^{-3}. \qquad (3.111)$$

4. **Choice of the upper bound**
   Here, we choose again the same upper bound $\tilde{F}$ as for the SMFLC:

$$\tilde{F} = 2500 \text{ kg m s}^{-4}. \qquad (3.112)$$

5. **Design of $K = K_{\max}$**
   Here, we choose the same $K = K_{\max}$ as for the SMFLC:

$$K = K_{\max} = 3900 \text{ kg m s}^{-4}. \qquad (3.113)$$

3.5.4 Simulation Results

The surface along which the robot effector is supposed to slide has three different slopes: zero, positive, and negative. Both the SMFLC and the SMC with BL have been tested according to the different types of slopes (see Fig. 3.32a–f). Because of their similar control parameters both controllers work in a similar way. However, the results of the ordinary SMC with BL tend to chatter around the force setpoint. This is due to the relatively steep slope of the s-u transfer characteristic around its origin. On the other hand, the slope of the transfer characteristic of the SMFLC is low around its origin and steep far from it, which causes fast and also smooth behavior of the system (3.92).

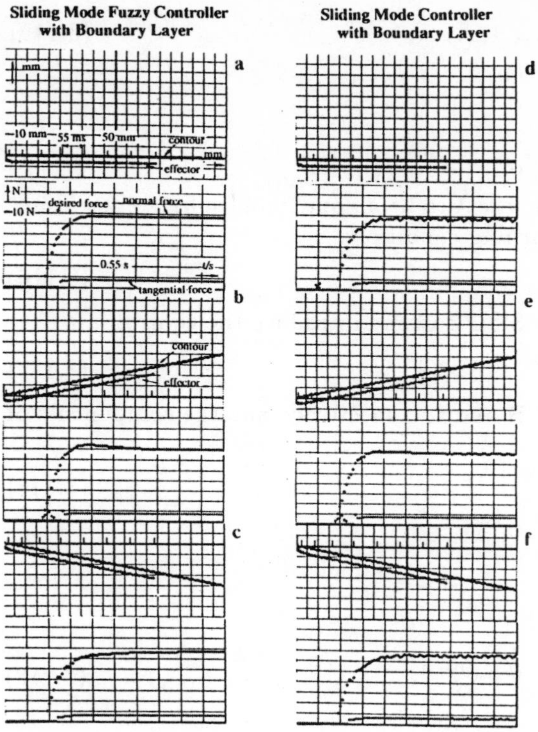

Fig. 3.32. Simulation results of the contour tracking

3.6 SMFLC for MIMO Systems

In the following we apply the results of Sects. 3.1 and 3.3 obtained for the design of a SISO sliding mode controller and an SMFLC, respectively, to MIMO systems.

Let a system with k inputs $u_1, u_2, \ldots, u_k$ and k outputs $x_1, x_2, \ldots, x_k$ be described by the state equation

$$\mathbf{x}^{(n)} = \mathbf{f}(\mathbf{x}, \dot{\mathbf{x}}, \ldots, \mathbf{x}^{(n-1)}) + \mathbf{B}(\mathbf{x}, \dot{\mathbf{x}}, \ldots, \mathbf{x}^{(n-1)}) \cdot \mathbf{u} + \tilde{\mathbf{d}} \tag{3.114}$$

with

$\mathbf{x} = (x_1, x_2, \ldots, x_k)^T$ – output vector,
$\mathbf{u} = (u_1, u_2, \ldots, u_k)^T$ – input control vector,
$\mathbf{f}$ – $(k \times 1)$ vector,
$\mathbf{B}$ – $(k \times k)$ positive definite invertible matrix,
$\tilde{\mathbf{d}}$ – $(k \times 1)$ vector of disturbances.

Since each of the k subsystems is controllable by an individual control variable u_i we may define k sliding surfaces independently from each other:

$$s_i = (\frac{\mathrm{d}}{\mathrm{d}t} + \lambda)^{(n-1)} e_{xi} \qquad i = 1, \ldots, k, \tag{3.115}$$

where

$e_{xi} = x_i - x^d{}_i$,
$x^d{}_i$ is the desired value of x_i.

Without loss of generality we choose λ to be unique for all subsystems. Moreover, we define k individual reaching conditions

$$s_i \cdot \dot{s}_i \leq -\eta_i \cdot |s_i|, \tag{3.116}$$

where $\eta_i > 0$. According to the SISO case we introduce the control law

$$\mathbf{u} = \hat{\mathbf{B}}^{-1} \cdot (\tilde{\mathbf{u}} - \hat{\mathbf{f}}), \tag{3.117}$$

where $\hat{\mathbf{B}}$ and $\hat{\mathbf{f}}$ are estimates of $\mathbf{B}$ and $\mathbf{f}$, respectively, and the components of $\tilde{\mathbf{u}}$ are

$$\tilde{u}_i = G_i \cdot (\hat{u}_i + u_{\mathrm{fuzz}i}), \tag{3.118}$$

where

$$\mathbf{e} = (e_{x1}, e_{x2}, \ldots, e_{xk})^T,$$

and

$$\hat{u}_i = x_i^{d(n)} - \sum_{l=1}^{n-1} \binom{n-1}{l} \cdot \lambda^l \cdot e_{xi}^{(n-l)}. \tag{3.119}$$

G_i is a multiplier to be considered later. The fuzzy part of this control law is derived as

$$u_{\mathrm{fuzz}i} = -K_{i\mathrm{fuzz}}(|s_i|) \cdot \mathrm{sgn}(s_i). \tag{3.120}$$

Each individual fuzzy part $u_{\mathrm{fuzz}i}$ is determined by a set of fuzzy rules like

R_{ci}^{j}: *if* s_i is LS_i^{j} *then* $u_{\mathrm{fuzz}i}$ is LU_i^{j}.

Substituting (3.117) into (3.114) we obtain

$$\mathbf{x}^{(n)} = \mathbf{f} - \mathbf{B}\hat{\mathbf{B}}^{-1} \cdot \hat{\mathbf{f}} + \mathbf{B}\hat{\mathbf{B}}^{-1} \cdot \tilde{\mathbf{u}} + \tilde{\mathbf{d}} = \Delta\mathbf{f} + \mathbf{B}\hat{\mathbf{B}}^{-1} \cdot \tilde{\mathbf{u}} + \tilde{\mathbf{d}}, \tag{3.121}$$

where

$$\Delta\mathbf{f} = \mathbf{f} - \mathbf{B}\hat{\mathbf{B}}^{-1} \cdot \hat{\mathbf{f}}.$$

In the following we apply a simple approach to obtain a reaching condition for each component i which is easy to implement [28]. Let $\mathbf{B}$ and $\hat{\mathbf{B}}^{-1}$ be symmetrical matrices

$$\mathbf{B} = (\mathbf{b}_1, \mathbf{b}_2, \ldots, \mathbf{b}_k)^T,$$
$$\hat{\mathbf{B}}^{-1} = (\hat{\mathbf{b}}_1^{-1}, \hat{\mathbf{b}}_2^{-1}, \ldots, \hat{\mathbf{b}}_k^{-1})^T. \tag{3.122}$$

Here, $\mathbf{b}_i$ denotes the i-th column vector of $\mathbf{B}$, and $\hat{\mathbf{b}}_i^{-1}$ denotes the i-th column vector of $\hat{\mathbf{B}}^{-1}$. Since $\mathbf{B}$ and $\hat{\mathbf{B}}^{-1}$ are symmetrical, we can assume that

$$\mathbf{b}_i^T \cdot \hat{\mathbf{b}}_i^{-1} > 0 \qquad i = 1, \ldots, k.$$

Then we define the bounds

$$0 \leq \beta_i^{\min} \leq \mathbf{b}_i^T \cdot \hat{\mathbf{b}}_i^{-1} \leq \beta_i^{\max}. \tag{3.123}$$

Now we define the multiplier G_i in (3.118)

$$G_i := \left(\beta_i^{\min} \cdot \beta_i^{\max}\right)^{-1/2}. \tag{3.124}$$

Finally, let the gain margins be defined by

$$\beta_i := \left(\frac{\beta_i^{\max}}{\beta_i^{\min}}\right)^{1/2}. \tag{3.125}$$

We then obtain from (3.121)

$$x_i^{(n)} = \Delta f_i + \sum_{j=1}^{k} \mathbf{b}_j^T \hat{\mathbf{b}}_i^{-1} \cdot \tilde{u}_j + \tilde{d}_i. \tag{3.126}$$

With the reaching condition (3.116) and

$$\dot{s}_i = x_i^{(n)} - \hat{u}_i, \tag{3.127}$$

we obtain

$$s_i \cdot (\Delta f_i + \tilde{d}_i - \hat{u}_i + \sum_{j=1}^{k} \mathbf{b}_j^T \hat{\mathbf{b}}_i^{-1} \cdot \tilde{u}_j) \leq -\eta_i \cdot |s_i|. \tag{3.128}$$

Introducing the control law (3.118) we have

$$|s_i| \cdot [(\Delta f_i + \tilde{d}_i - \hat{u}_i + \sum_{j \neq i} \mathbf{b}_j^T \hat{\mathbf{b}}_i^{-1} \cdot \tilde{u}_j) \cdot \operatorname{sgn}(s_i) + \mathbf{b}_i^T \hat{\mathbf{b}}_i^{-1} \cdot G_i \cdot \hat{u}_i \cdot \operatorname{sgn}(s_i)$$

$$- \mathbf{b}_i^T \hat{\mathbf{b}}_i^{-1} \cdot G_i \cdot K_{i\,\mathrm{fuzz}}(|s_i|) \cdot \operatorname{sgn}(s_i)^2] \leq -\eta_i \cdot |s_i|. \tag{3.129}$$

From the above inequality we obtain a sufficient stability condition for choosing the maximum value of $K_{i\,\mathrm{fuzz}}$

$$\mathbf{b}_i^T \hat{\mathbf{b}}_i^{-1} \cdot G_i \cdot K_{i\,\mathrm{fuzz}}|_{\max} >$$

$$\left|\Delta f_i + \tilde{d}_i + (\mathbf{b}_i^T \hat{\mathbf{b}}_i^{-1} \cdot G_i - 1) \cdot \hat{u}_i + \sum_{j \neq i} \mathbf{b}_j^T \hat{\mathbf{b}}_i^{-1} \cdot \tilde{u}_j\right| + \eta_i. \tag{3.130}$$

A stronger condition is

$$\mathbf{b}_i^T \hat{\mathbf{b}}_i^{-1} \cdot G_i \cdot K_{i\,\mathrm{fuzz}}|_{\max} >$$

$$|\Delta f_i| + |\tilde{d}_i| + |1 - \mathbf{b}_i^T \hat{\mathbf{b}}_i^{-1} \cdot G_i| \cdot |\hat{u}_i| + \sum_{j \neq i} |\mathbf{b}_j^T \hat{\mathbf{b}}_i^{-1}| \cdot |\tilde{u}_j| + \eta_i. \tag{3.131}$$

This requirement is even stronger if we set $\mathbf{b}_i^T\hat{\mathbf{b}}_i^{-1} = \beta_i^{\min}$. Because of (3.124) and (3.125) we have

$$\beta_i^{\min} \cdot G_i = \beta_i^{-1}, \tag{3.132}$$

so that we obtain

$$K_{i\,\mathrm{fuzz}}|_{\max} >$$

$$\beta_i \cdot \left(|\Delta f_i| + |\tilde{d}_i| + (1-\beta_i^{-1}) \cdot |\hat{u}_i| + \sum_{j \neq i} |\mathbf{b}_j^T\hat{\mathbf{b}}_i^{-1}| \cdot |\tilde{u}_j| + \eta_i \right) . \tag{3.133}$$

However, on the right hand side of (3.133) remain sums of unknown $|\tilde{u}_j|$'s that are not easy to derive. Therefore, we solve the problem by approximating $|\tilde{u}_j|$ with the desired value $|\tilde{u}_j^d|$ (see (3.118))

$$|\tilde{u}_j| \approx |\tilde{u}_j^d| = G_j \cdot |\hat{u}_j^d - K_{j\,\mathrm{fuzz}}(|s_j|) \cdot \mathrm{sgn}(s_j)|. \tag{3.134}$$

Since $\hat{u}_j^d = x^{d(n)}_j$ and $K_{j\,\mathrm{fuzz}}(|s_j|) = 0$ for $x_j = x_j^d; \ldots; x_j^{(n-1)} = x_j^{d(n-1)}$ we obtain

$$|\tilde{u}_j^d| = G_j \cdot |x^{d(n)}_j|. \tag{3.135}$$

On the other hand one has to determine the maximum values of $K_{i\,\mathrm{fuzz}}$ such that they are able to stabilize the system. With the upper bounds

$$|\Delta f_i| < \tilde{F}_i,$$
$$|\tilde{d}_i| < D_i,$$
$$|\hat{u}_i| < \hat{U}_i,$$
$$|\mathbf{b}_j^T\hat{\mathbf{b}}_i^{-1}| < B_{ij}; \quad i \neq j,$$
$$|x_j^{d(n)}| < Q_j,$$

which we assume obtain from the analysis of the sytem (3.114), we finally have the requirement

$$K_{i\,\mathrm{fuzz}}|_{\max} >$$

$$\beta_i \cdot \left(\tilde{F}_i + D_i + (1-\beta_i^{-1}) \cdot \hat{U}_i + \sum_{j \neq i} G_j \cdot B_{ij} \cdot Q_j + \eta_i \right) . \tag{3.136}$$

Inequality (3.136) gives a sufficient condition for the SMFLC in the i-th component to drive the system to the i-th sliding surface $s_i = 0$.

In Chap. 5 we will illustrate the design of a MIMO SMFLC by means of a tracking control problem for a robot arm with two degrees of freedom.

4. Model Based Design of Takagi–Sugeno FLCs

In this chapter we will present in detail the design methods for each of the different types of Takagi–Sugeno FLCs outlined in Chap. 1. For each particular type of Takagi–Sugeno FLC the presentation of its design method will emphasize the following:

1. The type of control problem, i.e., stabilization or tracking.
2. The type of design method, i.e., linearization, robust control, or gain scheduling.
3. The form of the open loop model of the system under control.
4. The form of the Takagi–Sugeno FLC and the form of the corresponding closed loop system.
5. The design of the Takagi–Sugeno FLC so that the closed loop system of a particular form satisfies the specifications of desired behavior in terms of stability, robustness, and performance.

In Sect. 4.1 we present the Takagi–Sugeno FLC-1. Despite the popularity which this type of FLC has gained in the fuzzy control literature its design is still plagued by a number of important unresolved issues, the most important ones being the following:

- The design depends cruicially on the identification of an open loop model in terms of a set of fuzzy rules of the form $R_{\mathrm{S}}^{\mathbf{i}}$. So far, no commonly accepted identification procedure exists. A number of different approaches to this identification problem have been proposed, but all these are still at research stage and no computerized identification tools using these different approaches have been made available.
- The design of the Takagi–Sugeno FLC-1 relies on methods of the trial-and-error type, as reported in the fuzzy control literature [36].
- With the exception of the stability properties of the closed loop system incorporating a Takagi–Sugeno FLC-1, very few results concerning robustness and performance have been reported and these, again, are at early research stage [35].

In this context, when presenting the Takagi–Sugeno FLC-1 we will confine ourselves only to the presentation of the form of the open loop system, the form of the Takagi–Sugeno FLC-1, the form of the closed loop system and its stability properties, and an outline of a trial-and-error type of design method considered in [36].

In Sect. 4.2 we present in detail the design of the Takagi–Sugeno FLC-2 and its use in local stabilization and tracking of a nonlinear autonomous system. With respect to local stabilization, a Takagi–Sugeno FLC-2 is able to stabilize a nonlinear autonomous system around **any** operating point without the need to change its gains. With respect to tracking, the FLC-2 performs gain scheduling on **any** reference state trajectory under the restriction that the reference state trajectories are slowly time varying.

4.1 Model Based Design of Takagi–Sugeno FLC-1

The model based design of a Takagi–Sugeno FLC-1 requires the existence of a fuzzy model for the nonlinear autonomous open loop system under control. Such a fuzzy model was first proposed in 1985 by Takagi and Sugeno [34] and is the result of identification from observed input-output data. The Takagi–Sugeno FLC-1 is then intended to solve the stabilization problem in the context of a given (identified) fuzzy model. Relevant publications on the fuzzy model based design and analysis of the Takagi–Sugeno FLC-1 include [36, 35, 17, 24]. Relevant publications on the identification of the fuzzy model include [34, 31, 1, 32, 33, 2, 3, 43, 9, 4, 20, 39, 30].

4.1.1 The Open Loop Fuzzy Model

The identified open loop autonomous fuzzy model consists of a set of fuzzy rules. The if-part of each fuzzy rule describes a particular fuzzy region in the state space and its corresponding then-part contains an open loop autonomous linear model.

The $\mathbf{i}$-th fuzzy rule describes the fuzzy model's dynamics within the fuzzy region $\mathbf{LX^i}$ specified in the rule's if-part. For nonlinear membership functions of the fuzzy values of the state variables, the dynamics is autonomous and linear for points constituting the center of $\mathbf{LX^i}$, while for the rest of the points in this fuzzy region the fuzzy model's dynamics is autonomous and nonlinear. In formal terms, such a fuzzy rule is written as

$$R_S^{\mathbf{i}}\text{: } \textit{if } \mathbf{x} = \mathbf{LX^i} \textit{ then } \dot{\mathbf{x}} = \mathbf{A_i} \cdot \mathbf{x} + \mathbf{B_i} \cdot \mathbf{u},$$

where:

- $R_S^{\mathbf{i}}$, $(\mathbf{i} = \mathbf{1}, \ldots, \mathbf{M})$ denotes the $\mathbf{i}$-th fuzzy rule describing the open loop fuzzy model's dynamics in the $\mathbf{i}$-th fuzzy region $\mathbf{LX^i}$ of the fuzzy state space.
- $\mathbf{LX^i} = (LX_1^{\mathbf{i}}, \ldots, LX_n^{\mathbf{i}})^T$, where $LX_k^{\mathbf{i}}$ denotes the fuzzy value which x_k takes in the $\mathbf{i}$-th fuzzy region. Each fuzzy value $LX_k^{\mathbf{i}}$ is determined by a

fuzzy set $\int_X \mu_{LX^{\mathbf{i}}_k}(x_k)/x_k$ of a standard triangular, trapezoidal, or bell-shaped type. The membership functions of any one of the previously mentioned types are nonlinear functions of x_k.

– $\dot{\mathbf{x}} = \mathbf{A_i} \cdot \mathbf{x} + \mathbf{B_i} \cdot \mathbf{u}$ is a linear autonomous model corresponding to the $\mathbf{i}$-th fuzzy region of the state space. The state vector denoted as $\dot{\mathbf{x}}$ is a $n \times 1$ linear vector-function of time and its components $x_1, x_2, \cdots, x_n$ denote time dependent state variables. The control input vector denoted as $\mathbf{u}$ is a $m \times 1$ vector function of time with components $u_1, u_2, \cdots, u_n$; the entries of the matrices $\mathbf{A_i}$ $(n \times n)$ and $\mathbf{B_i}$ $(n \times m)$ are constant.

Recall (see Sect. 2.3) that for each crisp state vector $\mathbf{x}^* = (x_1^*, x_2^*, \cdots, x_n^*)^T$ and each crisp input vector $\mathbf{u}^* = (u_1^*, u_2^*, \cdots, u_m^*)^T$, the computation with a single fuzzy rule proceeds as follows:

1. The degree of satisfaction $\mu^{\mathbf{i}}(\mathbf{x}^*)$ of the $\mathbf{i}$-th fuzzy region $\mathbf{LX^i}$ by $\mathbf{x}^* = (x_1^*, x_2^*, \cdots, x_n^*)^T$ is computed as

$$\mu^{\mathbf{i}}(\mathbf{x}^*) = \min\left(\mu_{LX^{\mathbf{i}}_1}(x_1^*), \mu_{LX^{\mathbf{i}}_2}(x_2^*) \ldots, \mu_{LX^{\mathbf{i}}_n}(x_n^*)\right). \tag{4.1}$$

2. $\dot{\mathbf{x}}^*$ is computed as

$$\mathbf{A_i} \cdot \mathbf{x}^* + \mathbf{B_i} \cdot \mathbf{u}^*. \tag{4.2}$$

3. The so computed $\dot{\mathbf{x}}^*$ is weighted by $\mu^{\mathbf{i}}(\mathbf{x}^*)$ as

$$\mu^{\mathbf{i}}(\mathbf{x}^*) \cdot (\mathbf{A_i} \cdot \mathbf{x}^* + \mathbf{B_i} \cdot \mathbf{u}^*). \tag{4.3}$$

Thus, in the general case, the system's dynamics corresponding to computation with a single fuzzy rule is given as

$$\mu^{\mathbf{i}}(\mathbf{x}) \cdot (\mathbf{A_i} \cdot \mathbf{x} + \mathbf{B_i} \cdot \mathbf{u}). \tag{4.4}$$

From the above expression, it is easily seen that:

1. For crisp state vectors that belong to the center of a fuzzy region $\mathbf{LX^i}$, the dynamics of the system's behavior is linear since whenever $\mathbf{x} = \mathbf{x^i}$, then $\mu^{\mathbf{i}}(\mathbf{x}) = \mu^{\mathbf{i}}(\mathbf{x^i}) = 1$. Thus, $\mu^{\mathbf{i}}(\mathbf{x}) \cdot (\mathbf{A_i} \cdot \mathbf{x} + \mathbf{B_i} \cdot \mathbf{u}) = \mathbf{A_i} \cdot \mathbf{x} + \mathbf{B_i} \cdot \mathbf{u}$.
2. For crisp state vectors that are not identical with $\mathbf{x^i}$, we have that $\mu^{\mathbf{i}}(\mathbf{x}) < 1$, Furthermore, $\mu^{\mathbf{i}}(\mathbf{x})$ is a nonlinear function of $\mathbf{x}$ due to the nonlinear character of the membership functions defining the fuzzy values of the components of the fuzzy state vector. Thus the expression (4.4) is nonlinear since its linear part $\mathbf{A_i} \cdot \mathbf{x} + \mathbf{B_i} \cdot \mathbf{u}$, itself a function of $\mathbf{x}$, is multiplied by the nonlinear function $\mu^{\mathbf{i}}(\mathbf{x})$.

The results computed for each individual rule via (4.4) are aggregated by simply taking their average:

$$\mathbf{u} = \frac{\sum_{\mathbf{i}} \mu^{\mathbf{i}}(\mathbf{x}) \cdot (\mathbf{A_i} \cdot \mathbf{x} + \mathbf{B_i} \cdot \mathbf{u})}{\sum_{\mathbf{i}} \mu^{\mathbf{i}}(\mathbf{x})}. \tag{4.5}$$

The above expression provides the overall result of the computation with the set of all fuzzy rules representing the open loop fuzzy model. The expression (4.5) can be simplified by normalizing the degrees of satisfaction $\mu^{\mathbf{i}}(\mathbf{x})$ and using instead their normalized counterparts $w^{\mathbf{i}}(\mathbf{x})$, i.e., $\sum_{\mathbf{i}} w^{\mathbf{i}}(\mathbf{x}) = 1$, which are obtained as follows: for any $\mu^{\mathbf{1}}(\mathbf{x})$, $\mu^{\mathbf{2}}(\mathbf{x})$, ...,$\mu^{\mathbf{M}}(\mathbf{x})$,

$$w^{\mathbf{i}}(\mathbf{x}) = \frac{\mu^{\mathbf{i}}(\mathbf{x})}{\sum\limits_{\mathbf{i}} \mu^{\mathbf{i}}(\mathbf{x})}. \tag{4.6}$$

Since we have now that $\sum_{\mathbf{i}} w^{\mathbf{i}}(\mathbf{x}) = 1$, the equation (4.5) can be rewritten in the more simple form:

$$\mathbf{u} = \sum_{\mathbf{i}} w^{\mathbf{i}}(\mathbf{x}) \cdot (\mathbf{A_i} \cdot \mathbf{x} + \mathbf{B_i} \cdot \mathbf{u}). \tag{4.7}$$

From (4.7) it is easily seen that the set of all fuzzy rules defines linear dynamics for all points that belong to the center of an arbitrary fuzzy region in the fuzzy state space. Take, for example, the **i**-th fuzzy region. For every point that belongs to its center, i.e., $\mathbf{x} = \mathbf{x^i}$, we have that $w^{\mathbf{i}}(\mathbf{x}) = w^{\mathbf{i}}(\mathbf{x^i}) = 1$ while for each $\mathbf{j} \neq \mathbf{i}$ we have that $w^{\mathbf{j}}(\mathbf{x}) = 0$, since $\sum_{\mathbf{i}} w^{\mathbf{i}}(\mathbf{x}) = 1$. Thus we have that (4.7) becomes (for each $\mathbf{x} = \mathbf{x^i}$),

$$\mathbf{u} = w^{\mathbf{i}}(\mathbf{x^i}) \cdot (\mathbf{A_i} \cdot \mathbf{x^i} + \mathbf{B_i} \cdot \mathbf{u}) = \mathbf{A_i} \cdot \mathbf{x^i} + \mathbf{B_i} \cdot \mathbf{u}. \tag{4.8}$$

On the other hand, (4.7) defines nonlinear dynamics for all points $\mathbf{x} \neq \mathbf{x^i}$. This is so, because in this case there is no $w^{\mathbf{i}}(\mathbf{x}) = 1$, and thus each linear part $(\mathbf{A_i} \cdot \mathbf{x^i} + \mathbf{B_i} \cdot \mathbf{u})$ in (4.7) is multiplied by the nonlinear function $w^{\mathbf{i}}(\mathbf{x})$.

4.1.2 The Takagi–Sugeno FLC-1

The Takagi–Sugeno FLC-1 is used for the stabilization problem in the context of the open loop fuzzy model given by (4.7). The authors of this book were unable to find any work related to the use of this type of FLC for the tracking problem. In this latter case, the linear models from the then-parts of the fuzzy rules defining the nonlinear open loop model have to be transformed into linear nonautonomous models (see Sect. 2.4.3). Thus computation with a single fuzzy rule, as well as computation with the set of all fuzzy rules, will define nonlinear nonautonomous dynamics for the open loop system.

The Takagi–Sugeno FLC-1 for the stabilization problem is given as a set of fuzzy rules where each fuzzy rule is of the form

$R_{\mathrm{C}}^{\mathbf{j}}$: *if* $\mathbf{x} = \mathbf{LX^j}$ *then* $\mathbf{u} = \mathbf{K_j} \cdot \mathbf{x}$

where:

- $R_{\mathrm{C}}^{\mathbf{j}}$, $(\mathbf{j} = \mathbf{1}, \cdots, \mathbf{M})$ denotes the **j**-th fuzzy rule intended to stabilize the open loop fuzzy system in the **j**-th fuzzy region $\mathbf{LX^j}$ of the fuzzy state space.

- $\mathbf{LX^j} = (LX_1^{\mathbf{j}}, \ldots, LX_n^{\mathbf{j}})^T$, where $LX_k^{\mathbf{j}}$ denotes the fuzzy value that x_k takes in the **j**-th fuzzy region. Each fuzzy value $LX_k^{\mathbf{j}}$ is determined by a fuzzy set $\int_X \mu_{LX_k^{\mathbf{j}}}(x_k)/x_k$ of a standard triangular, trapezoidal, or bell-shaped type. The membership functions of any one of the previously mentioned types are nonlinear functions of x_k.
- $\mathbf{u} = \mathbf{K_j} \cdot \mathbf{x}$ is a linear autonomous control law corresponding to the **j**-th fuzzy region of the state space. The matrix $\mathbf{K_j}$ is of dimension $m \times n$, its elements are constant, and it is called the *gain matrix* of the **j**-th fuzzy region.

For each crisp state vector $\mathbf{x}^* = (x_1^*, x_2^*, \cdots, x_n^*)^T$, the computation of the corresponding crisp input vector $\mathbf{u}^* = (u_1^*, u_2^*, \cdots, u_m^*)^T$ by a single fuzzy rule proceeds as follows:

1. The degree of satisfaction $\mu^{\mathbf{j}}(\mathbf{x}^*)$ of the **j**-th fuzzy region $\mathbf{LX^j}$ by $\mathbf{x}^* = (x_1^*, x_2^*, \cdots, x_n^*)^T$ is computed as
$$\mu^{\mathbf{j}}(\mathbf{x}^*) = \min\left(\mu_{LX_1^{\mathbf{j}}}(x_1^*), \mu_{LX_2^{\mathbf{j}}}(x_2^*) \ldots \mu_{LX_n^{\mathbf{j}}}(x_n)\right) \tag{4.9}$$
2. $\mathbf{u}^*$ is computed as
$$\mathbf{K_j} \cdot \mathbf{x}^*. \tag{4.10}$$
3. The so computed $\mathbf{u}^*$ is weighted by $\mu^{\mathbf{j}}(\mathbf{x}^*)$ as
$$\mu^{\mathbf{j}}(\mathbf{x}^*) \cdot \mathbf{K_j} \cdot \mathbf{x}^*. \tag{4.11}$$

Thus, in the general case, the control law's dynamics corresponding to computation with a single fuzzy rule is given as

$$\mu^{\mathbf{j}}(\mathbf{x}) \cdot \mathbf{K_j} \cdot \mathbf{x}. \tag{4.12}$$

From the above expression, it is easily seen that:

1. For crisp state vectors that belong to the center of a fuzzy region $\mathbf{LX^j}$, the dynamics of the control law is linear since whenever $\mathbf{x} = \mathbf{x^j}$, then $\mu^{\mathbf{j}}(\mathbf{x}) = \mu^{\mathbf{j}}(\mathbf{x^j}) = 1$. Thus, $\mu^{\mathbf{j}}(\mathbf{x}) \cdot \mathbf{K_j} \cdot \mathbf{x} = \mathbf{K_j} \cdot \mathbf{x}$.
2. For crisp state vectors that are not identical with $\mathbf{x^j}$, we have that $\mu^{\mathbf{j}}(\mathbf{x}) < 1$. Furthermore, $\mu^{\mathbf{j}}(\mathbf{x})$ is a nonlinear function of the state vector due to the nonlinear character of the membership functions defining the fuzzy values of the components of the fuzzy state vector. Thus the expression (4.12) is a nonlinear one since the linear part $\mathbf{K_j} \cdot \mathbf{x}$, a function of $\mathbf{x}$ itself, is multiplied by the nonlinear function $\mu^{\mathbf{j}}(\mathbf{x})$.

The results computed for each individual rule via (4.12) are aggregated by simply taking their average, that is,

$$\dot{\mathbf{x}} = \frac{\sum\limits_{\mathbf{j}} \mu^{\mathbf{j}}(\mathbf{x}) \cdot \mathbf{K_j} \cdot \mathbf{x}}{\sum\limits_{\mathbf{j}} \mu^{\mathbf{j}}(\mathbf{x})}. \tag{4.13}$$

The above expression provides the overall result of the computation with the set of fuzzy rules representing the Takagi–Sugeno FLC-1. The expression (4.13) can again be simplified by normalizing the degrees of satisfaction $\mu^{\mathbf{j}}(\mathbf{x})$ and using instead their normalized counterparts $w^{\mathbf{j}}(\mathbf{x})$, i.e., $\sum_{\mathbf{j}} w^{\mathbf{j}}(\mathbf{x}) = 1$, which are obtained as follows: for any given $\mu^{\mathbf{1}}(\mathbf{x})$, $\mu^{\mathbf{2}}(\mathbf{x})$,..., $\mu^{\mathbf{M}}(\mathbf{x})$,

$$w^{\mathbf{j}}(\mathbf{x}) = \frac{\mu^{\mathbf{j}}(\mathbf{x})}{\sum\limits_{\mathbf{j}} \mu^{\mathbf{j}}(\mathbf{x})}. \tag{4.14}$$

Since we have now that, $\sum_{\mathbf{j}} w^{\mathbf{j}}(\mathbf{x}) = 1$, equation (4.13) can be rewritten in the simpler form,

$$\dot{\mathbf{x}} = \sum_{\mathbf{j}} w^{\mathbf{j}}(\mathbf{x}) \cdot \mathbf{K_j} \cdot \mathbf{x}. \tag{4.15}$$

From (4.15) it is easily seen that the set of all fuzzy rules defines a control law with linear dynamics for all points that belong to the center of an arbitrary fuzzy region in the fuzzy state space. Take, for example, the $\mathbf{j}$-th fuzzy region. For every point that belongs to its center, i.e., $\mathbf{x} = \mathbf{x^j}$, we have that $w^{\mathbf{j}}(\mathbf{x}) = w^{\mathbf{j}}(\mathbf{x^j}) = 1$ while for each $\mathbf{i} \neq \mathbf{j}$ we have that $w^{\mathbf{i}}(\mathbf{x}) = 0$, since $\sum_{\mathbf{j}} w^{\mathbf{j}}(\mathbf{x}) = 1$. Thus we have that (4.15) becomes (for each $\mathbf{x} = \mathbf{x^j}$)

$$\dot{\mathbf{x}} = w^{\mathbf{j}}(\mathbf{x^j}) \cdot \mathbf{K_j} \cdot \mathbf{x^j} = \mathbf{K_j} \cdot \mathbf{x^j}. \tag{4.16}$$

On the other hand, (4.15) defines a control law with nonlinear dynamics for all points $\mathbf{x} \neq \mathbf{x^j}$. This is so, because in this case there is no $w^{\mathbf{j}}(\mathbf{x}) = 1$, and thus each linear expression $\mathbf{K_j} \cdot \mathbf{x^j}$ in (4.15) is multiplied by the nonlinear function $w^{\mathbf{j}}(\mathbf{x})$.

4.1.3 The Closed Loop Fuzzy Model

So far, by using fuzzy rules of the form

$R^{\mathbf{i}}_{\mathrm{S}}$: *if* $\mathbf{x} = \mathbf{LX^i}$ *then* $\dot{\mathbf{x}} = \mathbf{A_i} \cdot \mathbf{x} + \mathbf{B_i} \cdot \mathbf{u}$

and

$R^{\mathbf{i}}_{\mathrm{C}}$: *if* $\dot{\mathbf{x}} = \mathbf{LX^i}$ *then* $\mathbf{u} = \mathbf{K_i} \cdot \mathbf{x}$,

we have described the nonlinear autonomous open loop fuzzy model and the nonlinear Takagi–Sugeno FLC-1. We also saw that computation with the open loop fuzzy model is equivalent to

$$\dot{\mathbf{x}} = \sum_{\mathbf{i}} w^{\mathbf{i}}(\mathbf{x}) \cdot (\mathbf{A_i} \cdot \mathbf{x} + \mathbf{B_i} \cdot \mathbf{u}), \tag{4.17}$$

and computation with the Takagi–Sugeno FLC-1 is equivalent to

$$\mathbf{u} = \sum_{\mathbf{j}} w^{\mathbf{j}}(\mathbf{x}) \cdot \mathbf{K_j} \cdot \mathbf{x}. \tag{4.18}$$

Thus, replacing $\mathbf{u}$ from the former equation with its equivalent term, $\sum_{\mathbf{j}} w^{\mathbf{j}}(\mathbf{x}) \cdot \mathbf{K_j} \cdot \mathbf{x}$, from the latter equation, we obtain the expression for the nonlinear autonomous closed loop system as follows:

$$\dot{\mathbf{x}} = \frac{\sum_{\mathbf{i}} \sum_{\mathbf{j}} w^{\mathbf{i}}(\mathbf{x}) \cdot w^{\mathbf{j}}(\mathbf{x}) \cdot (\mathbf{A_i} + \mathbf{B_i} \cdot \mathbf{K_j}) \cdot \mathbf{x}}{\sum_{\mathbf{i}} \sum_{\mathbf{j}} w^{\mathbf{i}}(\mathbf{x}) \cdot w^{\mathbf{j}}(\mathbf{x})}. \tag{4.19}$$

Since we have that $\sum_{\mathbf{i}} w^{\mathbf{i}}(\mathbf{x}) = 1$ and $\sum_{\mathbf{j}} w^{\mathbf{j}}(\mathbf{x}) = 1$, then $\sum_{\mathbf{i}} \sum_{\mathbf{j}} w^{\mathbf{i}}(\mathbf{x}) \cdot w^{\mathbf{j}}(\mathbf{x}) = 1$. Thus (4.19) can be simplified as

$$\dot{\mathbf{x}} = \sum_{\mathbf{i}} \sum_{\mathbf{j}} w^{\mathbf{i}}(\mathbf{x}) \cdot w^{\mathbf{j}}(\mathbf{x}) \cdot (\mathbf{A_i} + \mathbf{B_i} \cdot \mathbf{K_j}) \cdot \mathbf{x}, \tag{4.20}$$

and further, denoting $(\mathbf{A_i} + \mathbf{B_i} \cdot \mathbf{K_j})$ by $\mathbf{A_{ij}}$, we can write

$$\dot{\mathbf{x}} = \sum_{\mathbf{i}} \sum_{\mathbf{j}} w^{\mathbf{i}}(\mathbf{x}) \cdot w^{\mathbf{j}}(\mathbf{x}) \cdot \mathbf{A_{ij}} \cdot \mathbf{x}. \tag{4.21}$$

From the above equation it is easily seen that the dynamics of the autonomous closed loop system is nonlinear since both $w^{\mathbf{i}}(\mathbf{x})$ and $w^{\mathbf{j}}(\mathbf{x})$ are nonlinear functions of the state vector $\mathbf{x}$. The dynamics of the closed loop autonomous system is again linear only for points in the fuzzy state space that belong to the center of an arbitrary fuzzy region. The problem now is to provide conditions under which the origin is an asymptotically stable equilibrium point of (4.21), where the domain of attraction of the origin is the whole fuzzy state space, i.e., every trajectory in the fuzzy state space converges to the origin as $t \to \infty$. The following result from [36] establishes these sufficient conditions as follows:

> The origin is an asymptotically stable equilibrium point of (4.21) whose domain of attraction is the whole fuzzy state space if there exists a common positive definite matrix $\mathbf{P}$ such that
>
> $$\mathbf{A}_{\mathbf{ij}}^T \cdot \mathbf{P} + \mathbf{P} \cdot \mathbf{A_{ij}} < \mathbf{0}. \tag{4.22}$$

Observe here that all of $\mathbf{A_{ij}}$ are Hurwitz matrices, if there exists a common positive definite matrix $\mathbf{P}$ such that $\mathbf{A}_{\mathbf{ij}}^T \cdot \mathbf{P} + \mathbf{P} \cdot \mathbf{A_{ij}} < \mathbf{0}$. However, such a common positive definite matrix $\mathbf{P}$ does not always exist even if all $\mathbf{A_{ij}}$ are Hurwitz matrices (see [40, Problem 5.24]). In this context, a necessary condition for the existence of a common positive definite matrix $\mathbf{P}$ can be derived by reformulating the following result from [36]:

> Let $\mathbf{A_{ij}}$ be Hurwitz matrices. Then $\mathbf{A_{ij}} \cdot \mathbf{A_{kl}}$, $\mathbf{i}, \mathbf{j}, \mathbf{k}, \mathbf{l} = \mathbf{1}, \ldots, \mathbf{M}$ are Hurwitz matrices if there exists a common positive definite matrix $\mathbf{P}$ such that ${\mathbf{A_{ij}}}^T \cdot \mathbf{P} + \mathbf{P} \cdot \mathbf{A_{ij}} < \mathbf{0}$

The above result implies the following necessary condition for the nonexistence of a common positive definite matrix $\mathbf{P}$ such that $\mathbf{A_{ij}}^T \cdot \mathbf{P} + \mathbf{P} \cdot \mathbf{A_{ij}} < \mathbf{0}$, when reformulated as:

> If one of $\mathbf{A_{ij}} \cdot \mathbf{A_{kl}}$ is not a Hurwitz matrix, where $\mathbf{A_{ij}}$ and $\mathbf{A_{kl}}$ are Hurwitz matrices, then there does not exist a common positive definite matrix $\mathbf{P}$ such that $\mathbf{A_{ij}}^T \cdot \mathbf{P} + \mathbf{P} \cdot \mathbf{A_{ij}} < \mathbf{0}$.

4.1.4 The Design of Takagi–Sugeno FLC-1

The design problem for a Takagi–Sugeno FLC-1 follows directly from the conditions under which the origin is an asymptotically stable equilibrium of (4.21). This condition requires the existence of a common positive matrix $\mathbf{P}$ such that for each $\mathbf{i}, \mathbf{j}$, $\mathbf{A}_{\mathbf{ij}}^T \cdot \mathbf{P} + \mathbf{P} \cdot \mathbf{A_{ij}} < \mathbf{0}$. In other words, it is required that $(\mathbf{A_i} + \mathbf{B_i} \cdot \mathbf{K_j})^T \cdot \mathbf{P} + \mathbf{P} \cdot (\mathbf{A_i} + \mathbf{B_i} \cdot \mathbf{K_j}) < \mathbf{0}$. The latter form of the required condition for asymptotic stability implies that the design problem for the Takagi–Sugeno FLC-1 can be formulated as follows.

> Given $\mathbf{A_i}$ and $\mathbf{B_i}$ $(\mathbf{i} = \mathbf{1}, \ldots, \mathbf{M})$ find $\mathbf{K_j}$ $(\mathbf{k} = \mathbf{1}, \ldots, \mathbf{M})$ such that $(\mathbf{A_i} + \mathbf{B_i} \cdot \mathbf{K_j})^T \cdot \mathbf{P} + \mathbf{P} \cdot (\mathbf{A_i} + \mathbf{B_i} \cdot \mathbf{K_j}) < \mathbf{0}$, where $\mathbf{P}$ is a positive definite matrix.

As already discussed, a common positive definite $\mathbf{P}$ does not exist if, $\mathbf{A_{ij}} \cdot \mathbf{A_{kl}}$ is not a Hurwitz matrix, though $\mathbf{A_{ij}}$ and $\mathbf{A_{kl}}$ are assumed to be Hurwitz matrices.

Thus the design begins with finding such $\mathbf{K_j}$, given $\mathbf{A_i}$ and $\mathbf{B_i}$, so that $(\mathbf{A_i} + \mathbf{B_i} \cdot \mathbf{K_j}) = \mathbf{A_{ij}}$ is a Hurwitz matrix. This can be achieved, for example, by constructing each $\mathbf{K_j}$ via the well-known *pole assignment method* (see [8]).

Second, one has to check out the possible nonexistence of a common positive $\mathbf{P}$ by forming all products $\mathbf{A_{ij}} \cdot \mathbf{A_{kl}}$ and verifying that each such product is a Hurwitz matrix. If at least one $\mathbf{A_{ij}} \cdot \mathbf{A_{kl}}$ is not a Hurwitz matrix, then one has to redesign the $\mathbf{K_j}$ and $\mathbf{K_l}$ involved in $\mathbf{A_{ij}}$ and $\mathbf{A_{kl}}$ so that the product in question becomes a Hurwitz matrix. No systematic procedure for finding such $\mathbf{K_j}$'s so that all products $\mathbf{A_{ij}} \cdot \mathbf{A_{kl}}$ are Hurwitz matrices is provided in the existing literature on the Takagi–Sugeno FLC-1.

Note that even when the nonexistence of a common positive matrix $\mathbf{P}$ such that for each $\mathbf{i}, \mathbf{j}$, $\mathbf{A}_{\mathbf{ij}}^T \cdot \mathbf{P} + \mathbf{P} \cdot \mathbf{A_{ij}} < \mathbf{0}$, is ruled out, one still has to find such a common positive $\mathbf{P}$. However, since each $\mathbf{A_{ij}}$ is a Hurwitz matrix, there exist unique positive definite $\mathbf{P_{ij}}$ such that each inequality $\mathbf{A}_{\mathbf{ij}}^T \cdot \mathbf{P_{ij}} + \mathbf{P_{ij}} \cdot \mathbf{A_{ij}} < \mathbf{0}$ holds.

Each inequality will, in general, have a different $\mathbf{P_{ij}}$ due to the different $\mathbf{A_i}$, $\mathbf{B_i}$, and $\mathbf{K_j}$ involved in the different inequalities. However, if among these $\mathbf{P_{ij}}$'s there is one that satisfies all inequalities, then the origin is the asymptotically stable equilibrium of (4.21). In this context, the trial-and-error design method proposed in [36] searches for such a $\mathbf{P_{ij}}$ that satisfies all inequalities, but the authors do not suggest any solution for the case when such a $\mathbf{P_{ij}}$ does not exist.

4.2 The Model Based Design of Takagi–Sugeno FLC-2

The Takagi–Sugeno FLC-2 is derived from an open loop fuzzy model which in turn is derived from the Lyapunov-linearized version of a nonlinear autonomous open loop model. Both the open loop fuzzy model and the Takagi–Sugeno FLC-2 have linear dynamics. Thus, the robustness and performance of the Takagi–Sugeno FLC-2 can be achieved by employing the already existing techniques from linear control theory for the design of robust and optimal linear controllers. This type of FLC can be used for both the stabilization and tracking control problems. With respect to stabilization it is able to stabilize a given nonlinear autonomous system at **any** operating point without changing the already designed gain matrices $\mathbf{K_i}$. With respect to tracking, it is able to locally track **any** trajectory again without changing the already designed gain matrices $\mathbf{K_i}$. In the latter case of tracking, it works as a gain scheduler on a given reference state trajectory, provided that trajectories are slowly time varying.

4.2.1 The Control Problem

Consider the nonlinear autonomous open loop system of the form

$$\dot{\mathbf{x}} = \mathbf{f}(\mathbf{x}, \mathbf{u}), \tag{4.23}$$

with $(\mathbf{0}, \mathbf{0})$ as its equilibrium point.

Let also $\mathbf{x^d}$ be a given operating point such that $\mathbf{x^d} \neq \mathbf{0}$ and $\mathbf{u^d}$ be the input corresponding to $\mathbf{x^d}$. Note that $\mathbf{x^d}$ and $\mathbf{u^d}$ are not functions of time while $\mathbf{x}$ and $\mathbf{u}$ are functions of time. By introducing the new state vector $\delta\mathbf{x} = \mathbf{x} - \mathbf{x^d}$ and the new input vector $\delta\mathbf{u} = \mathbf{u} - \mathbf{u^d}$ and substituting them for $\mathbf{x}$ and $\mathbf{u}$ in (4.23) we obtain the equivalent system

$$\delta\dot{\mathbf{x}} + \dot{\mathbf{x}}^{\mathbf{d}} = \mathbf{f}(\delta\mathbf{x} + \mathbf{x^d}, \delta\mathbf{u} + \mathbf{u^d}), \tag{4.24}$$

and, as already discussed in Sect. 2.4.2, the equilibrium point of (4.24) is now $(\delta\mathbf{x} = \mathbf{0}, \delta\mathbf{u} = \mathbf{0})$.

The stabilization control problem is then to find a control law

$$\delta\mathbf{u} = \mathbf{g}(\delta\mathbf{x}), \tag{4.25}$$

such that, starting anywhere in a region around $\mathbf{0}$, the state vector $\delta\mathbf{x}$ converges asymptotically to $\mathbf{0}$ as $t \to \infty$. In terms of the original state vector $\mathbf{x}$ this means that we want to design a control law such that $\mathbf{x}$ asymptotically converges to $\mathbf{x^d}$ as $t \to \infty$.

One way to solve this stabilization control problem is as follows. Let us first Lyapunov-linearize the modified nonlinear autonomous open loop system (4.24) at $(\mathbf{x^d}, \mathbf{u^d})$, thus obtaining the Lyapunov-linearized version of (4.24) given as

$$\delta\dot{\mathbf{x}} + \dot{\mathbf{x}}^{\mathbf{d}} = \mathbf{f}(\mathbf{x}^{\mathbf{d}}, \mathbf{u}^{\mathbf{d}}) + \mathbf{A}(\mathbf{x}^{\mathbf{d}}, \mathbf{u}^{\mathbf{d}}) \cdot \delta\mathbf{x} + \mathbf{B}(\mathbf{x}^{\mathbf{d}}, \mathbf{u}^{\mathbf{d}}) \cdot \delta\mathbf{u}, \tag{4.26}$$

where

$$\mathbf{A}(\mathbf{x}^{\mathbf{d}}, \mathbf{u}^{\mathbf{d}}) = \left(\frac{\delta\mathbf{f}(\mathbf{x}, \mathbf{u})}{\delta\mathbf{x}}\right)_{\mathbf{x}=\mathbf{x}^{\mathbf{d}}, \mathbf{u}=\mathbf{u}^{\mathbf{d}}}, \tag{4.27}$$

and

$$\mathbf{B}(\mathbf{x}^{\mathbf{d}}, \mathbf{u}^{\mathbf{d}}) = \left(\frac{\delta\mathbf{f}(\mathbf{x}, \mathbf{u})}{\delta\mathbf{u}}\right)_{\mathbf{x}=\mathbf{x}^{\mathbf{d}}, \mathbf{u}=\mathbf{u}^{\mathbf{d}}} \tag{4.28}$$

are the Jacobian matrices of $\mathbf{f}(\mathbf{x}, \mathbf{u})$ evaluated at $(\mathbf{x}^{\mathbf{d}}, \mathbf{u}^{\mathbf{d}})$.

Since we have that $\dot{\mathbf{x}}^{\mathbf{d}} = \mathbf{f}(\mathbf{x}^{\mathbf{d}}, \mathbf{u}^{\mathbf{d}})$ we can rewrite (4.26) in the equivalent form

$$\delta\dot{\mathbf{x}} = \mathbf{A}(\mathbf{x}^{\mathbf{d}}, \mathbf{u}^{\mathbf{d}}) \cdot \delta\mathbf{x} + \mathbf{B}(\mathbf{x}^{\mathbf{d}}, \mathbf{u}^{\mathbf{d}}) \cdot \delta\mathbf{u}. \tag{4.29}$$

We would like to point out here that the Lyapunov-linearized version (4.29) of (4.23) should in fact be augmented with a *linearization error.* This linearization error is the difference between $\mathbf{f}(\mathbf{x}, \mathbf{u})$ and its Lyapunov-linearized version for values of $\mathbf{x}$ and $\mathbf{u}$ that are different from $\mathbf{x}^{\mathbf{d}}$ and $\mathbf{u}^{\mathbf{d}}$. The linearization error is zero for $\mathbf{x} = \mathbf{x}^{\mathbf{d}}$ and $\mathbf{u} = \mathbf{u}^{\mathbf{d}}$ and increases as $\mathbf{x}$ and $\mathbf{u}$ move away from $\mathbf{x}^{\mathbf{d}}$ and $\mathbf{u}^{\mathbf{d}}$. That is why the Lyapunov-linearized version of (4.23) is a proper substitute for the original nonlinear autonomous open loop system only within a small region around $(\mathbf{x}^{\mathbf{d}}, \mathbf{u}^{\mathbf{d}})$ where the magnitude of the linearization error is such that the original nonlinear behavior can be considered as linear. Moreover, when $(\mathbf{x}^{\mathbf{d}}, \mathbf{u}^{\mathbf{d}})$ is an equilibrium point for the original nonlinear autonomous open loop system, the trajectories of this system have the same characteristic shape as the trajectories of its Lyapunov-linearized version within the small region around the equilibrium point. We omit the explicit reference to the linearization error by confining ourselves only to the small region around $(\mathbf{x}^{\mathbf{d}}, \mathbf{u}^{\mathbf{d}})$ where the linearization error can be neglected (see Fig. 4.2.1).

Second, let us formulate the following control law,

$$\delta\mathbf{u} = \mathbf{K}(\mathbf{x}^{\mathbf{d}}, \mathbf{x}^{\mathbf{d}}) \cdot \delta\mathbf{x}, \tag{4.30}$$

where $\mathbf{K}(\mathbf{x}^{\mathbf{d}}, \mathbf{x}^{\mathbf{d}})$ denotes the so-called *gain matrix* which is dependent on the operating point $(\mathbf{x}^{\mathbf{d}}, \mathbf{x}^{\mathbf{d}})$.

When the above control law is inserted in (4.29) we obtain the closed loop system

$$\delta\dot{\mathbf{x}} = (\mathbf{A}(\mathbf{x}^{\mathbf{d}}, \mathbf{u}^{\mathbf{d}}) + \mathbf{B}(\mathbf{x}^{\mathbf{d}}, \mathbf{u}^{\mathbf{d}}) \cdot \mathbf{K}(\mathbf{x}^{\mathbf{d}}, \mathbf{x}^{\mathbf{d}})) \cdot \delta\mathbf{x}. \tag{4.31}$$

From (4.31) one can see that $\delta\mathbf{x} = \mathbf{0}$, $\delta\mathbf{u} = \mathbf{0}$ is an equilibrium point of the above closed loop system. Equation (4.31) can be rewritten in the equivalent form

$$\dot{\mathbf{x}} = (\mathbf{A}(\mathbf{x}^{\mathbf{d}}, \mathbf{u}^{\mathbf{d}}) + \mathbf{B}(\mathbf{x}^{\mathbf{d}}, \mathbf{u}^{\mathbf{d}}) \cdot \mathbf{K}(\mathbf{x}^{\mathbf{d}}, \mathbf{x}^{\mathbf{d}})) \cdot (\mathbf{x} - \mathbf{x}^{\mathbf{d}}), \tag{4.32}$$

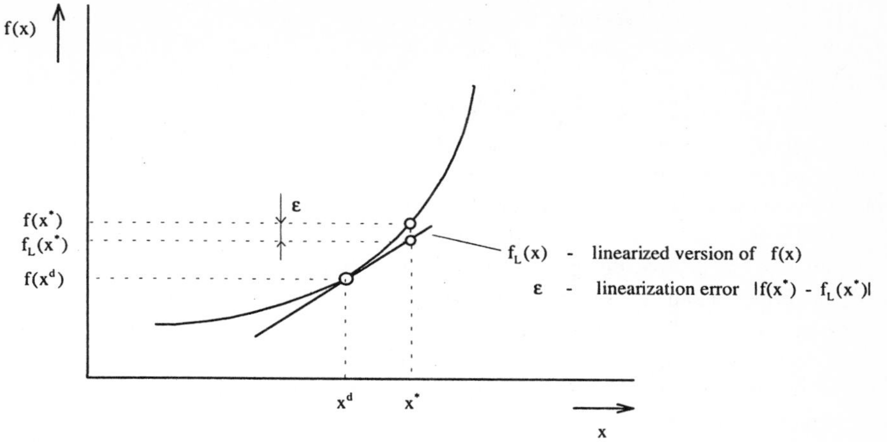

Fig. 4.1. Linearization errors

by using the equivalent expressions $\delta\mathbf{x} = \mathbf{x} - \mathbf{x^d}$, $\delta\dot{\mathbf{x}} = \dot{\mathbf{x}} - \dot{\mathbf{x}}^\mathbf{d}$, and the fact that $\dot{\mathbf{x}}^\mathbf{d} = \mathbf{0}$. Now it is easily seen that the equilibrium point of the above autonomous closed loop system is $\mathbf{x^d}$.

According to the results from Sect. 2.4.2, if the control law $\mathbf{K}(\mathbf{x^d}, \mathbf{x^d})$ is such that $\mathbf{x^d}$ is the asymptotically stable equilibrium of (4.32), then applying this control law to (4.23) will guarantee that $\mathbf{x^d}$ also is the asymptotically stable equilibrium of the resulting nonlinear autonomous closed loop system

$$\dot{\mathbf{x}} = \mathbf{f}(\mathbf{x}, \mathbf{K}(\mathbf{x^d}, \mathbf{u^d})). \tag{4.33}$$

Observe here that we can only guarantee the local asymptotic stability of the resulting nonlinear closed system (4.33) since the original nonlinear open loop system (4.24) behaves similarly to its Lyapunov-linearized version in a small region around $\mathbf{x^d}$. As it is well known from linear control theory, the control law for which $\mathbf{x^d}$ is the asymptotically stable equilibrium of (4.32) (and thus of (4.33)) should be such that $\mathbf{A}(\mathbf{x^d}, \mathbf{u^d}) + \mathbf{B}(\mathbf{x^d}, \mathbf{u^d}) \cdot \mathbf{K}(\mathbf{x^d}, \mathbf{u^d})$ is a Hurwitz matrix.

To achieve this one can construct the gain matrix $\mathbf{K}(\mathbf{x^d}, \mathbf{u^d})$, for example, by using the pole assignment method. This is done in three steps (for more details see [8]):

1. Compute the characteristic polynomial $p_\mathbf{K}(s)$ of $\mathbf{A}(\mathbf{x^d}, \mathbf{u^d}) + \mathbf{B}(\mathbf{x^d}, \mathbf{u^d}) \cdot \mathbf{K}(\mathbf{x^d}, \mathbf{u^d})$ in terms of the unknown components of $\mathbf{K}(\mathbf{x^d}, \mathbf{u^d})$.
2. Compute the desired characteristic polynomial $p_\mathbf{d}(s)$ using a set of desired eigenvalues.
3. Set $p_\mathbf{K}(s) = p_\mathbf{d}(s)$ and equate the coefficients of the powers of s to generate a system of equations to solve for the unknown components of $\mathbf{K}(\mathbf{x^d}, \mathbf{u^d})$.

In any case, one uses the matrices $\mathbf{A}(\mathbf{x^d}, \mathbf{u^d})$ and $\mathbf{B}(\mathbf{x^d}, \mathbf{u^d})$ in the construction of $\mathbf{K}(\mathbf{x^d}, \mathbf{u^d})$, and for this reason we write $\mathbf{K}(\mathbf{x^d}, \mathbf{u^d})$ as a function of $\mathbf{x^d}$ and $\mathbf{u^d}$.

Now suppose that we want to design a control law which when inserted in the original nonlinear autonomous open loop system is able to locally stabilize the resulting nonlinear autonomous closed loop system for **any** candidate operating point. Since $\mathbf{f}$ obeys the conditions from Sect. 2.4, Lyapunov-linearized versions of it can be constructed for any point in the state space. Then using the above design method we can design a control law which locally stabilizes each Lyapunov-linearized version of (4.24). When a particular operating point $\mathbf{x^d}$ (together with its corresponding $\mathbf{u^d}$) is specified one can simply select the corresponding control law $\mathbf{K}(\mathbf{x^d}, \mathbf{u^d})$ from the set of a priori designed control laws. However, since there are infinitely many points in the continuous state space this approach lacks any practical significance.

A practically feasible design method is as follows. Select a priori a number of operating points and for each such operating point design a control law based on the Lyapunov-linearized version of (4.24) for this particular operating point. Then, the question is how to locally stabilize (4.24) for operating points that are not amongst the ones selected a priori, i.e., intermediate operating points. The solution for such points would be to use a control law which is a combination of the known control laws for the operating points selected a priori. For example, let us select $\mathbf{M}$ operating points $\mathbf{x^i}$, together with their corresponding $\mathbf{u^i}$, and Lyapunov-linearize (4.24) at each $\mathbf{x^i}$ and its corresponding $\mathbf{u^i}$. Thus, one obtains $\mathbf{M}$ Lyapunov-linearized versions of (4.24),

$$\delta\dot{\mathbf{x}} = \mathbf{A}(\mathbf{x^i}, \mathbf{u^i}) \cdot \delta\mathbf{x} + \mathbf{B}(\mathbf{x^i}, \mathbf{u^i}) \cdot \delta\mathbf{u} \quad \mathbf{i} = \mathbf{1}, \ldots, \mathbf{M}, \tag{4.34}$$

with corresponding control laws

$$\delta\mathbf{u} = \mathbf{K}(\mathbf{x^i}, \mathbf{u^i}) \cdot \delta\mathbf{x} \quad \mathbf{i} = \mathbf{1}, \ldots, \mathbf{M}. \tag{4.35}$$

The above two expressions are equivalent to

$$\dot{\mathbf{x}} = \mathbf{A}(\mathbf{x^i}, \mathbf{u^i}) \cdot (\mathbf{x} - \mathbf{x^i}) + \mathbf{B}(\mathbf{x^i}, \mathbf{u^i}) \cdot (\mathbf{u} - \mathbf{u^i}) \quad \mathbf{i} = \mathbf{1}, \ldots, \mathbf{M}, \tag{4.36}$$

and

$$\mathbf{u} = \mathbf{K}(\mathbf{x^i}, \mathbf{u^i}) \cdot (\mathbf{x} - \mathbf{x^i}) + \mathbf{u^i} \quad \mathbf{i} = \mathbf{1}, \ldots, \mathbf{M}, \tag{4.37}$$

respectively, since $\delta\mathbf{x} = \mathbf{x} - \mathbf{x^i}$, $\delta\dot{\mathbf{x}} = \dot{\mathbf{x}} - \dot{\mathbf{x}}^\mathbf{i}$, $\dot{\mathbf{x}}^\mathbf{i} = \mathbf{0}$ and $\delta\mathbf{u} = \mathbf{u} - \mathbf{u^i}$. Substituting (4.37) for $\mathbf{u}$ in (4.36) (or equivalently, substituting (4.35) for $\mathbf{u}$ in (4.34)) we obtain $\mathbf{M}$ (linear) autonomous closed loop systems,

$$\dot{\mathbf{x}} = (\mathbf{A}(\mathbf{x^i}, \mathbf{u^i}) + \mathbf{B}(\mathbf{x^i}, \mathbf{u^i}) \cdot \mathbf{K}(\mathbf{x^i}, \mathbf{u^i})) \cdot (\mathbf{x} - \mathbf{x^i}) \quad \mathbf{i} = \mathbf{1}, \ldots, \mathbf{M}, \tag{4.38}$$

or equivalently,

$$\delta\dot{\mathbf{x}} = (\mathbf{A}(\mathbf{x^i}, \mathbf{u^i}) + \mathbf{B}(\mathbf{x^i}, \mathbf{u^i}) \cdot \mathbf{K}(\mathbf{x^i}, \mathbf{u^i})) \cdot \delta\mathbf{x} \quad \mathbf{i} = \mathbf{1}, \ldots, \mathbf{M}, \tag{4.39}$$

Now, consider an operating point $\mathbf{x^d}$ (with a corresponding $\mathbf{u^d}$) which is not among the selected operating points $\mathbf{x^i}$ a priori. We want to stabilize (4.24) at this operating point by using the already designed control laws $\mathbf{K}(\mathbf{x^i}, \mathbf{u^i})$, system matrices $\mathbf{A}(\mathbf{x^i}, \mathbf{u^i})$, and input matrices $\mathbf{B}(\mathbf{x^i}, \mathbf{u^i})$. This, as already mentioned, can be achieved by stabilizing the Lyapunov-linearized version of (4.24) at $\mathbf{x^d}$. That is, we want to stabilize (4.24) at $\mathbf{x^d}$ by using the already designed control laws $\mathbf{K}(\mathbf{x^i}, \mathbf{u^i})$, system matrices $\mathbf{A}(\mathbf{x^i}, \mathbf{u^i})$, and input matrices $\mathbf{B}(\mathbf{x^i}, \mathbf{u^i})$, instead of using the control law $\mathbf{K}(\mathbf{x^d}, \mathbf{u^d})$, the system matrix $\mathbf{A}(\mathbf{x^d}, \mathbf{u^d})$, and the input matrix $\mathbf{B}(\mathbf{x^i}, \mathbf{u^i})$.

Suppose that we define $\mathbf{K}(\mathbf{x^d}, \mathbf{u^d})$ as

$$\mathbf{K}(\mathbf{x^d}, \mathbf{u^d}) = \sum_{\mathbf{j}} w^{\mathbf{j}} \cdot \mathbf{K}(\mathbf{x^j}, \mathbf{u^j}), \tag{4.40}$$

where $w^{\mathbf{j}}$ is a constant weight of $\mathbf{K}(\mathbf{x^j}, \mathbf{u^j})$ which is a "measure" of the "appropriateness" of the control law $\mathbf{K}(\mathbf{x^j}, \mathbf{u^j})$ for the purpose of stabilizing the Lyapunov-linearized version of (4.24) at $\mathbf{x^d}$. The first problem here is how to determine the different $w^{\mathbf{j}}$'s. The second problem is that the Lyapunov-linearized version of (4.24) at $\mathbf{x^d}$ is not known. A solution to the latter problem would be to construct it (in similarity to the above control law (4.40)) as a weighted combination of the already available Lyapunov-linearized versions of (4.24), that is, we can define

$$\mathbf{A}(\mathbf{x^d}, \mathbf{u^d}) = \sum_{\mathbf{i}} w^{\mathbf{i}} \cdot \mathbf{A}(\mathbf{x^i}, \mathbf{u^i}) \tag{4.41}$$

and

$$\mathbf{B}(\mathbf{x^d}, \mathbf{u^d}) = \sum_{\mathbf{i}} w^{\mathbf{i}} \cdot \mathbf{B}(\mathbf{x^i}, \mathbf{u^i}) \tag{4.42}$$

where $w^{\mathbf{i}}$ is a constant weight which is a "measure" of the "extent" to which $\mathbf{A}(\mathbf{x^i}, \mathbf{u^i})$ and $\mathbf{B}(\mathbf{x^i}, \mathbf{u^i})$ can be used as substitutes for the "missing" $\mathbf{A}(\mathbf{x^d}, \mathbf{u^d})$ and $\mathbf{B}(\mathbf{x^d}, \mathbf{u^d})$ from the Lyapunov-linearized version of (4.24) at $\mathbf{x^d}$. Thus, we can approximate the "missing" Lyapunov-linearized version

$$\dot{\mathbf{x}} = \mathbf{A}(\mathbf{x^d}, \mathbf{u^d}) \cdot (\mathbf{x} - \mathbf{x^d}) + \mathbf{B}(\mathbf{x^d}, \mathbf{u^d}) \cdot (\mathbf{u} - \mathbf{u^d}), \tag{4.43}$$

of (4.24) at $\mathbf{x^d}$ by

$$\dot{\mathbf{x}} = \sum_{\mathbf{i}} w^{\mathbf{i}} \cdot (\mathbf{A}(\mathbf{x^i}, \mathbf{u^i}) \cdot (\mathbf{x} - \mathbf{x^d}) + \mathbf{B}(\mathbf{x^i}, \mathbf{u^i}) \cdot (\mathbf{u} - \mathbf{u^d})). \tag{4.44}$$

Here again the problem is the determination of the measures of the extent to which $\mathbf{A}(\mathbf{x^i}, \mathbf{u^i})$ and $\mathbf{B}(\mathbf{x^i}, \mathbf{u^i})$ can be used as a substitute for the "missing" $\mathbf{A}(\mathbf{x^d}, \mathbf{u^d})$ and $\mathbf{B}(\mathbf{x^d}, \mathbf{u^d})$ from Lyapunov-linearized version (4.43) of (4.24) at $\mathbf{x^d}$. Another problem is whether the weight associated with $\mathbf{A}(\mathbf{x^i}, \mathbf{u^i})$ and $\mathbf{B}(\mathbf{x^i}, \mathbf{u^i})$ should be the same as the weight of the corresponding control law

$\mathbf{K}(\mathbf{x^i}, \mathbf{u^i})$ for each $\mathbf{i}$. Let us assume that these weights are the same, the intuition being that $\mathbf{K}(\mathbf{x^i}, \mathbf{u^i})$ was derived on the basis of $\mathbf{A}(\mathbf{x^i}, \mathbf{u^i})$ and $\mathbf{B}(\mathbf{x^i}, \mathbf{u^i})$. Now we can use (4.40), which approximates the "missing" $\mathbf{K}(\mathbf{x^d}, \mathbf{u^d})$ with the available $\mathbf{K}(\mathbf{x^j}, \mathbf{u^j})$, to define the control law

$$\mathbf{u} = \sum_{\mathbf{j}} w^{\mathbf{j}} \cdot (\mathbf{K}(\mathbf{x^j}, \mathbf{u^j}) \cdot (\mathbf{x} - \mathbf{x^d}) + \mathbf{u^d}), \tag{4.45}$$

This control law is the approximation of the "missing" control law

$$\mathbf{u} = \mathbf{K}(\mathbf{x^d}, \mathbf{u^d}) \cdot (\mathbf{x} - \mathbf{x^d}) + \mathbf{u^d}, \tag{4.46}$$

intended to stabilize the "missing" (4.43) at $\mathbf{x^d}$.

Substituting (4.45) in (4.44) we obtain that

$$\dot{\mathbf{x}} = \sum_{\mathbf{i}} \sum_{\mathbf{j}} w^{\mathbf{i}} \cdot w^{\mathbf{j}} \cdot (\mathbf{A}(\mathbf{x^i}, \mathbf{u^i}) + \mathbf{B}(\mathbf{x^i}, \mathbf{u^i}) \cdot \mathbf{K}(\mathbf{x^j}, \mathbf{u^j})) \cdot (\mathbf{x} - \mathbf{x^d}), \tag{4.47}$$

is the closed loop Lyapunov-linearized version of the original nonlinear autonomous closed loop system

$$\dot{\mathbf{x}} = \mathbf{f}(\mathbf{x}, \sum_{\mathbf{j}} w^{\mathbf{j}} \cdot \mathbf{K}(\mathbf{x^j}, \mathbf{u^j})) \tag{4.48}$$

that was to be stabilized at a unspecified in advance $\mathbf{x^d}$.

Now the problem is (besides the problem with the determination of the weights $w^{\mathbf{i}}$), to provide conditions under which (4.47) will have $\mathbf{x^d}$ as its locally asymptotically stable equilibrium point. We will derive such conditions in the next section. However, it is easily seen that the practical applicability of above outlined design alternative is crucially dependent upon the determination of the weights involved in the the design of the weighted combination of control laws and the weighted combination of the Lyapunov-linearized versions of (4.24). The fuzzification of this design alternative in terms of partitioning the crisp state space into fuzzy regions, provides a natural, and computationally very efficient way for determining the above mentioned weights as the normalized degrees of satisfaction of these fuzzy regions to which an operating point belongs.

Another problem is that (4.47) is just an approximation of the actual Lyapunov-linearized version of (4.24) at $(\mathbf{x^d}, \mathbf{u^d})$. Thus, one can expect an approximation error whose size may affect the stability robustness of (4.47). In Sect. 4.2.6 we will describe the allowed range for this approximation error, such that if this error is within the allowed range the stability of (4.47) cannot be disturbed.

4.2.2 The Open Loop Fuzzy Model

Let us first Lyapunov-linearize the original nonlinear autonomous open loop system (4.24) at the center $\mathbf{x^i}$ of each fuzzy region $\mathbf{LX^i}$ of the fuzzy state space. As a result we obtain $\mathbf{M}$ Lyapunov-linearized versions of (4.24), each of the form

$$\dot{\mathbf{x}} = \mathbf{A}(\mathbf{x^i}, \mathbf{u^i}) \cdot (\mathbf{x} - \mathbf{x^i}) + \mathbf{B}(\mathbf{x^i}, \mathbf{u^i}) \cdot (\mathbf{u} - \mathbf{u^i}). \tag{4.49}$$

The fuzzy counterpart of each Lyapunov-linearized version (4.49) of the original nonlinear autonomous open loop system (4.24) is given as a fuzzy rule of the form

$$R_S^{\mathbf{i}}\text{: } \textit{if } \mathbf{x^d} = \mathbf{LX^i} \textit{ then } \dot{\mathbf{x}} = \mathbf{A}(\mathbf{x^i}, \mathbf{u^i}) \cdot (\mathbf{x} - \mathbf{x^d}) + \mathbf{B}(\mathbf{x^i}, \mathbf{u^i}) \cdot (\mathbf{u} - \mathbf{u^d}).$$

For any crisp state vector $\mathbf{x}^* = (x_1^*, x_2^*, \cdots, x_n^*)^T$, its corresponding crisp input vector $\mathbf{u}^* = (u_1^*, u_2^*, \cdots, u_m^*)^T$, a given operating point $\mathbf{x^d} = (x_1^d, x_2^d, \cdots, x_n^d)^T$, and its corresponding input $\mathbf{u^d} = (u_1^d, u_2^d, \cdots, u_m^d)^T$ the computation with a single fuzzy rule proceeds as follows:

1. The degree of satisfaction $\mu^{\mathbf{i}}(\mathbf{x^d})$ of the $\mathbf{i}$-th fuzzy region $\mathbf{LX^i}$ by $\mathbf{x^d} = (x_1^d, x_2^d, \ldots, x_n^d)^T$ is computed as

$$\mu^{\mathbf{i}}(\mathbf{x^d}) = \min\left(\mu_{LX_1^{\mathbf{i}}}(x_1^d), \mu_{LX_2^{\mathbf{i}}}(x_2^d), \ldots, \mu_{LX_n^{\mathbf{i}}}(x_n^d)\right). \tag{4.50}$$

2. $\dot{\mathbf{x}}^*$ is computed as

$$\dot{\mathbf{x}}^* = \mathbf{A}(\mathbf{x^i}, \mathbf{u^i}) \cdot (\mathbf{x}^* - \mathbf{x^d}) + \mathbf{B}(\mathbf{x^i}, \mathbf{u^i}) \cdot (\mathbf{u}^* - \mathbf{u^d}). \tag{4.51}$$

3. The so computed $\dot{\mathbf{x}}^*$ is weighted by $\mu^{\mathbf{i}}(\mathbf{x^d})$ as

$$\mu^{\mathbf{i}}(\mathbf{x^d}) \cdot \dot{\mathbf{x}}^*. \tag{4.52}$$

Thus, in the general case, the dynamics of the fuzzy model corresponding to computation with a single fuzzy rule is given as

$$\mu^{\mathbf{i}}(\mathbf{x^d}) \cdot (\mathbf{A}(\mathbf{x^i}, \mathbf{u^i}) \cdot (\mathbf{x} - \mathbf{x^d}) + \mathbf{B}(\mathbf{x^i}, \mathbf{u^i}) \cdot (\mathbf{u} - \mathbf{u^d})). \tag{4.53}$$

From the above expression, it is easily seen that its dynamics is linear everywhere in the fuzzy region $\mathbf{LX^i}$ since for a given $\mathbf{x^d}$, $\mu^{\mathbf{i}}(\mathbf{x^d})$ is constant and $(\mathbf{A}(\mathbf{x^i}, \mathbf{u^i}) \cdot (\mathbf{x} - \mathbf{x^d}) + \mathbf{B}(\mathbf{x^i}, \mathbf{u^i}) \cdot (\mathbf{u} - \mathbf{u^d}))$ is a linear function. However, with respect to the original nonlinear system (4.23), the expression (4.53) is a proper subsitute for (4.23) only within a small region around $\mathbf{x^d}$ where the magnitude of the linearization error is such that the original nonlinear behavior can be considered as linear.

Let us recall here (see Sect. 4.2.1) that computation with the fuzzy rule

$$R_S^{\mathbf{i}}\text{: } \textit{if } \mathbf{x^d} = \mathbf{LX^i} \textit{ then } \dot{\mathbf{x}} = \mathbf{A}(\mathbf{x^i}, \mathbf{u^i}) \cdot (\mathbf{x} - \mathbf{x^d}) + \mathbf{B}(\mathbf{x^i}, \mathbf{u^i}) \cdot (\mathbf{u} - \mathbf{u^d}),$$

simply approximates computation with the "missing" Lyapunov-linearized version

$$\dot{\mathbf{x}} = \mathbf{A}(\mathbf{x^d}, \mathbf{u^d}) \cdot (\mathbf{x} - \mathbf{x^d}) + \mathbf{B}(\mathbf{x^d}, \mathbf{u^d}) \cdot (\mathbf{u} - \mathbf{u^d}), \tag{4.54}$$

of (4.24) at $(\mathbf{x^d}, \mathbf{u^d})$. Computation with the above "missing" Lyapunov-linearized version of (4.24) is replaced by computation with

$$\dot{\mathbf{x}} = \mathbf{A}(\mathbf{x^i}, \mathbf{u^i}) \cdot (\mathbf{x} - \mathbf{x^d}) + \mathbf{B}(\mathbf{x^i}, \mathbf{u^i}) \cdot (\mathbf{u} - \mathbf{u^d}), \tag{4.55}$$

weighted with $\mu^{\mathbf{i}}(\mathbf{x^d})$, which is a measure of the extent to which the "missing" Lyapunov-linearized version of (4.24) at $(\mathbf{x^d}, \mathbf{u^d})$ can be replaced by the given Lyapunov-linearized versions of (4.24) at $(\mathbf{x^i}, \mathbf{u^i})$. If $\mathbf{x^d} = \mathbf{x^i}$ then $\mu^{\mathbf{i}}(\mathbf{x^d})$ is equal to one and in this case

$$\begin{aligned}&\mathbf{A}(\mathbf{x^i}, \mathbf{u^i}) \cdot (\mathbf{x} - \mathbf{x^d}) + \mathbf{B}(\mathbf{x^i}, \mathbf{u^i}) \cdot (\mathbf{u} - \mathbf{u^d}) = \\ &\quad \mathbf{A}(\mathbf{x^d}, \mathbf{u^d}) \cdot (\mathbf{x} - \mathbf{x^d}) + \mathbf{B}(\mathbf{x^d}, \mathbf{u^d}) \cdot (\mathbf{u} - \mathbf{u^d}).\end{aligned} \tag{4.56}$$

If $\mathbf{x^d} \neq \mathbf{x^i}$ then $\mu^{\mathbf{i}}(\mathbf{x^d})$ is not equal to one and in this case

$$\begin{aligned}&\mathbf{A}(\mathbf{x^i}, \mathbf{u^i}) \cdot (\mathbf{x} - \mathbf{x^d}) + \mathbf{B}(\mathbf{x^i}, \mathbf{u^i}) \cdot (\mathbf{u} - \mathbf{u^d}) \neq \\ &\quad \mathbf{A}(\mathbf{x^d}, \mathbf{u^d}) \cdot (\mathbf{x} - \mathbf{x^d}) + \mathbf{B}(\mathbf{x^d}, \mathbf{u^d}) \cdot (\mathbf{u} - \mathbf{u^d}).\end{aligned} \tag{4.57}$$

Then, the smaller/bigger $\mu^{\mathbf{i}}(\mathbf{x^d})$ is, the smaller/bigger the difference between

$$\mathbf{A}(\mathbf{x^i}, \mathbf{u^i}) \cdot (\mathbf{x} - \mathbf{x^d}) + \mathbf{B}(\mathbf{x^i}, \mathbf{u^i}) \cdot (\mathbf{u} - \mathbf{u^d}) \tag{4.58}$$

and

$$\mathbf{A}(\mathbf{x^d}, \mathbf{u^d}) \cdot (\mathbf{x} - \mathbf{x^d}) + \mathbf{B}(\mathbf{x^d}, \mathbf{u^d}) \cdot (\mathbf{u} - \mathbf{u^d}). \tag{4.59}$$

The results computed for each individual rule via (4.53) are aggregated by simply taking their weighted sum:

$$\dot{\mathbf{x}} = \frac{\sum_{\mathbf{i}} \mu^{\mathbf{i}}(\mathbf{x^d}) \cdot (\mathbf{A}(\mathbf{x^i}, \mathbf{u^i}) \cdot (\mathbf{x} - \mathbf{x^d}) + \mathbf{B}(\mathbf{x^i}, \mathbf{u^i}) \cdot (\mathbf{u} - \mathbf{u^d}))}{\sum_{\mathbf{i}} \mu^{\mathbf{i}}(\mathbf{x^d})}. \tag{4.60}$$

Thus, the above expression provides the overall result of the computation with the set of all fuzzy rules representing the fuzzy model of the Lyapunov-linearized version of the original nonlinear autonomous open loop system. Expression (4.60) can be simplified by normalizing the degrees of satisfaction $\mu^{\mathbf{i}}(\mathbf{x^d})$ and using instead their normalized counterparts $w^{\mathbf{i}}(\mathbf{x^d})$, i.e. $\sum_{\mathbf{i}} w^{\mathbf{i}}(\mathbf{x^d}) = 1$, that are obtained as follows: for any given $\mu^{\mathbf{1}}(\mathbf{x^d})$, $\mu^{\mathbf{2}}(\mathbf{x^d})$,..., $\mu^{\mathbf{M}}(\mathbf{x^d})$,

$$w^{\mathbf{i}}(\mathbf{x^d}) = \frac{\mu^{\mathbf{i}}(\mathbf{x^d})}{\sum_{\mathbf{i}} \mu^{\mathbf{i}}(\mathbf{x^d})}. \tag{4.61}$$

Since we have now that, $\sum_{\mathbf{i}} w^{\mathbf{i}}(\mathbf{x^d}) = 1$, equation (4.60) can be rewritten in the equivalent simpler form,

$$\dot{\mathbf{x}} = \sum_{\mathbf{i}} w^{\mathbf{i}}(\mathbf{x^d}) \cdot (\mathbf{A}(\mathbf{x^i}, \mathbf{u^i}) \cdot (\mathbf{x} - \mathbf{x^d}) + \mathbf{B}(\mathbf{x^i}, \mathbf{u^i}) \cdot (\mathbf{u} - \mathbf{u^d})). \tag{4.62}$$

Since for any $\mathbf{x^d}$, all of $\mu^{\mathbf{i}}(\mathbf{x^d})$ are constant and the right hand side of the above expression is a linear function, the dynamics of the fuzzy model are linear for any given $\mathbf{x^d}$. Here again, (4.62) is a proper substitute for the original nonlinear open loop system (4.23) only within a small region around $\mathbf{x^d}$.

4.2.3 The Takagi–Sugeno FLC-2

The Takagi–Sugeno FLC-2 is intended to locally asymptotically stabilize the open loop fuzzy model at any candidate operating point and thus locally asymptotically stabilize the resulting nonlinear closed loop system when this type of FLC is inserted in (4.24). The Takagi–Sugeno FLC-2 is given as a set of fuzzy rules, each fuzzy rule being of the form

$R^{\mathbf{i}}_{\mathrm{C}}$: *if* $\mathbf{x^d} = \mathbf{LX^j}$ *then* $\mathbf{u} = \mathbf{K}(\mathbf{x^j}, \mathbf{u^j}) \cdot (\mathbf{x} - \mathbf{x^d}) + \mathbf{u^d}$

where $\mathbf{K}(\mathbf{x^j}, \mathbf{u^j})$ is the gain matrix of the Lyapunov-linearized version of (4.24) for the $\mathbf{j}$-th fuzzy region as represented in the then-part of the fuzzy rule $R^{\mathbf{j}}_{\mathrm{S}}$. Thus the control law from the then-part of the above fuzzy rule is intended to locally asymptotically stabilize the open loop fuzzy model

$$\dot{\mathbf{x}} = w^{\mathbf{j}}(\mathbf{x^d}) \cdot (\mathbf{A}(\mathbf{x^j}, \mathbf{u^j}) \cdot (\mathbf{x} - \mathbf{x^d}) + \mathbf{B}(\mathbf{x^j}, \mathbf{u^j}) \cdot (\mathbf{u} - \mathbf{u^d})) \tag{4.63}$$

at $(\mathbf{x^d}, \mathbf{u^d})$.

For each crisp state vector $\mathbf{x}^* = (x_1^*, x_2^*, \cdots, x_n^*)^T$, a given operating point $\mathbf{x^d} = (x_1^d, x_2^d, \cdots, x_n^d)^T$, and its corresponding $\mathbf{u^d} = (u_1^d, u_2^d, \cdots, u_n^d)^T$, the computation of the corresponding crisp input vector $\mathbf{u}^* = (u_1^*, u_2^*, \cdots, u_m^*)^T$ by a single fuzzy rule proceeds as follows:

1. The degree of satisfaction $\mu^{\mathbf{i}}(\mathbf{x^d})$ of the $\mathbf{i}$-th fuzzy region $\mathbf{LX^j}$ by $\mathbf{x^d} = (x_1^d, x_2^d, \ldots, x_n^d)^T$ is computed as

$$\mu^{\mathbf{j}}(\mathbf{x^d}) = \min\left(\mu_{LX_1^{\mathbf{j}}}(x_1^d), \mu_{LX_2^{\mathbf{j}}}(x_2^d), \ldots, \mu_{LX_n^{\mathbf{j}}}(x^d)\right). \tag{4.64}$$

2. $\mathbf{u}^*$ is computed as

$$\mathbf{K}(\mathbf{x^j}, \mathbf{u^j}) \cdot (\mathbf{x}^* - \mathbf{x^d}) + \mathbf{u^d}. \tag{4.65}$$

3. $\mathbf{u}^*$ is weighted by $\mu^{\mathbf{j}}(\mathbf{x^d})$ as

$$\mu^{\mathbf{j}}(\mathbf{x^d}) \cdot (\mathbf{K}(\mathbf{x^j}, \mathbf{u^j}) \cdot (\mathbf{x}^* - \mathbf{x^d}) + \mathbf{u^d}) \tag{4.66}$$

Thus, in the general case, the control law's dynamics corresponding to computation with a single fuzzy rule is given as

$$\mathbf{u} = \mu^{\mathbf{j}}(\mathbf{x^d}) \cdot (\mathbf{K}(\mathbf{x^j}, \mathbf{u^j}) \cdot (\mathbf{x} - \mathbf{x^d}) + \mathbf{u^d}). \tag{4.67}$$

From the above expression, it is easily seen that for all crisp state vectors the dynamics of the control law is linear since for any $\mathbf{x^d}$, $\mu^{\mathbf{j}}(\mathbf{x^d})$ is constant and $(\mathbf{K}(\mathbf{x^j}, \mathbf{u^j}) \cdot (\mathbf{x} - \mathbf{x^d}) + \mathbf{u^d})$ is a linear function. Note also that computation with the above expression approximates computation with the "missing" control law

$$\mathbf{u} = \mathbf{K}(\mathbf{x^d}, \mathbf{u^d}) \cdot (\mathbf{x} - \mathbf{x^d}) + \mathbf{u^d}, \tag{4.68}$$

intended for the asymptotic stabilization of the "missing" Lyapunov-linearized version

$$\dot{\mathbf{x}} = \mathbf{A}(\mathbf{x^d}, \mathbf{u^d}) \cdot (\mathbf{x} - \mathbf{x^d}) + \mathbf{B}(\mathbf{x^d}, \mathbf{u^d}) \cdot (\mathbf{u} - \mathbf{u^d}), \tag{4.69}$$

of (4.24) at $(\mathbf{x^d}, \mathbf{u^d})$. This approximation of $\mathbf{K}(\mathbf{x^d}, \mathbf{u^d})$ by $\mathbf{K}(\mathbf{x^j}, \mathbf{u^j})$ is simply done by weighting the latter control law with the degree to which $\mathbf{x^d}$ satisfies the fuzzy region for which $\mathbf{K}(\mathbf{x^j}, \mathbf{u^j})$ is intended. Thus one again can expect approximation errors reflecting the difference between the weighted $\mathbf{K}(\mathbf{x^j}, \mathbf{u^j})$ and the "missing" $\mathbf{K}(\mathbf{x^d}, \mathbf{u^d})$.

The results computed for each individual rule via (4.67) are aggregated by simply taking their weighted sum, that is,

$$\mathbf{u} = \frac{\sum_{\mathbf{j}} \mu^{\mathbf{j}}(\mathbf{x^d}) \cdot (\mathbf{K}(\mathbf{x^j}, \mathbf{u^j}) \cdot (\mathbf{x} - \mathbf{x^d}) + \mathbf{u^d})}{\sum_{\mathbf{j}} \mu^{\mathbf{j}}(\mathbf{x^d})}. \tag{4.70}$$

Thus, the above expression provides the overall result of computation with the set of fuzzy rules representing the Takagi–Sugeno FLC-2. The expression (4.70) can again be simplified by normalizing the degrees of satisfaction $\mu^{\mathbf{j}}(\mathbf{x^d})$ and using instead their normalized counterparts $w^{\mathbf{j}}(\mathbf{x^d})$, i.e. $\sum_{\mathbf{j}} w^{\mathbf{j}}(\mathbf{x^d}) = 1$, which are obtained as follows: for any given $\mu^{\mathbf{1}}(\mathbf{x^d})$, $\mu^{\mathbf{2}}(\mathbf{x^d}), \ldots, \mu^{\mathbf{M}}(\mathbf{x^d})$,

$$w^{\mathbf{j}}(\mathbf{x^d}) = \frac{\mu^{\mathbf{j}}(\mathbf{x^d})}{\sum_{\mathbf{j}} \mu^{\mathbf{j}}(\mathbf{x^d})}. \tag{4.71}$$

Since we have now that, $\sum_{\mathbf{j}} w^{\mathbf{j}}(\mathbf{x^d}) = 1$, the equation (4.70) can be rewritten in the equivalent more simple form,

$$\mathbf{u} = \sum_{\mathbf{j}} w^{\mathbf{j}}(\mathbf{x^d}) \cdot (\mathbf{K}(\mathbf{x^j}, \mathbf{u^j}) \cdot (\mathbf{x} - \mathbf{x^d}) + \mathbf{u^d}). \tag{4.72}$$

4.2.4 The Closed Loop Fuzzy Model

So far, by using fuzzy rules of the form

$$R_S^i\text{: } \textit{if } \mathbf{x^d} = \mathbf{LX^i} \textit{ then } \dot{\mathbf{x}} = \mathbf{A}(\mathbf{x^i}, \mathbf{u^i}) \cdot (\mathbf{x} - \mathbf{x^d}) + \mathbf{B}(\mathbf{x^i}, \mathbf{u^i}) \cdot (\mathbf{u} - \mathbf{u^d}),$$

and

$$R_C^j\text{: } \textit{if } \mathbf{x^d} = \mathbf{LX^j} \textit{ then } \mathbf{u} = \mathbf{K}(\mathbf{x^j}, \mathbf{u^j}) \cdot (\mathbf{x} - \mathbf{x^d}) + \mathbf{u^d},$$

we have described the open loop fuzzy model and the Takagi–Sugeno FLC-2. Furthermore, we saw that computation with the fuzzy model is equivalent to

$$\dot{\mathbf{x}} = \sum_{\mathbf{i}} w^{\mathbf{i}}(\mathbf{x^d}) \cdot (\mathbf{A}(\mathbf{x^i}, \mathbf{u^i}) \cdot (\mathbf{x} - \mathbf{x^d}) + \mathbf{B}(\mathbf{x^i}, \mathbf{u^i}) \cdot (\mathbf{u} - \mathbf{u^d})), \tag{4.73}$$

and computation with the Takagi–Sugeno FLC-2 is equivalent to

$$\mathbf{u} = \sum_{\mathbf{j}} w^{\mathbf{j}}(\mathbf{x^d}) \cdot (\mathbf{K}(\mathbf{x^j}, \mathbf{x^j}) \cdot (\mathbf{x} - \mathbf{x^d}) + \mathbf{u^d}), \tag{4.74}$$

where both of the above expressions have linear dynamics. Thus replacing **u** from the former equation with its equivalent term from the latter one, we obtain the equation for the closed loop fuzzy model

$$\begin{aligned}\dot{\mathbf{x}} &= \sum_{\mathbf{i}} w^{\mathbf{i}}(\mathbf{x^d}) \cdot (\mathbf{A}(\mathbf{x^i}, \mathbf{u^i}) \cdot (\mathbf{x} - \mathbf{x^d}) + \mathbf{B}(\mathbf{x^i}, \mathbf{u^i}) \cdot \\ &\quad \left(\sum_{\mathbf{j}} w^{\mathbf{j}}(\mathbf{x^d}) \cdot (\mathbf{K}(\mathbf{x^j}, \mathbf{u^j}) \cdot (\mathbf{x} - \mathbf{x^d})) + \mathbf{u^d}) - \mathbf{u^d} \right),\end{aligned} \tag{4.75}$$

which is equivalent to

$$\begin{aligned}\dot{\mathbf{x}} &= \sum_{\mathbf{i}} \sum_{\mathbf{j}} w^{\mathbf{i}}(\mathbf{x^d}) \cdot w^{\mathbf{j}}(\mathbf{x^d}) \cdot (\mathbf{A}(\mathbf{x^i}, \mathbf{u^i}) \\ &\quad + \mathbf{B}(\mathbf{x^i}, \mathbf{u^i}) \cdot \mathbf{K}(\mathbf{x^j}, \mathbf{u^j})) \cdot (\mathbf{x} - \mathbf{x^d}),\end{aligned} \tag{4.76}$$

since $\sum_{\mathbf{i}} w^{\mathbf{i}}(\mathbf{x^d}) = \sum_{\mathbf{j}} w^{\mathbf{j}}(\mathbf{x^d}) = 1$ and because of this $\sum_{\mathbf{i}} \sum_{\mathbf{j}} w^{\mathbf{i}}(\mathbf{x^d}) \cdot w^{\mathbf{j}}(\mathbf{x^d}) = \sum_{\mathbf{i}} w^{\mathbf{i}}(\mathbf{x^d}) = 1$.

Now let us derive the conditions under which (4.76) is asymptotically stable. In order to do this we first present the following result about robust stability reported in [44]:

Consider a linear system with linear perturbations

$$\dot{\mathbf{x}} = \mathbf{A} \cdot \mathbf{x} + \sum_{i=1}^{M} k_i \delta \mathbf{A}_i \cdot \mathbf{x} \tag{4.77}$$

where $\mathbf{A}$ is a Hurwitz matrix, $\delta\mathbf{A}_i$ are constant matrices of the same dimension as $\mathbf{A}$, and k_i are uncertain parameters with values in an arbitrary interval around zero. Let $\mathbf{P}$ be the unique solution of the Lyapunov equation

$$\mathbf{A}^T \cdot \mathbf{P} + \mathbf{P} \cdot \mathbf{A} = -2 \cdot \mathbf{I}, \tag{4.78}$$

and let us define the matrices $\mathbf{P}_i$ as

$$\mathbf{P}_i = \frac{\delta\mathbf{A}_i^T \cdot \mathbf{P} + \mathbf{P} \cdot \delta\mathbf{A}_i}{2}. \tag{4.79}$$

Then the linear system (4.77) is asymptotically stable if

$$\sum_{i=1}^{M} |k_i| \cdot \sigma_{\max}(\mathbf{P}_i) < 1 \tag{4.80}$$

where $\sigma_{\max}(\bullet)$ denotes the largest *singular value* of a matrix. See [21, Sect. 2.9] about computation of singular values.

Now consider (4.76) and let

$$\begin{aligned} \mathbf{A}(\mathbf{x^1}, \mathbf{u^1}) &+ \mathbf{B}(\mathbf{x^1}, \mathbf{u^1}) \cdot \mathbf{K}(\mathbf{x^1}, \mathbf{u^1}) \\ &= \mathbf{A}(\mathbf{x^2}, \mathbf{u^2}) + \mathbf{B}(\mathbf{x^2}, \mathbf{u^2}) \cdot \mathbf{K}(\mathbf{x^2}, \mathbf{u^2}) \\ &\vdots \\ &= \mathbf{A}(\mathbf{x^M}, \mathbf{u^M}) + \mathbf{B}(\mathbf{x^M}, \mathbf{u^M}) \cdot \mathbf{K}(\mathbf{x^M}, \mathbf{u^M}) \\ &= \mathbf{A}, \end{aligned} \tag{4.81}$$

be Hurwitz matrices. Furthermore, let us denote $\mathbf{A}(\mathbf{x^i}, \mathbf{u^i}) + \mathbf{B}(\mathbf{x^i}, \mathbf{u^i}) \cdot \mathbf{K}(\mathbf{x^j}, \mathbf{u^j})$ by $\mathbf{A_{ij}}$ and define $\delta\mathbf{A_{ij}}$ as

$$\delta\mathbf{A_{ij}} + \mathbf{A} = \mathbf{A_{ij}}. \tag{4.82}$$

Now (4.76) can be rewritten as

$$\dot{\mathbf{x}} = \sum_{\mathbf{i}} \sum_{\mathbf{j}} w^{\mathbf{i}}(\mathbf{x^d}) \cdot w^{\mathbf{j}}(\mathbf{x^d}) \cdot \mathbf{A_{ij}} \cdot (\mathbf{x} - \mathbf{x^d}), \tag{4.83}$$

which is equivalent to

$$\dot{\mathbf{x}} = \mathbf{A} \cdot (\mathbf{x} - \mathbf{x^d}) + \sum_{\mathbf{i}} \sum_{\mathbf{j}} w^{\mathbf{i}}(\mathbf{x^d}) \cdot w^{\mathbf{j}}(\mathbf{x^d}) \cdot \delta\mathbf{A_{ij}} \cdot (\mathbf{x} - \mathbf{x^d}), \tag{4.84}$$

It is easily seen that the above equation is of the same form as (4.77) where the constant k_i corresponds to the constant product $w^{\mathbf{i}}(\mathbf{x^d}) \cdot w^{\mathbf{j}}(\mathbf{x^d})$, and $\delta\mathbf{A}_i$ corresponds to $\delta\mathbf{A_{ij}}$. However, observe here that at least one product $w^{\mathbf{i}}(\mathbf{x^d}) \cdot w^{\mathbf{j}}(\mathbf{x^d})$ is greater than zero and less or equal to one since at least one $w^{\mathbf{i}}(\mathbf{x^d})$

is greater than zero and less or equal to one and $\sum_{\mathbf{i}}\sum_{\mathbf{j}} w^{\mathbf{i}}(\mathbf{x^d}) \cdot w^{\mathbf{j}}(\mathbf{x^d}) = 1$. With these observations in mind let us now reformulate the result about the robust asymptotic stability of the linear system (4.77) in terms of the linear system (4.84):

Consider the linear system with linear perturbations

$$\dot{\mathbf{x}} = \mathbf{A} \cdot (\mathbf{x} - \mathbf{x^d}) + \sum_{\mathbf{i}}\sum_{\mathbf{j}} w^{\mathbf{i}}(\mathbf{x^d}) \cdot w^{\mathbf{j}}(\mathbf{x^d}) \cdot \delta\mathbf{A_{ij}} \cdot (\mathbf{x} - \mathbf{x^d}), \qquad (4.85)$$

where $\mathbf{A}$ is a Hurwitz matrix, $\delta\mathbf{A_{ij}}$ are constant matrices of the same dimension as $\mathbf{A}$, and $w^{\mathbf{i}}(\mathbf{x^d}) \cdot w^{\mathbf{j}}(\mathbf{x^d})$ are uncertain parameters with values in an arbitrary interval around zero. Let $\mathbf{P}$ be the unique solution of the Lyapunov equation

$$\mathbf{A}^T \cdot \mathbf{P} + \mathbf{P} \cdot \mathbf{A} = -2 \cdot \mathbf{I}, \qquad (4.86)$$

and let us define the matrices $\mathbf{P_{ij}}$ as

$$\mathbf{P_{ij}} = \frac{\delta\mathbf{A_{ij}}^T \cdot \mathbf{P} + \mathbf{P} \cdot \delta\mathbf{A_{ij}}}{2}. \qquad (4.87)$$

Then the linear system (4.84) (equivalent to (4.76)) is asymptotically stable if

$$\sum_{i}\sum_{j} w^{\mathbf{i}}(\mathbf{x^d}) \cdot w^{\mathbf{j}}(\mathbf{x^d}) \cdot \sigma_{\max}(\mathbf{P_{ij}}) < 1. \qquad (4.88)$$

Since in our case the products $w^{\mathbf{i}}(\mathbf{x^d}) \cdot w^{\mathbf{j}}(\mathbf{x^d})$ are known, at least one such product is greater than zero, and $\sum_i \sum_j w^{\mathbf{i}}(\mathbf{x^d}) \cdot w^{\mathbf{j}}(\mathbf{x^d}) = 1$, it is obvious that the above condition holds if the stronger condition

$$\sigma_{\max}(\mathbf{P_{ij}}) < 1 \quad \text{for each} \quad \mathbf{i}, \mathbf{j} = \mathbf{1}, \mathbf{2}, \ldots, \mathbf{M} \qquad (4.89)$$

also holds. It is easilly seen that the weaker condition (4.88) is easy to use when the operating point $\mathbf{x^d}$ is known in advance. In this case all of the $w^{\mathbf{i}}(\mathbf{x^d})$'s are available as well as the matrices $\mathbf{P_{ij}}$. However, when the operating point $\mathbf{x^d}$ is not known, then the only known component of (4.88) is $\sigma_{\max}(\mathbf{P_{ij}})$, since the matrices $\mathbf{P_{ij}}$ are available even without $\mathbf{x^d}$ being known.

Note that both conditions guarantee the asymptotic stability of (4.76) only if (4.81) and (4.82) hold. Based on this observation we will present the design of a Takagi–Sugeno FLC-2 in the next section.

4.2.5 The Design of Takagi–Sugeno FLC-2

As already described in the previous section the original nonlinear autonomous system (4.23) can be locally asymptotically stabilized at an arbitrary setpoint $\mathbf{x^d}$ if we can design gain matrices $\mathbf{K}(\mathbf{x^i}, \mathbf{u^i})$ that can locally asymptotically stabilize the closed loop fuzzy system (4.76) at $\mathbf{x^d}$, that is the system

$$\begin{aligned}\dot{\mathbf{x}} &= \sum_{\mathbf{i}}\sum_{\mathbf{j}} w^{\mathbf{i}}(\mathbf{x^d}) \cdot w^{\mathbf{j}}(\mathbf{x^d}) \cdot (\mathbf{A}(\mathbf{x^i}, \mathbf{u^i}) \\ &\quad + \mathbf{B}(\mathbf{x^i}, \mathbf{u^i}) \cdot \mathbf{K}(\mathbf{x^j}, \mathbf{u^j})) \cdot (\mathbf{x} - \mathbf{x^d}). \end{aligned} \tag{4.90}$$

Furthermore, in order to derive condition (4.89) which guaranteed that $\mathbf{x^d}$ is the locally asymptotically stable equilibrium point of the above system, we transformed this system into the form (4.84), that is

$$\dot{\mathbf{x}} = \mathbf{A} \cdot (\mathbf{x} - \mathbf{x^d}) + \sum_{\mathbf{i}}\sum_{\mathbf{j}} w^{\mathbf{i}}(\mathbf{x^d}) \cdot w^{\mathbf{j}}(\mathbf{x^d}) \cdot \delta\mathbf{A_{ij}} \cdot (\mathbf{x} - \mathbf{x^d}), \tag{4.91}$$

where $\mathbf{A}$ was a Hurwitz matrix defined by (4.81) and $\delta\mathbf{A_{ij}}$ were defined by (4.82). In other words, according to (4.81) we have to make each one of $\mathbf{A}(\mathbf{x^i}, \mathbf{u^i}) + \mathbf{B}(\mathbf{x^i}, \mathbf{u^i}) \cdot \mathbf{K}(\mathbf{x^i}, \mathbf{u^i})$ a Hurwitz matrix. Both $\mathbf{A}(\mathbf{x^i}, \mathbf{u^i})$ and $\mathbf{B}(\mathbf{x^i}, \mathbf{u^i})$ are known since they were obtained via the Lyapunov-linearization of (4.24) at $(\mathbf{x^i}, \mathbf{u^i})$. Then one can determine the unknown matrices $\mathbf{K}(\mathbf{x^i}, \mathbf{u^i})$ by the pole assignment method so that each one of $\mathbf{A}(\mathbf{x^i}, \mathbf{u^i}) + \mathbf{B}(\mathbf{x^i}, \mathbf{u^i}) \cdot \mathbf{K}(\mathbf{x^i}, \mathbf{u^i})$ becomes a Hurwitz matrix. Furthermore, by using the same set of desired poles to determine the unknown $\mathbf{K}(\mathbf{x^i}, \mathbf{u^i})$ one obtains exactly the required equalities from (4.81). Note that using the same set of desired poles we still obtain different $\mathbf{K}(\mathbf{x^i}, \mathbf{u^i})$ because for each $\mathbf{i} \neq \mathbf{j}$ we have that $\mathbf{A}(\mathbf{x^i}, \mathbf{u^i}) \neq \mathbf{A}(\mathbf{x^j}, \mathbf{u^j})$ and $\mathbf{B}(\mathbf{x^i}, \mathbf{u^i}) \neq \mathbf{B}(\mathbf{x^j}, \mathbf{u^j})$. However, since the set of desired poles is the same we have that for each $\mathbf{i} \neq \mathbf{j}$, $\mathbf{A}(\mathbf{x^i}, \mathbf{u^i}) + \mathbf{B}(\mathbf{x^i}, \mathbf{u^i}) \cdot \mathbf{K}(\mathbf{x^i}, \mathbf{u^i}) = \mathbf{A}(\mathbf{x^j}, \mathbf{u^j}) + \mathbf{B}(\mathbf{x^j}, \mathbf{u^j}) \cdot \mathbf{K}(\mathbf{x^j}, \mathbf{u^j})$. Thus by using the pole assignment method on the same set of desired poles we can design the gain matrices $\mathbf{K}(\mathbf{x^i}, \mathbf{u^i})$ $(\mathbf{i} = \mathbf{1}, \mathbf{2}, \ldots, \mathbf{M})$ such that (4.81) holds.

Next, in order to obtain the matrices $\mathbf{P_{ij}}$ whose largest singular values have to obey condition (4.89) for robust asymptotic stability, we have to construct the matrices $\delta\mathbf{A_{ij}}$. According to (4.82) these were defined as

$$\delta\mathbf{A_{ij}} + \mathbf{A} = \mathbf{A_{ij}}, \tag{4.92}$$

which is equivalent to

$$\begin{aligned}\delta\mathbf{A_{ij}} &= \mathbf{A}(\mathbf{x^i}, \mathbf{u^i}) + \mathbf{B}(\mathbf{x^i}, \mathbf{u^i}) \cdot \mathbf{K}(\mathbf{x^j}, \mathbf{u^j}) \\ &\quad - \mathbf{A}(\mathbf{x^i}, \mathbf{u^i}) - \mathbf{B}(\mathbf{x^i}, \mathbf{u^i}) \cdot \mathbf{K}(\mathbf{x^i}, \mathbf{u^i}),\end{aligned} \tag{4.93}$$

and thus we obtain

$$\delta\mathbf{A_{ij}} = \mathbf{B}(\mathbf{x^i}, \mathbf{u^i}) \cdot (\mathbf{K}(\mathbf{x^j}, \mathbf{u^j}) - \mathbf{K}(\mathbf{x^i}, \mathbf{u^i})). \tag{4.94}$$

In other words, the matrices $\delta\mathbf{A_{ij}}$ can be easily obtained by the already known matrices $\mathbf{B}(\mathbf{x^i}, \mathbf{u^i})$ and $\mathbf{K}(\mathbf{x^i}, \mathbf{u^i})$.

Finally, we have to determine the matrices $\mathbf{P_{ij}}$ from condition (4.89). These were defined in (4.87) as

$$\mathbf{P_{ij}} = \frac{\delta\mathbf{A_{ij}}^T \cdot \mathbf{P} + \mathbf{P} \cdot \delta\mathbf{A_{ij}}}{2} \tag{4.95}$$

where $\mathbf{P}$ was the unique solution of the Lyapunov equation (4.86), that is,

$$\mathbf{A}^T \cdot \mathbf{P} + \mathbf{P} \cdot \mathbf{A} = -2 \cdot \mathbf{I}. \tag{4.96}$$

Thus, the determination of the matrices $\mathbf{P_{ij}}$ requires solving the above Lyapunov equation for $\mathbf{P}$. Recall here (see Sect. 2.4.2) that this equation has a unique solution if and only if $\mathbf{A}$ is a Hurwitz matrix. In our case, the matrix $\mathbf{A}$ from the above equation is such that

$$\begin{aligned} \mathbf{A} &= \mathbf{A}(\mathbf{x^1}, \mathbf{u^1}) + \mathbf{B}(\mathbf{x^1}, \mathbf{u^1}) \cdot \mathbf{K}(\mathbf{x^1}, \mathbf{u^1}) = \dots \\ &= \mathbf{A}(\mathbf{x^M}, \mathbf{u^M}) + \mathbf{B}(\mathbf{x^M}, \mathbf{u^M}) \cdot \mathbf{K}(\mathbf{x^M}, \mathbf{u^M}), \end{aligned} \tag{4.97}$$

and is also a Hurwitz matrix because each one of $\mathbf{A}(\mathbf{x^i}, \mathbf{u^i}) + \mathbf{B}(\mathbf{x^i}, \mathbf{u^i})\mathbf{K}(\mathbf{x^i}, \mathbf{u^i})$ was already designed as a Hurwitz matrix. Thus the above Lyapunov equation does have a unique solution $\mathbf{P}$. Furthermore, since the different $\delta\mathbf{A_{ij}} = \mathbf{B}(\mathbf{x^i}, \mathbf{u^i}) \cdot (\mathbf{K}(\mathbf{x^j}, \mathbf{u^j}) - \mathbf{K}(\mathbf{x^i}, \mathbf{u^i}))$ are known, the matrices $\mathbf{P_{ij}}$ can be determined, according to (4.87) as

$$\begin{aligned} \mathbf{P_{ij}} &= \frac{(\mathbf{B}(\mathbf{x^i}, \mathbf{u^i}) \cdot (\mathbf{K}(\mathbf{x^j}, \mathbf{u^j}) - \mathbf{K}(\mathbf{x^i}, \mathbf{u^i})))^T \cdot \mathbf{P}}{2} \\ &+ \frac{\mathbf{P} \cdot \mathbf{B}(\mathbf{x^i}, \mathbf{u^i}) \cdot (\mathbf{K}(\mathbf{x^j}, \mathbf{u^j}) - \mathbf{K}(\mathbf{x^i}, \mathbf{u^i}))}{2}. \end{aligned} \tag{4.98}$$

Now, in order to verify whether the gain matrices $\mathbf{K}(\mathbf{x^i}, \mathbf{u^i})$, designed via the pole assignment method, satisfy condition (4.89) for local asymptotic stability, we have to compute the set of singular values for each $\mathbf{P_{ij}}$, take the largest singular value $\sigma_{\max}(\mathbf{P_{ij}})$ for each $\mathbf{P_{ij}}$, and check whether the inequalities (4.89) are satisfied, that is, whether

$$\sigma_{\max}(\mathbf{P_{ij}}) < 1 \quad \text{for each} \quad \mathbf{i}, \mathbf{j} = \mathbf{1}, \mathbf{2}, \dots, \mathbf{M}. \tag{4.99}$$

If each of the above inequalities is satisfied, then we have that the gain matrices $\mathbf{K}(\mathbf{x^i}, \mathbf{u^i})$, designed via the pole assignment method, are such that the fuzzy closed loop system (4.76) has the given operating point $\mathbf{x^d}$ as its locally asymptotically stable equilibrium point. This in turn, guarantees that $\mathbf{x^d}$ is also the locally asymptotically stable equilibrium point of the original nonlinear autonomous system (4.23).

It has to be stressed here that the design method for the Takagi–Sugeno FLC-2, as presented in this section, does not guarantee that the gain matrices $\mathbf{K}(\mathbf{x^i}, \mathbf{u^i})$, designed via the pole assignment method, are such that (4.89) is automatically satisfied once these gain matrices are determined. This in turn implies that $\mathbf{K}(\mathbf{x^i}, \mathbf{u^i})$ may have to be redesigned over and over again until gain matrices are found that satisfy the above inequalities.

However, once the proper (in the context of (4.89)) gain matrices are found they can be used to locally asymptotically stabilize the original nonlinear autonomous system (4.23) for **any** operating point $(\mathbf{x^d}, \mathbf{u^d})$. If this operating point is one of $(\mathbf{x^i}, \mathbf{u^i})$, i.e., belongs to the center of a fuzzy region, this implies that only the corresponding, already available, gain matrix $\mathbf{K}(\mathbf{x^i}, \mathbf{u^i})$ will be used for stabilization since in this case $w^{\mathbf{i}}(\mathbf{x^d}) = 1$ while $\forall \mathbf{j} \neq \mathbf{i}\ w^{\mathbf{j}}(\mathbf{x^d}) = 0$. If $(\mathbf{x^d}, \mathbf{u^d})$ is not among the $(\mathbf{x^i}, \mathbf{u^i})$ then it is an intermediate operating point which satisfies a number of fuzzy regions, each to a different degree of satisfaction. In this case a weighted combination of the already available gain matrices for these fuzzy regions will be used to locally asymptotically stabilize (4.23). Thus for any operating point in the fuzzy state space there always exists an already available gain matrix, or a weighted combination of already available gain matrices.

4.2.6 Approximation Errors

The so-called *approximation errors* were briefly mentioned in Sects. 4.2.2–4.2.3. Now we will consider these errors in detail.

Let $(\mathbf{x^d}, \mathbf{u^d})$ be an arbitrary intermediate operating point, that is, it is not among the already available operating points $(\mathbf{x^i}, \mathbf{u^i})$, $(\mathbf{i} = \mathbf{1}, \mathbf{2}, \ldots, \mathbf{M})$. As we saw in Sect. 4.2.4, the fuzzy closed loop linear system for such an arbitrary intermediate operating point is given by

$$\begin{aligned} \dot{\mathbf{x}} &= \sum_{\mathbf{i}} \sum_{\mathbf{j}} w^{\mathbf{i}}(\mathbf{x^d}) \cdot w^{\mathbf{j}}(\mathbf{x^d}) \cdot (\mathbf{A}(\mathbf{x^i}, \mathbf{u^i}) \\ &\quad + \mathbf{B}(\mathbf{x^i}, \mathbf{u^i}) \cdot \mathbf{K}(\mathbf{x^j}, \mathbf{u^j})) \cdot (\mathbf{x} - \mathbf{x^d}), \end{aligned} \tag{4.100}$$

where $w^{\mathbf{i}}(\mathbf{x^d})$ are the degrees of satisfaction of the different fuzzy regions by $\mathbf{x^d}$, $\mathbf{A}(\mathbf{x^i}, \mathbf{u^i})$ and $\mathbf{B}(\mathbf{x^i}, \mathbf{u^i})$ are the system and input matrices obtained via Lyapunov-linearization at $(\mathbf{x^i}, \mathbf{u^i})$, and $\mathbf{K}(\mathbf{x^j}, \mathbf{u^j})$ are the gain matrices designed via the use of $\mathbf{A}(\mathbf{x^j}, \mathbf{u^j})$ and $\mathbf{B}(\mathbf{x^j}, \mathbf{u^j})$.

If, instead of using (4.100), we Lyapunov-linearize the original nonlinear autonomous system (4.23) at $(\mathbf{x^d}, \mathbf{u^d})$ and then design an appropriate gain matrix $\mathbf{K}(\mathbf{x^d}, \mathbf{u^d})$ we will obtain the following closed loop system

$$\dot{\mathbf{x}} = (\mathbf{A}(\mathbf{x^d}, \mathbf{u^d}) + \mathbf{B}(\mathbf{x^d}, \mathbf{u^d}) \cdot \mathbf{K}(\mathbf{x^d}, \mathbf{u^d})) \cdot (\mathbf{x} - \mathbf{x^d}). \tag{4.101}$$

The difference between the matrix

$$\sum_{\mathbf{i}} \sum_{\mathbf{j}} w^{\mathbf{i}}(\mathbf{x^d}) \cdot w^{\mathbf{j}}(\mathbf{x^d}) \cdot (\mathbf{A}(\mathbf{x^i}, \mathbf{u^i}) + \mathbf{B}(\mathbf{x^i}, \mathbf{u^i}) \cdot \mathbf{K}(\mathbf{x^j}, \mathbf{u^j})), \tag{4.102}$$

from (4.100) and the matrix

$$\mathbf{A}(\mathbf{x^d}, \mathbf{u^d}) + \mathbf{B}(\mathbf{x^d}, \mathbf{u^d}) \cdot \mathbf{K}(\mathbf{x^d}, \mathbf{u^d}), \tag{4.103}$$

from (4.101), for any $\mathbf{x}$, is constant since both (4.100) and (4.101) describe linear behaviors. This difference constitutes the approximation error matrix due to the use of (4.100) instead of (4.101). We treat this approximation error as an unknown disturbance matrix $\mathbf{E}$ in the context of the result about robust stability reported in [44], and already used in the design of the Takagi–Sugeno FLC-2 in Sect. 4.2.4. To utilize this result for the particular case of an approximation error we proceed as follows.

Suppose that the condition (4.89) which guaranteed the stability of (4.100) holds, and thus the latter linear closed loop system has $\mathbf{x^d}$ as its local asymptotically stable equilibrium point. Now we have to establish the condition under which (4.100) remains asymptotically stable at $\mathbf{x^d}$ despite of an approximation error in terms of an unknown perturbation matrix $\mathbf{E}$. For the sake of simplicity, let us denote the right hand side of (4.100) by $\mathbf{A}'$. Thus (4.100) can be rewritten in the equivalent form

$$\dot{\mathbf{x}} = \mathbf{A}' \cdot (\mathbf{x} - \mathbf{x^d}) \tag{4.104}$$

where

$$\mathbf{A}' = \sum_{\mathbf{i}} \sum_{\mathbf{j}} w^{\mathbf{i}}(\mathbf{x^d}) \cdot w^{\mathbf{j}}(\mathbf{x^d}) \cdot (\mathbf{A}(\mathbf{x^i}, \mathbf{u^i}) + \mathbf{B}(\mathbf{x^i}, \mathbf{u^i}) \cdot \mathbf{K}(\mathbf{x^j}, \mathbf{u^j})). \tag{4.105}$$

In other words, the problem of studying the stability of (4.100) in the presence of an unknown perturbation matrix $\mathbf{E}$ can be reduced to studying the stability of the linear system

$$\dot{\mathbf{x}} = (\mathbf{A}' + \mathbf{E}) \cdot (\mathbf{x} - \mathbf{x^d}), \tag{4.106}$$

where the unknown perturbation matrix $\mathbf{E}$ with unknown elements e_{ij} is of the same dimension as $\mathbf{A}'$, i.e., $(n \times n)$, and is defined as

$$\mathbf{E} = \sum_{m=1}^{n \times n} k_m \cdot \mathbf{E}^m, \tag{4.107}$$

where k_m are unknown parameters, and the elements e_{ij}^m, $(i, j = 1, 2, ..., n)$ of each E^m are obtained as follows. Let us number the elements a_{ij} of $\mathbf{A}'$ from 1 to $n \times n$. Thus we can rewrite each element of $\mathbf{A}'$ as a_{ij}^m where $m = 1, 2, \ldots, n \times n$. Then the elements e_{ij}^m of each $\mathbf{E}^m$ are defined as

if $a_{ij}^m \neq 0$ then $e_{ij}^m = 1$, and $e_{pq}^m = 0, \forall p, q \neq i, j$,
otherwise $e_{ij}^m = 0, \forall i, j = 1, 2, \ldots, n$.

It is easily seen that if $a_{ij}^m \neq 0$, then $\mathbf{E}^m$ has only one element equal to one, namely e_{ij}^m, and the rest of its elements are equal to zero.

Thus, according to (4.107), for each i, j we have that

$$e_{ij} = \sum_{m=1}^{n\times n} k_m \cdot e_{ij}^m = k_m. \tag{4.108}$$

if $a_{ij}^m \neq 0$, otherwise we have that $e_{ij} = 0$. Hence, for each i, j, the elements $a_{ij}^m + e_{ij}$ of $\mathbf{A}' + \mathbf{E}$ are equal to zero whenever $a_{ij}^m = 0$ and equal to $a_{ij}^m + k_m$ whenever $a_{ij}^m \neq 0$.

Example 4.2.1. Let the matrix $\mathbf{A}'$ be given as

$$\mathbf{A}' = \begin{pmatrix} 1 & 0 \\ 2 & -1 \end{pmatrix}. \tag{4.109}$$

In other words we have that $a_{11}^1 = 1$, $a_{12}^2 = 0$, $a_{21}^3 = 2$, and $a_{22}^4 = -1$. Thus the matrices $\mathbf{E}^m$ $(m = 1, 2, 3, 4)$ are given as

$$\mathbf{E}^1 = \begin{pmatrix} 1 & 0 \\ 0 & 0 \end{pmatrix}. \tag{4.110}$$

$$\mathbf{E}^2 = \begin{pmatrix} 0 & 0 \\ 0 & 0 \end{pmatrix}. \tag{4.111}$$

$$\mathbf{E}^3 = \begin{pmatrix} 0 & 0 \\ 1 & 0 \end{pmatrix}. \tag{4.112}$$

$$\mathbf{E}^4 = \begin{pmatrix} 0 & 0 \\ 0 & 1 \end{pmatrix}. \tag{4.113}$$

Furthermore, we have that

$$\begin{aligned} \mathbf{E} &= k_1 \cdot \mathbf{E}^1 + k_2 \cdot \mathbf{E}^2 + k_3 \cdot \mathbf{E}^3 + k_4 \cdot \mathbf{E}^4 \\ &= k_1 \cdot \begin{pmatrix} 1 & 0 \\ 0 & 0 \end{pmatrix} + k_2 \cdot \begin{pmatrix} 0 & 0 \\ 0 & 0 \end{pmatrix} \\ &+ k_3 \cdot \begin{pmatrix} 0 & 0 \\ 1 & 0 \end{pmatrix} + k_4 \cdot \begin{pmatrix} 0 & 0 \\ 0 & 1 \end{pmatrix} \\ &= \begin{pmatrix} k_1 & 0 \\ k_3 & k_4 \end{pmatrix}. \end{aligned} \tag{4.114}$$

Thus we obtain that

$$\begin{aligned} \mathbf{A}' + \mathbf{E} &= \begin{pmatrix} 1 & 0 \\ 2 & -1 \end{pmatrix} + \begin{pmatrix} k_1 & 0 \\ k_3 & k_4 \end{pmatrix} \\ &= \begin{pmatrix} 1 + k_1 & 0 \\ 2 + k_3 & -1 + k_4 \end{pmatrix}. \end{aligned} \tag{4.115}$$

Now, in the context of (4.80) from Sect. 4.2.4, we have that

- $\mathbf{A}'$ is stable, since the condition (4.89) was assumed to hold, and thus is a Hurwitz matrix,
- $\mathbf{E}^{ij}$ are known perturbation matrices (by construction),
- k_{ij} are unknown parameters in an interval around zero.

In this case, the system (4.106) is stable if the condition (4.80) is fulfilled. In our case this condition means that the following inequality should hold for each i, j

$$\sum_{i=1}^{n}\sum_{j=1}^{n} |k_{ij}| \cdot \sigma_{\mathbf{max}}(\mathbf{F}_{ij}) < 1 \tag{4.116}$$

where

$$\mathbf{F}_{ij} = \frac{\mathbf{E}^{ijT} \cdot \mathbf{P} + \mathbf{P} \cdot \mathbf{E}^{ij}}{2}, \tag{4.117}$$

where $\mathbf{P}$ is the unique solution of the Lyapunov equation

$$\mathbf{A}'^{T} \cdot \mathbf{P} + \mathbf{P} \cdot \mathbf{A}' = -2 \cdot \mathbf{I}. \tag{4.118}$$

Thus, as long as the approximation error, in terms of the perturbation matrix $\mathbf{E}$, is such that the above inequality holds, the system (4.106) is stable. In other words, despite the approximation error the matrix $\mathbf{A}'$ remains a Hurwitz matrix. Since $\mathbf{A}'$ remains a Hurwitz matrix, then (4.104) also remains stable. However, (4.104) is equivalent to (4.100). Thus, whenever the approximation error in terms of the perturbation matrix $\mathbf{E}$ is such that (4.116) is fulfilled, the system (4.100) remains stable.

4.3 The Takagi–Sugeno FLC-2 as a Gain Scheduler

As already described in Sect. 2.4.3, the tracking control problem for a nonlinear autonomous system can be transformed into a stabilization control problem of a nonlinear nonautonomous system. This transformation is done as follows.

Consider a nonlinear autonomous system of the form

$$\dot{\mathbf{x}} = \mathbf{f}(\mathbf{x}, \mathbf{u}), \tag{4.119}$$

and let $\mathbf{x}^{\mathbf{d}}(t)$ be a known state reference trajectory (a solution of (4.119)) starting at initial time $t_0 = 0$ and initial condition (or initial state $\mathbf{x}(0)$) and corresponding to a given reference input $\mathbf{u}^{\mathbf{d}}(t)$. The tracking control problem for (4.119) is then transformed into the stabilization problem for the nonlinear nonautonomous system

$$\delta\dot{\mathbf{x}} = \mathbf{f}(\delta\mathbf{x} + \mathbf{x}^{\mathbf{d}}, \delta\mathbf{u} + \mathbf{u}^{\mathbf{d}}, t) - \mathbf{f}(\mathbf{x}^{\mathbf{d}}, \mathbf{u}^{\mathbf{d}}, t), \tag{4.120}$$

where $\delta\mathbf{x} = \mathbf{x}(t) - \mathbf{x^d}(t)$, $\delta\mathbf{u} = \mathbf{u}(t) - \mathbf{u^d}(t)$, and $\delta\dot{\mathbf{x}} = \dot{\mathbf{x}}(t) - \dot{\mathbf{x}}^\mathbf{d}(t)$. Observe that (4.120) is now a nonlinear nonautonomous open loop system, the stability of which is to be studied at $(\delta\mathbf{x} = \mathbf{0}, \delta\mathbf{u} = \mathbf{0})$ rather than along the state reference trajectory $\mathbf{x^d}(t)$. Observe furthermore that $\dot{\mathbf{x}}^\mathbf{d}(t)$ may be different from zero. The Lyapunov-linearized version of (4.120) around $(\mathbf{0}, \mathbf{0})$ results in the linear nonautonomous system

$$\delta\dot{\mathbf{x}} = \mathbf{A}(\mathbf{x^d}, \mathbf{u^d}, t) \cdot \delta\mathbf{x} + \mathbf{B}(\mathbf{x^d}, \mathbf{u^d}, t) \cdot \delta\mathbf{u}, \tag{4.121}$$

which is equivalent to

$$\dot{\mathbf{x}} = \dot{\mathbf{x}}^\mathbf{d} + \mathbf{A}(\mathbf{x^d}, \mathbf{u^d}, t) \cdot (\mathbf{x}(t) - \mathbf{x^d}(t)) + \mathbf{B}(\mathbf{x^d}, \mathbf{u^d}, t) \cdot (\mathbf{u}(t) - \mathbf{u^d}(t)), \tag{4.122}$$

where the equilibrium point of the latter system is now the trajectory $\mathbf{x^d}(t)$. Because of the equivalence between (4.121) and (4.122), the local uniform exponential stability of (4.122) at $\mathbf{x^d}(t)$ guarantees under certain conditions (see Sect. 4.4.3) that $\mathbf{x^d}(t)$ is also the locally uniformly exponentially stable trajectory of (4.120) or (4.119). Thus the control problem is the design of such a nonautonomous control law which, when inserted in (4.122), will locally uniformly exponentially stabilize the resulting linear nonautonomous closed loop system at the state reference trajectory $\mathbf{x^d}(t)$. Gain scheduling is one approach to the design of the control law discussed above. In the next section we will summarize the essential steps of the gain scheduling design method as described in [25], [26], [15].

4.3.1 The Gain Scheduling Design Method

The gain scheduling design method proceeds as follows (see [25, 15, 26]). Consider first the known reference trajectory $\mathbf{x^d}(t)$ used in the derivation of (4.120). If this trajectory is evaluated at a particular *frozen time* τ then the value $\mathbf{x^d}(\tau)$ is obtained and is called the *frozen-time value* of $\mathbf{x^d}(t)$ for $t = \tau$. A set $\{\mathbf{x^d}(\tau)\}$ of such frozen values obtained for equidistant frozen times $\tau = \tau_1, \tau_2, \ldots, \tau_N$, is chosen in advance.

Second, the linear nonautonomous open loop system (4.122) is obtained via Lyapunov-linearization of the nonlinear nonautonomous open loop system (4.121) at $\mathbf{x^d}(t)$ and its corresponding $\mathbf{u^d}(t)$. Then, N frozen-time linear autonomous open loop systems of the form (4.122) are obtained by replacing $\mathbf{x^d}(t)$ and $\mathbf{u^d}(t)$ from (4.122) by pairs of their frozen-time values $(\mathbf{x^d}(\tau_1), \mathbf{u^d}(\tau_1)), (\mathbf{x^d}(\tau_2), \mathbf{u^d}(\tau_2)), \ldots, (\mathbf{x^d}(\tau_N), \mathbf{u^d}(\tau_N))$. That is,

$$\begin{aligned} \dot{\mathbf{x}} \; &= \; \dot{\mathbf{x}}^\mathbf{d}(\tau) + \mathbf{A}(\mathbf{x^d}(\tau), \mathbf{u^d}(\tau)) \cdot (\mathbf{x} - \mathbf{x^d}(\tau)) \\ &\quad + \mathbf{B}(\mathbf{x^d}(\tau), \mathbf{u^d}(\tau)) \cdot (\mathbf{u} - \mathbf{u^d}(\tau)), \end{aligned} \tag{4.123}$$

where $\tau = \tau_1, \tau_2, \ldots, \tau_N$.

Third, N linear autonomous control laws are designed, one for each of the frozen-time linear autonomous open loop systems. These control laws are of the form (for $\tau = \tau_1, \tau_2, \ldots, \tau_N$)

$$\mathbf{u} = \mathbf{K}(\mathbf{x^d}(\tau), \mathbf{u^d}(\tau)) \cdot (\mathbf{x} - \mathbf{x^d}(\tau)) + \mathbf{u^d}(\tau). \tag{4.124}$$

Thus one obtains **N** frozen-time closed loop systems (for $\tau = \tau_1, \tau_2, \ldots, \tau_N$)

$$\begin{aligned} \dot{\mathbf{x}} &= \dot{\mathbf{x}}^{\mathbf{d}}(\tau) + (\mathbf{A}(\mathbf{x^d}(\tau), \mathbf{u^d}(\tau)) \\ &\quad + \mathbf{B}(\mathbf{x^d}(\tau), \mathbf{u^d}(\tau)) \cdot \mathbf{K}(\mathbf{x^d}(\tau), \mathbf{u^d}(\tau))) \cdot (\mathbf{x} - \mathbf{x^d}(\tau)). \end{aligned} \tag{4.125}$$

The control law (4.124) is designed in such a manner so that each $\mathbf{x^d}(\tau_i)$ is a local uniformly exponentially stable equilibrium point of its corresponding (4.125).

Fourth, the already available autonomous control laws from (4.124) are interpolated (or gain scheduled). The autonomous gain scheduled control law so obtained should be such that each intermediate operating point $\mathbf{x^d}(\tau)$, where $\tau_i < \tau < \tau_{i+1}$, is a local uniformly exponentially stable equilibrium point of the frozen-time Lyapunov-linearized version of (4.119) at $\mathbf{x^d}(\tau)$ and its corresponding $\mathbf{u^d}(\tau)$. Observe that the autonomous gain scheduled control law for an intermediate operating point $\mathbf{x^d}(\tau)$ is not derived on the basis of the *interpolated* version of (4.123) for the intermediate point $\mathbf{x^d}(\tau)$ and its corresponding $\mathbf{u^d}(\tau)$. This interpolated version of (4.123) can, in principle, be constructed from the frozen-time linear autonomous open loop systems of the form (4.123) for $\tau = \{\tau_i, \tau_{i+1}\}$. Instead, the autonomous gain scheduled control law is obtained directly by interpolating the already available control laws from (4.125) for $\tau = \{\tau_i, \tau_{i+1}\}$.

However, even if the gain scheduled control law is able to locally uniformly exponentially stabilize each frozen-time autonomous closed loop system from (4.125) and each such system obeys certain robustness and performance requirements, these properties need not carry over to the linear nonautonomous closed loop system (that is, the system (4.122) in which the gain scheduled control law is inserted). However, under the condition that the linear nonautonomous open loop system (4.122) is slowly time varying (see Sect. 2.4.4), all of the above mentioned properties of the frozen-time linear autonomous closed loop systems are inherited by the the linear nonautonomous closed loop system. This implies in turn that the same local properties carry over to the nonlinear autonomous closed loop system obtained by inserting the gain scheduled control law in (4.120) or (4.119). Observe here that in the case of gain scheduling on a state reference trajectory the condition requiring that (4.122) be slowly time varying is equivalent to the requirement that the state reference trajectory $\mathbf{x^d}(t)$ should vary slowly [25, Theorem 4.2–1].

We stress here that no general and formally motivated method for the interpolation of the already available autonomous control laws from (4.124) into a gain scheduled control law is available. The interpolation is done in an ad hoc manner by the use of heuristic guidelines [15] and additional information about the plant [25]. One consequence is that at intermediate operating points the poles locations of the linear closed loop system obtained by inserting the gain scheduled control law in the frozen-time Lyapunov-linearized version of (4.119) are, in general, incorrect [25].

In this context, the fuzzy gain scheduler described in the next section is immune to incorrect poles since the gain scheduled control law is derived on the basis of the fuzzily interpolated Lyapunov-linearized version of (4.119) at a given frozen-time value of $\mathbf{x^d}(t)$. This fuzzily interpolated Lyapunov-linearized version of (4.119) is constructed from the frozen-time linear autonomous open loop systems of the form (4.123). Hence, the gain scheduled control law is designed with a particular frozen-time open loop system in mind, and thus, the poles of the resulting frozen-time closed loop system do not migrate from the desired pole locations used for the design of the gain scheduled control law. Thus, the design of the gain scheduled control law of a fuzzy gain scheduler is formally motivated.

Yet another advantage of the fuzzy gain scheduler is that the method for determining the weights used in the construction of the fuzzily interpolated Lyapunov-linearized version of (4.119) from the frozen-time linear autonomous open loop systems (4.123) is general and computationally efficient. These weights are simply obtained as the degrees of satisfaction of the different fuzzy regions from the fuzzy state space by a given intermediate frozen-time value of $\mathbf{x^d}(t)$.

4.3.2 The Design of a Fuzzy Gain Scheduler

Suppose first that given an arbitrary state reference trajectory $\mathbf{x^d}(t)$ together with its corresponding reference input $\mathbf{u^d}(t)$, the nonlinear autonomous open loop system (4.119) is transformed into the linear nonautonomous open loop system (4.122). Furthermore, consider a set $\{\mathbf{x^d}(\tau)\}$ of frozen-time values of $\mathbf{x^d}(t)$ obtained for equidistant frozen times $\tau_1, \tau_2, \ldots, \tau_N$ and the corresponding set $\{\mathbf{u^d}(\tau)\}$ of frozen-time values of $\mathbf{u^d}(t)$. The set $\{\mathbf{x^d}(\tau)\}$ of frozen-time values is then used in the derivation of the $\mathbf{N}$ frozen-time autonomous open loop systems from (4.123) which were of the form

$$\begin{aligned}\dot{\mathbf{x}} &= \dot{\mathbf{x}}^{\mathbf{d}}(\tau) + \mathbf{A}(\mathbf{x^d}(\tau), \mathbf{u^d}(\tau)) \cdot (\mathbf{x} - \mathbf{x^d}(\tau)) \\ &\quad + \mathbf{B}(\mathbf{x^d}(\tau), \mathbf{u^d}(\tau)) \cdot (\mathbf{u} - \mathbf{u^d}(\tau)). \end{aligned} \tag{4.126}$$

Now recall here that the linear autonomous open loop fuzzy model (4.62) used in the design of the Takagi–Sugeno FLC-2 (see Sect. 4.2.2) was of the form

$$\dot{\mathbf{x}} = \dot{\mathbf{x}}^{\mathbf{d}}(\tau) + \sum_{\mathbf{i}} w^{\mathbf{i}}(\mathbf{x^d}) \cdot (\mathbf{A}(\mathbf{x^i}, \mathbf{u^i}) \cdot (\mathbf{x} - \mathbf{x^d})$$

$$+ \mathbf{B}(\mathbf{x^i}, \mathbf{u^i}) \cdot (\mathbf{u} - \mathbf{u^d})), \tag{4.127}$$

and was obtained by Lyapunov-linearization of the autonomous counterpart (4.24) of (4.120) at the points $(\mathbf{x^i}, \mathbf{u^i})$ where $\mathbf{x^i}$ were the centers of the fuzzy regions from the fuzzy state space and $\mathbf{u^i}$ were the input values corresponding to these centers. In the case of the nonlinear autonomous open loop system (4.119), the above expression can be derived by considering each pair $(\mathbf{x^i}, \mathbf{u^i})$ as a pair of frozen-time values associated with the centers of the fuzzy regions from the fuzzy state space of (4.119) and different from $(\mathbf{x^d}(\tau), \mathbf{u^d}(\tau))$. Then, by replacing $\mathbf{x^d}(t)$ and $\mathbf{u^d}(t)$ from (4.122) with the pairs $(\mathbf{x^i}, \mathbf{u^i})$ in $\mathbf{A}(\mathbf{x^d}, \mathbf{u^d})$ und $\mathbf{B}(\mathbf{x^d}, \mathbf{u^d})$ we obtain $\mathbf{M}$ linear autonomous open loop systems

$$\dot{\mathbf{x}} = \dot{\mathbf{x}}^{\mathbf{d}} + \mathbf{A}(\mathbf{x^i}, \mathbf{u^i}) \cdot (\mathbf{x} - \mathbf{x^d}) + \mathbf{B}(\mathbf{x^i}, \mathbf{u^i}) \cdot (\mathbf{u} - \mathbf{u^d}). \tag{4.128}$$

Observe here that (4.123) and (4.128) are equivalent for $\mathbf{x^d}(\tau) = \mathbf{x^i}$ and $\mathbf{u^d}(\tau) = \mathbf{u^i}$. However, for $\mathbf{x^d}(\tau) \neq \mathbf{x^i}$ and $\mathbf{u^d}(\tau) \neq \mathbf{u^i}$ each one of (4.123) can be approximated using the already available (4.128). This is so because the linear autonomous fuzzy open loop expression (4.127) approximates the behavior of a “missing”(autonomous) Lyapunov-linearized system at any intermediate operating point $(\mathbf{x^d}, \mathbf{u^d})$. Thus, (4.127) can be used to approximate the behavior of the “missing” (from (4.128)) frozen-time Lyapunov-linearized versions (4.123) for any intermediate operating points $(\mathbf{x^d}, \mathbf{u^d}) = (\mathbf{x^d}(\tau), \mathbf{u^d}(\tau))$. Hence, the expression

$$\begin{aligned} \dot{\mathbf{x}} &= \dot{\mathbf{x}}^{\mathbf{d}}(\tau) + \sum_{\mathbf{i}} w^{\mathbf{i}}(\mathbf{x^d}(\tau)) \cdot (\mathbf{A}(\mathbf{x^i}, \mathbf{u^i}) \cdot (\mathbf{x} - \mathbf{x^d}(\tau)) \\ &\quad + \mathbf{B}(\mathbf{x^i}, \mathbf{u^i}) \cdot (\mathbf{u} - \mathbf{u^d}(\tau))) \end{aligned} \tag{4.129}$$

approximates the behavior of each one of (4.123) by a weighted combination of (4.128).

Recall also that the set of all rules of the Takagi–Sugeno FLC-2 defines a control law of the form

$$\mathbf{u} = \sum_{\mathbf{j}} w^{\mathbf{j}}(\mathbf{x^d}) \cdot (\mathbf{K}(\mathbf{x^j}, \mathbf{u^j}) \cdot (\mathbf{x} - \mathbf{x^d}) + \mathbf{u^d}) \tag{4.130}$$

which can be designed in such a way (see Sects. 4.2.5–4.2.6) that it can locally uniformly exponentially stabilize (4.127) at an arbitrary operating point $\mathbf{x^d}$ and its corresponding $\mathbf{u^d}$, despite approximation errors of known magnitude. That is, even around operating points $\mathbf{x^d} = \mathbf{x^d}(\tau)$. Thus, the control law of the form

$$\mathbf{u} = \sum_{\mathbf{j}} w^{\mathbf{j}}(\mathbf{x^d}(\tau)) \cdot (\mathbf{K}(\mathbf{x^j}, \mathbf{u^j}) \cdot (\mathbf{x} - \mathbf{x^d}(\tau)) + \mathbf{u^d}(\tau)) \tag{4.131}$$

will be able to locally uniformly exponentially stabilize (4.129) at an arbitrary operating point $\mathbf{x^d}(\tau)$ as well since the latter system is obtained from (4.127) only by substituting the operating point $\mathbf{x^d}$ with the different operating point $\mathbf{x^d}(\tau)$ and $\mathbf{u^d}$ with $\mathbf{u^d}(\tau)$.

Recall also that the closed loop system obtained by inserting (4.130) in (4.127) was of the form

$$\begin{aligned}\dot{\mathbf{x}} &= \dot{\mathbf{x}}^{\mathbf{d}} + \sum_{\mathbf{i}}\sum_{\mathbf{j}} w^{\mathbf{i}}(\mathbf{x^d}) \cdot w^{\mathbf{j}}(\mathbf{x^d}) \cdot (\mathbf{A}(\mathbf{x^i}, \mathbf{u^i}) \\ &\quad + \mathbf{B}(\mathbf{x^i}, \mathbf{u^i}) \cdot \mathbf{K}(\mathbf{x^j}, \mathbf{u^j})) \cdot (\mathbf{x} - \mathbf{x^d}), \qquad (4.132)\end{aligned}$$

and as long as the approximation errors for (4.132) (see Sects. 4.2.5–4.2.6), are in certain range, the above closed loop system has $\mathbf{x^d}$ as its local uniformly exponentially stable equilibrium point. Now inserting (4.131) in (4.129) we obtain the fuzzily approximated version of (4.125):

$$\begin{aligned}\dot{\mathbf{x}} &= \dot{\mathbf{x}}^{\mathbf{d}}(\tau) + \sum_{\mathbf{i}}\sum_{\mathbf{j}} w^{\mathbf{i}}(\mathbf{x^d}(\tau)) \cdot w^{\mathbf{j}}(\mathbf{x^d}(\tau)) \cdot (\mathbf{A}(\mathbf{x^i}, \mathbf{u^i}) \\ &\quad + \mathbf{B}(\mathbf{x^i}, \mathbf{u^i}) \cdot \mathbf{K}(\mathbf{x^j}, \mathbf{u^j})) \cdot (\mathbf{x} - \mathbf{x^d}(\tau)). \qquad (4.133)\end{aligned}$$

It is easily seen that the latter closed loop system is obtained from (4.132) only by substituting the operating point $\mathbf{x^d}$ with the different operating point $\mathbf{x^d}(\tau)$ and $\mathbf{u^d}$ with $\mathbf{u^d}(\tau)$. Thus, (4.133) will have $\mathbf{x^d}(\tau)$ as its local uniformly exponentially stable equilibrium point provided that the approximation errors are in a certain range.

Thus we have seen that a Takagi–Sugeno FLC-2 such that computation with all of its rules can be represented by (4.131) is able to locally uniformly exponentially stabilize the frozen-time closed loop system (4.125) at all points $\mathbf{x^d}(\tau)$. Furthermore, under the assumption that the linear nonautonomous system (4.122) is slowly time varying, such a Takagi–Sugeno FLC-2 can also locally uniformly exponentially stabilize the latter system, when inserted in it, since it can locally uniformly exponentially stabilize all of its frozen-time counterparts (4.125).

It is easily seen that a Takagi–Sugeno FLC-2 such that computation with all of its rules results can be represented by (4.131) has rules of the form

$R^{\mathbf{i}}_{\mathrm{C}}$: *if* $\mathbf{x^d}(\tau) = \mathbf{LX^j}$ *then* $\mathbf{u} = \mathbf{K}(\mathbf{x^j}, \mathbf{u^j}) \cdot (\mathbf{x} - \mathbf{x^d}(\tau)) + \mathbf{u^d}(\tau)$.

Obviously, the construction of the gain matrices of a Takagi–Sugeno FLC-2 with rules of the above type requires an open loop system, the fuzzy rule based representation of which has the form

$R^{\mathbf{i}}_{\mathrm{S}}$: *if* $\mathbf{x^d}(\tau) = \mathbf{LX^i}$ *then* $\dot{\mathbf{x}} = \dot{\mathbf{x}}^{\mathbf{d}}(\tau) + \mathbf{A}(\mathbf{x^i}, \mathbf{u^i}) \cdot (\mathbf{x} - \mathbf{x^d}(\tau)) + \mathbf{B}(\mathbf{x^i}, \mathbf{u^i}) \cdot (\mathbf{u} - \mathbf{u^d}(\tau))$,

since computation with all the above rules results exactly in (4.129).

Both of the above types of fuzzy rules can be designed in exactly the same manner as in the case of the stabilization control problem from the previous section. This is so, since the only difference between the use of the Takagi–Sugeno FLC-2 for stabilization around an operating point and its use as a gain scheduler for tracking a state reference trajectory is purely syntactic, i.e., the use of $\mathbf{x}^{\mathbf{d}}$ instead of $\mathbf{x}^{\mathbf{d}}(\tau)$ and vice versa.

5. Examples

5.1 A Robot Arm Example for a MIMO SMFLC

5.1.1 Basic Equations

Let the basic equation describing the motion of a robot arm be

$$\mathbf{M}(\mathbf{q}) \cdot \ddot{\mathbf{q}} + \mathbf{N}(\mathbf{q}, \dot{\mathbf{q}}) = \mathbf{u}, \tag{5.1}$$

where

$\mathbf{q}$ is a $(k \times 1)$ position vector,
$\dot{\mathbf{q}}$ is a $(k \times 1)$ velocity vector,
$\ddot{\mathbf{q}}$ is a $(k \times 1)$ acceleration vector,
$\mathbf{M}(\mathbf{q})$ is a $(k \times k)$ matrix of inertia (invertible)
$\mathbf{N}(\mathbf{q}, \dot{\mathbf{q}})$ is a $(k \times 1)$ vector of damping, centrifugal, coriolis, gravitational forces,
$\mathbf{u}$ is a $(k \times 1)$ vector of generalized forces and torques.

Furthermore, let the open loop system (5.1) have k degrees of freedom (d.o.f.). Normally, $k = 6$, so that the number of d.o.f. in the Cartesian space $\mathbf{R}_{\mathbf{x}}^{\mathbf{k}}$ is equal to the number of d.o.f. in the joint space $\mathbf{R}_{\mathbf{q}}^{\mathbf{k}}$. The control problem is to follow a given trajectory $\mathbf{q}^{\mathbf{d}}(t)$ and to produce a torque vector $\mathbf{u}$ such that the tracking error approaches 0 as $t \to \infty$. The control design steps are related to the design steps of the TISO SMFLC in Sect. 3.5.2:

1. Introduction of the overall control law,
2. Choice of the fuzzy values for the normalized controller inputs s_{iN} and the controller outputs $u_{\mathrm{fuzz}iN}$,
3. Design of the fuzzy rules for each link,
4. Choice of the slopes λ_i of the sliding lines $s_i = 0$,
5. Choice of the normalization factors N_{ei} and $N_{\dot{e}i}$ for e_{q_i} and $\dot{e}_{q_i}$,
6. Choice of the upper bounds from (3.136) in Sect. 3.6,
7. Design $|K_{i\mathrm{fuzz}}|_{\mathrm{max}}$.

Introduction of the overall control law

In order to solve the tracking control problem we introduce the control torques

$$\mathbf{u} = \hat{\mathbf{M}}(\mathbf{q}) \cdot \tilde{\mathbf{u}} + \hat{\mathbf{N}}(\mathbf{q}, \dot{\mathbf{q}}), \tag{5.2}$$

where $\hat{\mathbf{M}}$ and $\hat{\mathbf{N}}$ are estimates of $\mathbf{M}$ and $\mathbf{N}$, respectively. Substituting (5.2) into (5.1) yields

$$\ddot{\mathbf{q}} = \mathbf{M}(\mathbf{q})^{-1} \cdot (\hat{\mathbf{M}}(\mathbf{q}) \cdot \tilde{\mathbf{u}} + \Delta\mathbf{N}), \tag{5.3}$$

where

$\tilde{\mathbf{u}}$ is the control law and $\Delta\mathbf{N} = \hat{\mathbf{N}}(\mathbf{q}, \dot{\mathbf{q}}) - \mathbf{N}(\mathbf{q}, \dot{\mathbf{q}})$.

According to (3.118) in Sect. 3.6 we choose the components of the control law in (5.3) as

$$\tilde{u}_i = G_i(\mathbf{q}, \dot{\mathbf{q}}) \cdot (\hat{u}_i + u_{\mathrm{fuzz}i}) \tag{5.4}$$

where $u_{\mathrm{fuzz}i}$ is the fuzzy control part and $G_i(\mathbf{q}, \dot{\mathbf{q}})$ is the gain to be determined.

Choice of the fuzzy values for s_{iN} and $u_{\mathrm{fuzz}iN}$

The structure of the SMFLCs for link 1 and link 2 are chosen to be identical. The membership functions for both s_{iN} and $u_{\mathrm{fuzz}iN}$ $(i = 1, 2)$ are defined within the interval $(-255, 255)$. Figure 5.1 shows the 9 membership functions chosen for s_{iN} and $u_{\mathrm{fuzz}iN}$, respectively. They are distributed in such a way that the gain around $s_{iN} = 0$ is small in contrast to higher values of $s_{iN} = 0$.

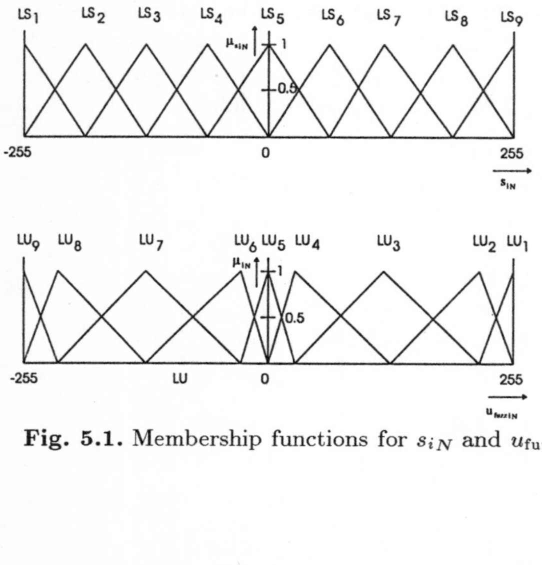

Fig. 5.1. Membership functions for s_{iN} and $u_{\mathrm{fuzz}iN}$

Design of the fuzzy rules for each link

Each fuzzy control part $u_{\mathrm{fuzz}iN}$ is determined by the set of fuzzy rules

R_{ci}: *if* s_{iN} is LS_i *then* $u_{\mathrm{fuzz}iN}$ is LU_i.

The corresponding analytical expression for $u_{\mathrm{fuzz}i}$ is given as

$$u_{\mathrm{fuzz}i} = -K_{i\mathrm{fuzz}}(\mathbf{q}, \dot{\mathbf{q}}) \cdot \mathrm{sgn}(s_i) \quad (5.5)$$

where

$$\begin{aligned} s_i &= \lambda \cdot e_{q_i} + \dot{e}_{q_i} \qquad i = 1, \ldots, k, \\ e_{q_i} &= q_i - q_i^d, \end{aligned}$$

and q_i^d is the desired value of q_i.

Choice of the slopes λ_i of the sliding lines $s_i = 0$

The slopes λ_i of the sliding lines $s_i = 0$ have been chosen to be identical for both links. λ_i represents the bandwidth of the i-th closed loop subsystem and has to be chosen to be much less than the minimum of unmodeled frequencies $\nu_{u\min}$:

$$\lambda \ll \nu_{u\min}. \quad (5.6)$$

Choice of the normalization factors for e_{q_i} and $\dot{e}_{q_i}$

The choice of the normalization factors N_{ei} and $N_{\dot{e}i}$ for e_{q_i} and $\dot{e}_{q_i}$ depends on λ and on the range for e_{q_i} or $\dot{e}_{q_i}$. For example, once $N_{\dot{e}i}$ is determined so N_{ei} can be calculated by

$$N_{ei} = \lambda_i \cdot N_{\dot{e}i}. \quad (5.7)$$

Choice of the upper bounds and design $|K_{i\mathrm{fuzz}}|_{\max}$

The control term $\hat{u}_i$ in (5.4) is given as

$$\hat{u}_i = \ddot{q}_i^d - \lambda \cdot \dot{e}_{q_i}. \quad (5.8)$$

Equation (5.3) can be rewritten as

$$\ddot{\mathbf{q}} = \mathbf{M}(\mathbf{q})^{-1} \cdot \Delta\mathbf{N} + \mathbf{M}(\mathbf{q})^{-1} \cdot \hat{\mathbf{M}}(\mathbf{q}) \cdot \tilde{\mathbf{u}}. \quad (5.9)$$

Comparing (5.9) and (3.121) in Sect. 3.6 we obtain the following correspondences

$\mathbf{M}(\mathbf{q})^{-1} \cdot \Delta\mathbf{N}$ corresponds to $\Delta\mathbf{f}$
$\mathbf{M}(\mathbf{q})^{-1}$ corresponds to $\mathbf{B}$
$\hat{\mathbf{M}}(\mathbf{q})^{-1}$ corresponds to $\hat{\mathbf{B}}^{-1}$.

$\mathbf{M}^{-1}$ and $\hat{\mathbf{M}}$ are symmetrical matrices with

$$\begin{aligned} \mathbf{M}^{-1} &= (\mathbf{m}_1^{-1}, \ldots, \mathbf{m}_k^{-1})^T, \text{ and} \\ \hat{\mathbf{M}} &= (\hat{\mathbf{m}}_1, \ldots, \hat{\mathbf{m}}_k)^T, \end{aligned} \tag{5.10}$$

where $(\mathbf{m}_i^{-1})^T \cdot (\hat{\mathbf{m}}_\mathbf{i}) > 0, \qquad i = 1, \ldots, k$. Setting the bounds

$$0 \leq \beta_i^{\min} \leq (\mathbf{m}_i^{-1})^T \cdot (\hat{\mathbf{m}}_i) \leq \beta_i^{\max}, \tag{5.11}$$

we obtain the multiplier G_i of (3.124) and the gain margin β_i of (3.125) in Sect. 3.6, respectively.

From (5.9) we obtain

$$\ddot{q}_i = \Delta f_i + \sum_{j=1}^{k} (\mathbf{m}_j^{-1})^T \cdot (\hat{\mathbf{m}}_i) \cdot \tilde{u}_j, \tag{5.12}$$

where

$$\Delta f_i = \sum_{r=1}^{k} m_{ir}^{-1} \cdot \Delta N_r. \tag{5.13}$$

With the reaching condition (3.116) in Sect. 3.6 and (5.6) we have,

$$\dot{s}_i = \ddot{q}_i - \ddot{q}_i^d + \lambda \cdot \dot{e}_{q_i}. \tag{5.14}$$

Hence

$$s_i \cdot [\Delta f_i - \ddot{q}_i^d + \lambda \cdot \dot{e}_{q_i} + \sum_{j=1}^{k} (\mathbf{m}_j^{-1})^T \cdot (\hat{\mathbf{m}}_i) \cdot \tilde{u}_j)] \leq -\eta_i \cdot |s_i|. \tag{5.15}$$

Finally we obtain from (3.136) in Sect. 3.6

$$K_{i_{\text{fuzz}}}|_{\max} > \beta_i \cdot \left(F_i + (1 - \beta_i^{-1}) \cdot \hat{U}_i + \sum_{j \neq i} G_j \cdot B_{ij} \cdot Q_j + \eta_i \right), \tag{5.16}$$

where we define the upper bounds

$$\begin{aligned} &|\Delta f_i| < F_i \\ &|\hat{u}_i| < \hat{U}_i \\ &|(\mathbf{m}_i^{-1})^T \cdot (\hat{\mathbf{m}}_i)| < M_{ij}; \quad i \neq j \\ &|\ddot{q}_j^d| < Q_j. \end{aligned}$$

5.1.2 The Two-Link Robot Arm

In this section we concentrate on the equation of motion of the two-link robot arm and on the computation of the maximum values $K_{1_{\text{fuzz}}}|_{\max}$ and $K_{2_{\text{fuzz}}}|_{\max}$ of $u_{\text{fuzz}i}$.

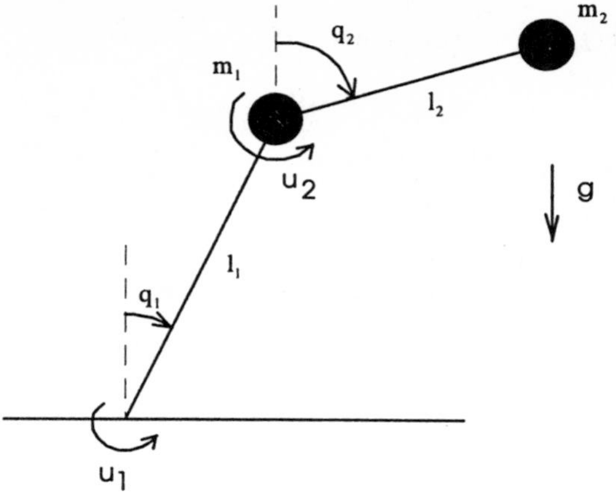

Fig. 5.2. Scheme of a two-link robot arm

The equation of motion. Consider the following two-link robot arm with its masses concentrated at the ends of each link and where the motor inertias are neglected (see Fig. 5.2):

According to (5.1) we have the equations of motion

$$\mathbf{M}(\mathbf{q}) \cdot \ddot{\mathbf{q}} = -\mathbf{N}(\mathbf{q}, \dot{\mathbf{q}}) + \mathbf{u}. \tag{5.17}$$

In this equation

$$\mathbf{M}(\mathbf{q}) = \begin{pmatrix} m_{11} & m_{12} \\ m_{21} & m_{22} \end{pmatrix} = \tag{5.18}$$

$$\begin{pmatrix} (m_1 + m_2) \cdot l_1^2 & m_2 \cdot l_1 \cdot l_2 \cdot \cos(q_1 - q_2) \\ m_2 \cdot l_1 \cdot l_2 \cdot \cos(q_1 - q_2) & m_2 l_2^2 \end{pmatrix},$$

and

$$\mathbf{N}(\mathbf{q}, \dot{\mathbf{q}}) = \begin{pmatrix} n_1 \\ n_2 \end{pmatrix} = \tag{5.19}$$

$$\begin{pmatrix} \dot{q}_2^2 \cdot m_2 \cdot l_1 \cdot l_2 \cdot \sin(q_1 - q_2) - (m_1 + m_2) \cdot g \cdot l_1 \cdot \sin q_1 + K_{q1} \cdot \dot{q}_1 \\ -\dot{q}_1^2 \cdot m_2 \cdot l_1 \cdot l_2 \cdot \sin(q_1 - q_2) - m_2 \cdot g \cdot l_2 \cdot \sin q_2 + K_{q2} \cdot \dot{q}_2 \end{pmatrix},$$

where K_{q1} and K_{q2} are the damping coefficients for the coordinates q_1 and q_2, respectively.

Computation of the maximum values $K_{1_{\mathrm{fuzz}}}|_{\max}$ and $K_{2_{\mathrm{fuzz}}}|_{\max}$. The inverse of $\mathbf{M}(\mathbf{q})$ in the control law (5.2) is given as

$$\mathbf{M}^{-1}(\mathbf{q}) = \begin{pmatrix} m_{11}^{-1} & m_{12}^{-1} \\ m_{21}^{-1} & m_{22}^{-1} \end{pmatrix} = \tag{5.20}$$

$$\begin{pmatrix} m_2 l_2^2/D & -m_2 \cdot l_1 \cdot l_2 \cdot \cos(q_1 - q_2)/D \\ -m_2 \cdot l_1 \cdot l_2 \cdot \cos(q_1 - q_2)/D & (m_1 + m_2) \cdot l_1^2/D \end{pmatrix},$$

with

$$D = m_2 \cdot l_1^2 \cdot l_2^2 \cdot (m_1 + m_2 \cdot \sin^2(q_1 - q_2)). \tag{5.21}$$

Then we have

$$\mathbf{M}^{-1}(\mathbf{q})\Delta\mathbf{N} = \begin{pmatrix} \Delta f_1 \\ \Delta f_2 \end{pmatrix} = \begin{pmatrix} m_{11}^{-1} \cdot \Delta n_1 + m_{12}^{-1} \cdot \Delta n_2 \\ m_{21}^{-1} \cdot \Delta n_1 + m_{22}^{-1} \cdot \Delta n_2 \end{pmatrix}, \tag{5.22}$$

where $\Delta n_1 = \hat{n}_1 - n_1$ and $\Delta n_2 = \hat{n}_2 - n_2$. We obtain the mixed products $(\mathbf{m}_j^{-1})^T \cdot (\hat{\mathbf{m}}_i)$ for $i \neq j$ from (5.15) as follows:

$$\begin{aligned} m_{ji} &= (m_{11}^{-1}, m_{21}^{-1}) \cdot \begin{pmatrix} \hat{m}_{12} \\ \hat{m}_{22} \end{pmatrix} = (m_{11}^{-1} \cdot \hat{m}_{12} + m_{21}^{-1} \cdot \hat{m}_{22}), \\ m_{ij} &= (m_{12}^{-1}, m_{22}^{-1}) \cdot \begin{pmatrix} \hat{m}_{11} \\ \hat{m}_{21} \end{pmatrix} = (m_{12}^{-1} \cdot \hat{m}_{11} + m_{22}^{-1} \cdot \hat{m}_{21}). \end{aligned} \tag{5.23}$$

For the products $(\mathbf{m}_i^{-1})^T \cdot (\hat{\mathbf{m}}_i)$ we obtain

$$\begin{aligned} m_{ii1} &= (m_{11}^{-1}, m_{21}^{-1}) \cdot \begin{pmatrix} \hat{m}_{11} \\ \hat{m}_{21} \end{pmatrix} = (m_{11}^{-1} \cdot \hat{m}_{11} + m_{21}^{-1} \cdot \hat{m}_{21}), \\ m_{ii2} &= (m_{12}^{-1}, m_{22}^{-1}) \cdot \begin{pmatrix} \hat{m}_{12} \\ \hat{m}_{22} \end{pmatrix} = (m_{12}^{-1} \cdot \hat{m}_{12} + m_{22}^{-1} \cdot \hat{m}_{22}). \end{aligned} \tag{5.24}$$

From (5.24) we establish $\beta_i^{\min}$ and $\beta_i^{\max}$:

$$\begin{aligned} &\beta_1^{\min} \leq (m_{11}^{-1} \cdot \hat{m}_{11} + m_{21}^{-1} \cdot \hat{m}_{21}) \leq \beta_1^{\max}, \\ &\beta_2^{\min} \leq (m_{12}^{-1} \cdot \hat{m}_{12} + m_{22}^{-1} \cdot \hat{m}_{22}) \leq \beta_2^{\max}. \end{aligned} \tag{5.25}$$

Then we fix G_i as

$$G_1 = \frac{1}{\sqrt{\beta_1^{\min} \cdot \beta_1^{\max}}}; \qquad G_2 = \frac{1}{\sqrt{\beta_2^{\min} \cdot \beta_2^{\max}}}, \tag{5.26}$$

and β_i as

$$\beta_1 = \sqrt{\frac{\beta_1^{\max}}{\beta_1^{\min}}}; \quad \beta_2 = \sqrt{\frac{\beta_2^{\max}}{\beta_2^{\min}}}. \tag{5.27}$$

Then, the control torque $\mathbf{u}$ can easily be obtained from (5.2) as

$$\mathbf{u} = \begin{pmatrix} \hat{m}_{11} & \hat{m}_{12} \\ \hat{m}_{21} & \hat{m}_{22} \end{pmatrix} \cdot \begin{pmatrix} \tilde{u}_1 \\ \tilde{u}_2 \end{pmatrix} + \begin{pmatrix} \hat{n}_1 \\ \hat{n}_2 \end{pmatrix}, \tag{5.28}$$

where

$$\tilde{u}_1 = G_1 \cdot (\hat{u}_1 - K_{1_{\rm fuzz}}|_{\rm max} \cdot \mathrm{sgn}(s_1))$$
$$\tilde{u}_2 = G_2 \cdot (\hat{u}_2 - K_{2_{\rm fuzz}}|_{\rm max} \cdot \mathrm{sgn}(s_2))$$

and where

$$\hat{u}_1 = \ddot{q}_{1d} - \lambda \cdot \dot{e}_{q1},$$
$$\hat{u}_2 = \ddot{q}_{2d} - \lambda \cdot \dot{e}_{q2},$$
$$s_1 = \lambda \cdot e_{q1} + \dot{e}_{q1},$$
$$s_2 = \lambda \cdot e_{q2} + \dot{e}_{q2}.$$

In addition we have to determine the upper bounds $F_i, \hat{U}_i, M_{ij}$, and Q_i $(i, j = 1, 2)$:

$$|\Delta f_1| \leq F_1; \qquad |\Delta f_2| < F_2,$$
$$|\hat{u}_1| \leq \hat{U}_1; \qquad |\hat{u}_2| < \hat{U}_2. \tag{5.29}$$

From (5.23) we obtain

$$|m_{11}^{-1} \cdot \hat{m}_{12} + m_{21}^{-1} \cdot \hat{m}_{22}| < M_{12},$$
$$|m_{12}^{-1} \cdot \hat{m}_{11} + m_{22}^{-1} \cdot \hat{m}_{21}| < M_{21}, \tag{5.30}$$

and finally

$$\ddot{q}_1^d < Q_1,$$
$$\ddot{q}_2^d < Q_2. \tag{5.31}$$

Then, we obtain the maximum values $K_{i_{\rm fuzz}}|_{\rm max}$ as

$$K_{1_{\rm fuzz}}|_{\rm max} > \beta_1 \cdot \left(F_1 + (1 - \beta_1^{-1}) \cdot \hat{U}_1 + \sum_{j \neq i} G_j \cdot M_{1j} \cdot Q_j + \eta_1 \right)$$
$$K_{2_{\rm fuzz}}|_{\rm max} > \beta_2 \cdot \left(F_2 + (1 - \beta_2^{-1}) \cdot \hat{U}_2 + \sum_{j \neq i} G_j \cdot M_{2j} \cdot Q_j + \eta_2 \right). \tag{5.32}$$

Numerical example. The mechanical parameters of the robot are

$m_1 = 1$ kg, $\hat{m}_1 \in [0.9, 1.1]$ kg
$m_2 = 2$ kg, $\hat{m}_2 \in [1.8, 2.2]$ kg
$l_1 = 0.2$ m, $\hat{l}_1 \in [0.18, 0.22]$ m
$l_2 = 0.2$ m, $\hat{l}_2 \in [0.18, 0.22]$ m
$K_{q1} = 10$ kg m^2 s^{-1}, $\hat{K}_{q1} \in [9, 11]$ kg m^2 s^{-1}
$K_{q2} = 10$ kg m^2 s^{-1}, $\hat{K}_{q2} \in [9, 11]$ kg m^2 s^{-1}

where $\hat{}$ denotes the estimate of the corresponding parameter. The restrictions of the angles and their velocities are

$$
\begin{aligned}
q_1 &\in [-1.047, 1.047] \text{ rad}, \\
q_2 &\in [0.523, 2.617] \text{ rad}, \\
\dot{q}_1 &\in [-1.57, 1.57] \text{ rad s}^{-1}, \\
\dot{q}_2 &\in [-1.57, 1.57] \text{ rad s}^{-1}.
\end{aligned} \tag{5.33}
$$

The minimum of unmodeled frequencies is assumed to be $\nu_{u\min} = 100\ \text{s}^{-1}$. Now we determine the bounds of the right hand side of (5.32). From that we obtain the maximum values of $K_{1_{\text{fuzz}}}$ and $K_{1_{\text{fuzz}}}$ that suffice for a stable motion of the robot within the fuzzy regions determined by the restictions (5.33). Tables 5.1.2 and 5.1.2 show the calculated values m_{ii1}, m_{ii2}, m_{ji}, m_{ij}, Δf_1, Δf_2 of (5.22–5.24) for the lower and upper bounds of the parameter estimates and the lower and upper restrictions of q_i and $\dot{q}_i$ $(i = 1, 2)$.

Table 5.1. Values of m_{ii1}, m_{ii2}, m_{ji}, m_{ij}, Δf_1, Δf_2 for $\hat{m}_1 = 1.1$ kg, $\hat{m}_2 = 2.2$ kg, $\hat{l}_1 = 0.22$ m, $\hat{l}_2 = 0.22$ m, $\hat{K}_{q1} = 11$ kg m^2 s^{-1}, $\hat{K}_{q2} = 11$ kg m^2 s^{-1}

$\dot{q}_1$	-1.57	-1.57	-1.57	0	0	0	1.57	1.57	1.57
$\dot{q}_2$	-1.57	0	1.57	-1.57	0	1.57	-1.57	0	1.57
$m_{ii1\max}$	1.4	1.4	1.4	1.4	1.4	1.4	1.4	1.4	1.4
$m_{ii1\min}$	1.4	1.4	1.4	1.4	1.4	1.4	1.4	1.4	1.4
$m_{ii2\max}$	1.4	1.4	1.4	1.4	1.4	1.4	1.4	1.4	1.4
$m_{ii2\min}$	1.4	1.4	1.4	1.4	1.4	1.4	1.4	1.4	1.4
$m_{ji\max}$	0	0	0	0	0	0	0	0	0
$m_{ji\min}$	0	0	0	0	0	0	0	0	0
$m_{ij\max}$	0	0	0	0	0	0	0	0	0
$m_{ij\min}$	0	0	0	0	0	0	0	0	0
$\Delta f_{1\max}$	20	0	20	50	10	45	80	45	80
$\Delta f_{1\min}$	-70	-45	-70	-50	-10	-45	-10	5	-10
$\Delta f_{2\max}$	0	50	100	-10	10	60	-10	45	90
$\Delta f_{2\min}$	-90	-50	0	-60	-10	10	-100	-45	10

From these values we obtain

$$|m_{ii1}|_{\max} = 1.4,\ |m_{ii1}|_{\min} = 0.75,\ |m_{ii2}|_{\max} = 1.4,\ |m_{ii2}|_{\min} = 0.75,$$

$$|m_{ji}|_{\max} = 2,\ |m_{ij}|_{\max} = 5,\ |\Delta f_1|_{\max} = 100,\ |\Delta f_2|_{\max} = 100,$$

so that

$$
\begin{aligned}
&\beta_1^{\min} = |m_{ii1}|_{\min} = 0.75,\ \beta_1^{\max} = |m_{ii1}|_{\max} = 1.4, \\
&\beta_2^{\min} = |m_{ii2}|_{\min} = 0.75,\ \beta_2^{\max} = |m_{ii2}|_{\max} = 1.4.
\end{aligned}
$$

From (5.26) and (5.27) we obtain

$$
\begin{aligned}
&G_1 = G_2 = 0.975, \\
&\beta_1 = \beta_2 = 1.366.
\end{aligned}
$$

Further we obtain from (5.29) and (5.29)

Table 5.2. Values of m_{ii1}, m_{ii2}, m_{ji}, m_{ij}, Δf_1, Δf_2 for $\hat{m}_1 = 0.9$ kg, $\hat{m}_2 = 1.8$ kg, $\hat{l}_1 = 0.18$ m, $\hat{l}_2 = 0.18$ m, $\hat{K}_{q1} = 9$ kg m^2 s^{-1}, $\hat{K}_{q2} = 9$ kg m^2 s^{-1}

$\dot{q}_1$	-1.57	-1.57	-1.57	0	0	0	1.57	1.57	1.57
$\dot{q}_2$	-1.57	0	1.57	-1.57	0	1.57	-1.57	0	1.57
$m_{ii1\,\max}$	0.75	0.75	0.75	0.75	0.75	0.75	0.75	0.75	0.75
$m_{ii1\,\min}$	0.75	0.75	0.75	0.75	0.75	0.75	0.75	0.75	0.75
$m_{ii2\,\max}$	0.75	0.75	0.75	0.75	0.75	0.75	0.75	0.75	0.75
$m_{ii2\,\min}$	0.75	1.4	0.75	0.75	0.75	0.75	0.75	1.4	0.75
$m_{ji\,\max}$	2	2	0	2	2	2	0	2	2
$m_{ji\,\min}$	-2	-2	-2	0	0	-2	-2	0	-2
$m_{ij\,\max}$	5	5	5	5	5	5	5	5	5
$m_{ij\,\min}$	-5	-5	-5	-5	-5	-5	-5	-5	-5
$\Delta f_{1\,\max}$	100	50	90	50	10	45	10	-5	20
$\Delta f_{1\,\min}$	-5	5	-10	-50	-10	-45	-80	-45	-80
$\Delta f_{2\,\max}$	100	45	-10	60	7.5	-10	100	45	-10
$\Delta f_{2\,\min}$	10	-45	-90	1	-7.5	-55	10	-45	-90

$$F_1 = F_2 = 100,$$
$$M_{12} = 2,\ M_{21} = 5.$$

We choose furthermore

$$\ddot{q}_1^d = \ddot{q}_1^d = 0,$$
$$\lambda = 10,$$
$$\eta_1 = \eta_2 = 1,$$
$$|\dot{e}_{q1}|_{\max} = |\dot{e}_{q2}|_{\max} = 1.57.$$

Then we have

$$\hat{U}_1 = \hat{U}_2 = 15.7.$$

Finally, we choose

$$Q_1 = Q_2 = 1.$$

With that we obtain from (5.32)

$$K_{1\text{fuzz}}|_{\max} > 1.366 \cdot (100 + (1 - 0.732) \cdot 15.7 + 0.975 \cdot 2 \cdot 1 + 1) = 146.4,$$
$$K_{2\text{fuzz}}|_{\max} > 1.366 \cdot (100 + (1 - 0.732) \cdot 15.7 + 0.975 \cdot 5 \cdot 1 + 1) = 150.4.$$

For another case, where there is no model for compensation and for the damping coefficients $\hat{K}_{q1} = \hat{K}_{q2} = 0.5$ kg m^2 s^{-1} we obtain the higher maximum values

$$K_{1\text{fuzz}}|_{\max} = 252,$$
$$K_{2\text{fuzz}}|_{\max} = 227,$$

because of higher upper bounds F_i. Again, it has to be emphasized here that the transfer characteristics of the pure SMFLCs for links 1 and 2 are chosen to be identical (see Fig. 5.3). The characteristics show the dependence of the normalized value $K_{i\text{fuzz}} \cdot \text{sgn}(s_i)|_N$ on the normalized value s_{iN}. The

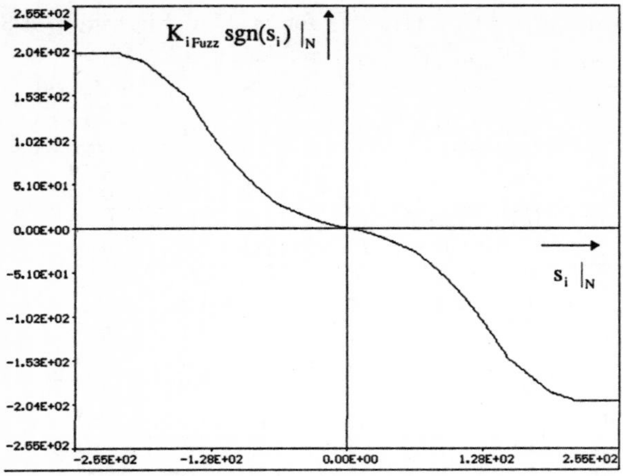

Fig. 5.3. Transfer characteristics of the SMFLC

membership functions (see Fig. 5.1) were chosen such that for small values of s_i the gain is smaller than for bigger values of s_i.

The robot motion can be divided into two separate phases (see Fig. 5.4). Phase 1 denotes the motion from $(q_1^d, q_2^d) = (0, 1.57)$ to $(q_1^d, q_2^d) = (-0.5, 2.05)$. Phase 2 denotes the motion from $(q_1^d, q_2^d) = (-0.5, 2.05)$ to $(q_1^d, q_2^d) = (0, 1.57)$. Without using any compensation model and for $\hat{K}_{q1} = \hat{K}_{q2} = 0.5$ kg m^2 s^{-1} we obtain a phase plane for link 1 as shown in Fig. 5.5.

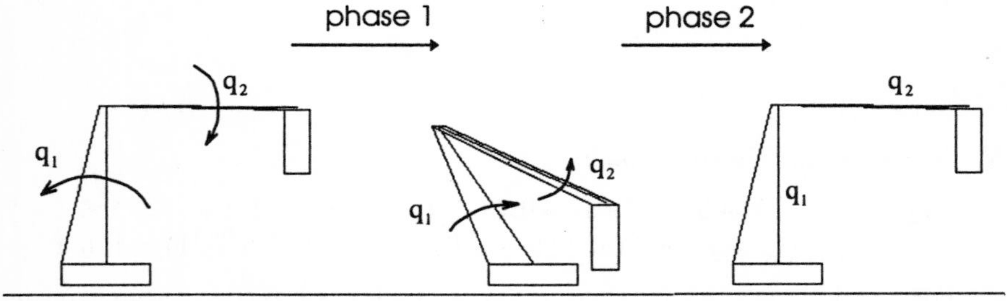

Fig. 5.4. Two phases of robot motion

The time plot of Fig. 5.6 shows the corresponding torque u_1 and the error e_{q_1}. Observe the clear deviation of the error from zero in the stationary phase.

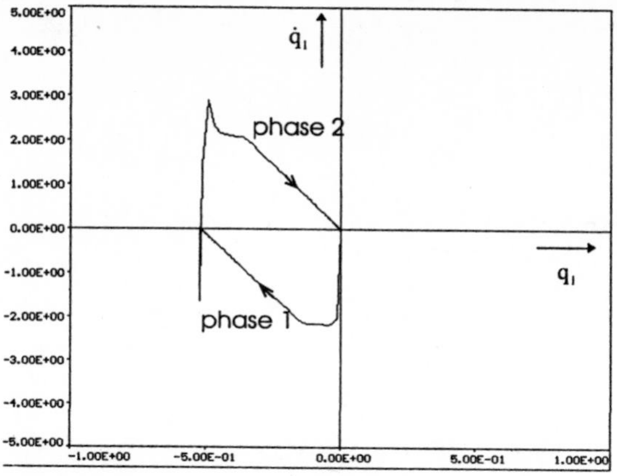

Fig. 5.5. Phase plane for link 1

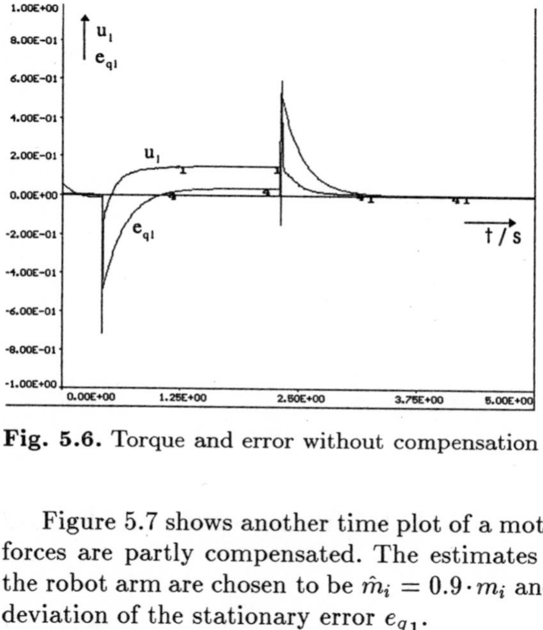

Fig. 5.6. Torque and error without compensation (link 1)

Figure 5.7 shows another time plot of a motion at which the gravitational forces are partly compensated. The estimates of the masses and lengths of the robot arm are chosen to be $\hat{m}_i = 0.9 \cdot m_i$ and $\hat{l}_i = 0.9 \cdot l_i$. Note the smaller deviation of the stationary error e_{q_1}.

Figures 5.8–5.10 show the corresponding phase planes and time plots for link 2.

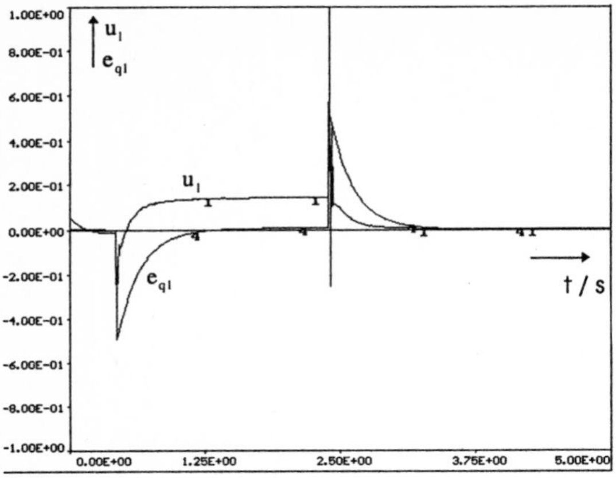

Fig. 5.7. Torque and error with compensation of the gravitational forces (link 1)

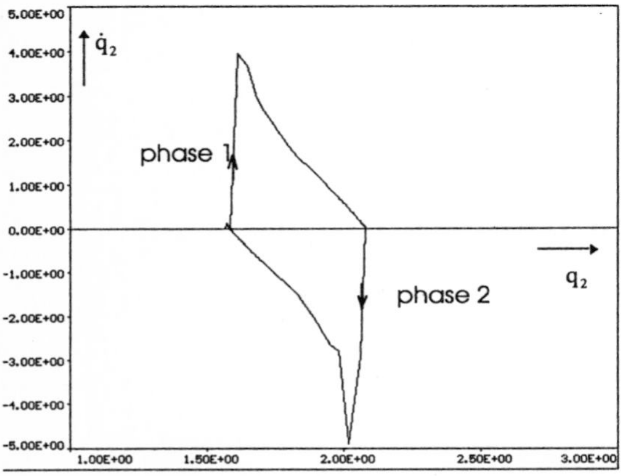

Fig. 5.8. Phase plane for link 2

5.2 Robotic Example for a MIMO Takagi–Sugeno FLC-2

5.2.1 Basic Equations

The example deals with the same two-link robot arm described in the last section. In order to apply the FLC-2 approach we rewrite the equations of motion (5.1) as the following set of state equations

$$\mathbf{M}(\mathbf{x}) \cdot \dot{\mathbf{x}} + \mathbf{N}(\mathbf{x}) = \mathbf{u}(\mathbf{x}), \tag{5.34}$$

with

$\mathbf{x} = (x_1, \ldots, x_n)^T = (q_1, \dot{q}_1, \ldots, q_k, \dot{q}_k)^T$ is the $(n \times 1)$ state vector $(n = 2k)$,

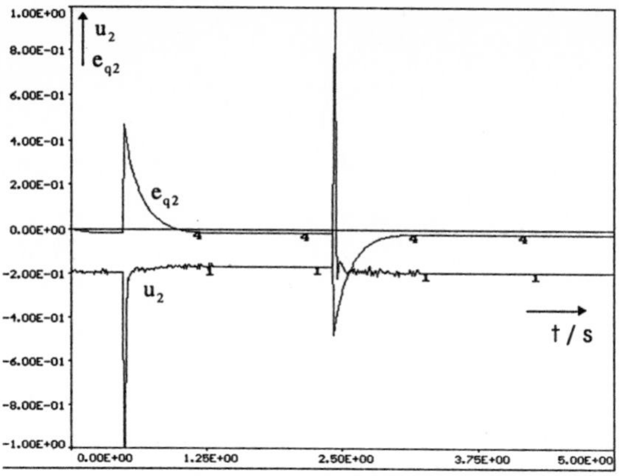

Fig. 5.9. Torque and error without compensation (link 2)

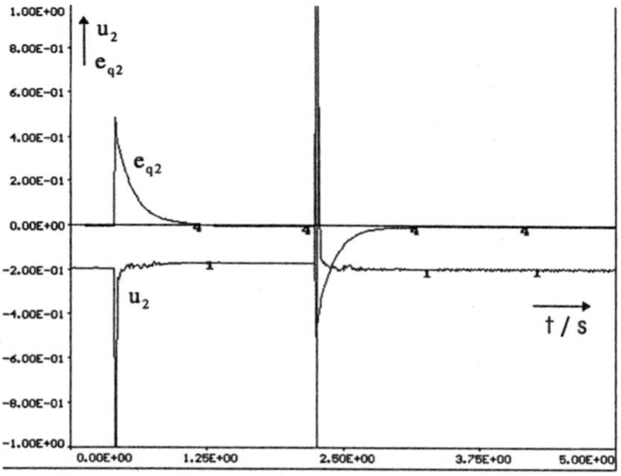

Fig. 5.10. Torque and error with compensation of the gravitational forces (link 2)

$\mathbf{u}(\mathbf{x})$ is the $(n \times 1)$ vector of generalized forces and torques,
$\mathbf{M}(\mathbf{x})$ is the $(n \times n)$ matrix of inertia (invertible),
$\mathbf{N}(\mathbf{x})$ is the $(n \times 1)$ vector of damping, centrifugal, coriolis, gravitational forces.

The Lyapunov-linearization of (5.34) around a desired operating point $\mathbf{x^d}$ or a slowly varying trajectory $\mathbf{x^d}(\tau)$ results in

$$\mathbf{M}(\mathbf{x^d} + \delta\mathbf{x}) \cdot (\dot{\mathbf{x}} + \delta\dot{\mathbf{x}}) = -\mathbf{N}(\mathbf{x^d} + \delta\mathbf{x}) + \mathbf{u^d} + \delta\mathbf{u} \tag{5.35}$$

where

$\mathbf{x} = \mathbf{x^d} + \delta\mathbf{x}$,
$\mathbf{u} = \mathbf{u^d} + \delta\mathbf{u}$,

$\mathbf{x^d}$ is the desired state vector,
$\mathbf{u^d}$ is the control vector corresponding to $\mathbf{x^d}$,
$\delta\mathbf{x}$ is the error,
$\delta\mathbf{u}$ is the control input error.

In what follows we neglect higher-order terms of $\delta\mathbf{x}$ and $\delta\mathbf{u}$ and assume further that

$$\mathbf{M}(\mathbf{x^d} + \delta\mathbf{x}) \cdot \dot{\mathbf{x}} \approx \mathbf{M}(\mathbf{x^d}) \cdot \dot{\mathbf{x}}. \tag{5.36}$$

This simplification cane be done for slow changes of $\mathbf{x^d}$ and, with that, of $\mathbf{M}(\mathbf{x^d})$. Then we obtain from (5.35)

$$\mathbf{M}(\mathbf{x^d}) \cdot (\dot{\mathbf{x}}^\mathbf{d} + \delta\dot{\mathbf{x}}) = -\mathbf{N}(\mathbf{x^d}) + \mathbf{A}(\mathbf{x^d}) \cdot \delta\mathbf{x} + \mathbf{u^d} + \delta\mathbf{u}, \tag{5.37}$$

where

$$\mathbf{A}(\mathbf{x_d}) = -\left.\frac{\partial \mathbf{N}(\mathbf{x})}{\partial \mathbf{x}}\right|_{\mathbf{x}=\mathbf{x^d}} \text{ is the Jacobian.}$$

From (5.34) we directly obtain the specific solution

$$\mathbf{M}(\mathbf{x^d}) \cdot \dot{\mathbf{x}}^\mathbf{d} = -\mathbf{N}(\mathbf{x^d}) + \mathbf{u^d}, \tag{5.38}$$

so that (5.37) transforms into

$$\mathbf{M}(\mathbf{x^d}) \cdot \delta\dot{\mathbf{x}} = \mathbf{A}(\mathbf{x^d}) \cdot \delta\mathbf{x} + \delta\mathbf{u} \tag{5.39}$$

or equivalently into

$$\delta\dot{\mathbf{x}} = \mathbf{M}^{-1}(\mathbf{x^d}) \cdot \mathbf{A}(\mathbf{x^d}) \cdot \delta\mathbf{x} + \mathbf{M}^{-1}(\mathbf{x^d}) \cdot \delta\mathbf{u}. \tag{5.40}$$

This is a linear state equation with an equilibrium point at $\delta\mathbf{x} = \mathbf{0}$ for $\delta\mathbf{u} = 0$. In (5.40) we introduce the linear control law

$$\delta\mathbf{u} = \mathbf{K}(\mathbf{x^d}) \cdot \delta\mathbf{x}, \tag{5.41}$$

and thus we obtain

$$\delta\dot{\mathbf{x}} = \mathbf{M}^{-1}(\mathbf{x^d}) \cdot (\mathbf{A}(\mathbf{x^d}) + \mathbf{K}(\mathbf{x^d})) \cdot \delta\mathbf{x}. \tag{5.42}$$

The control law (5.41) is now reformulated into

$$\mathbf{u} = \mathbf{u^d} + \mathbf{K}(\mathbf{x^d}) \cdot \delta\mathbf{x}, \tag{5.43}$$

where the desired control input $\mathbf{u^d}$ is chosen to be

$$\mathbf{u^d} = \mathbf{M}(\mathbf{x^d}) \cdot \dot{\mathbf{x}}^\mathbf{d} + \mathbf{N}(\mathbf{x^d}). \tag{5.44}$$

Since the actual values of $\mathbf{M}(\mathbf{x^d})$ and $\mathbf{N}(\mathbf{x^d})$ can only be estimated, one has to take into account the estimate $\hat{\mathbf{u}}^\mathbf{d}$ instead of $\mathbf{u^d}$, that is,

$$\hat{\mathbf{u}}^\mathbf{d} = \hat{\mathbf{M}}(\mathbf{x^d}) \cdot \dot{\mathbf{x}}^\mathbf{d} + \hat{\mathbf{N}}(\mathbf{x^d}). \tag{5.45}$$

With that, the system equation (5.42) transforms into

$$\begin{aligned} \delta\dot{\mathbf{x}} &= \mathbf{M}^{-1}(\mathbf{x^d}) \cdot (\mathbf{A}(\mathbf{x^d}) + \mathbf{K}(\mathbf{x^d})) \cdot \delta\mathbf{x} + \mathbf{M}^{-1}(\mathbf{x^d}) \cdot \Delta\mathbf{u^d}, \\ \Delta\mathbf{u^d} &= \hat{\mathbf{u}}^\mathbf{d} - \mathbf{u^d} = (\hat{\mathbf{M}}(\mathbf{x^d}) - \mathbf{M}(\mathbf{x^d})) \cdot \dot{\mathbf{x}}^\mathbf{d} + (\hat{\mathbf{N}}(\mathbf{x^d}) - \mathbf{N}(\mathbf{x^d})). \end{aligned} \tag{5.46}$$

Observe that $\mathbf{M}(\mathbf{x^d})$ and $\mathbf{N}(\mathbf{x^d})$ should be estimated as accurately as possible in order not to invalidate the linearization results.

According to (4.36), every possible control law (5.41) in the bounded state space is now approximated by a Takagi–Sugeno FLC-2 that is represented by $\mathbf{M}$ individual control laws

$$\delta\mathbf{u} = \mathbf{K}(\mathbf{x^j}) \cdot \delta\mathbf{x} \quad \mathbf{j} = \mathbf{1}, \ldots, \mathbf{M}. \tag{5.47}$$

Considering (5.43) and (5.45), this control law can be reformulated as

$$\begin{aligned} \mathbf{u} &= \hat{\mathbf{u}}^{\mathbf{d}}(\mathbf{x^j}) + \mathbf{K}(\mathbf{x^j}) \cdot \delta\mathbf{x} \quad \mathbf{j} = \mathbf{1}, \ldots, \mathbf{M}, \\ \hat{\mathbf{u}}^{\mathbf{d}}(\mathbf{x^j}) &= \hat{\mathbf{M}}(\mathbf{x^j}) \cdot \dot{\mathbf{x}}^{\mathbf{d}} + \mathbf{N}(\mathbf{x^j}). \end{aligned} \tag{5.48}$$

The corresponding fuzzy controller rules are

$$R_{\mathrm{C}}^{\mathbf{j}}\text{: } \textit{if } \mathbf{x^d} = \mathbf{LX^j} \textit{ then } \mathbf{u} = \mathbf{K}(\mathbf{x^j}) \cdot (\mathbf{x} - \mathbf{x^d}) + \hat{\mathbf{M}}(\mathbf{x^i}) \cdot \dot{\mathbf{x}}^{\mathbf{d}} + \mathbf{N}(\mathbf{x^i}),$$

The fuzzy system rules that approximate (5.40) are

$$R_{\mathrm{S}}^{\mathbf{i}}\text{: } \textit{if } \mathbf{x^d} = \mathbf{LX^i} \textit{ then } \delta\dot{\mathbf{x}} = \mathbf{M^{-1}}(\mathbf{x^i}) \cdot \mathbf{A}(\mathbf{x^i}) \cdot \delta\mathbf{x} + \mathbf{M^{-1}}(\mathbf{x^i}) \cdot \delta\mathbf{u}$$

Following the results from Sect. 4.2.4 we obtain the approximated version of (5.46), that is,

$$\begin{aligned} \delta\dot{\mathbf{x}} &= \sum_{\mathbf{i}}\sum_{\mathbf{j}} w^{\mathbf{i}}(\mathbf{x^d}) \cdot w^{\mathbf{j}}(\mathbf{x^d}) \cdot \mathbf{M^{-1}}(\mathbf{x^i}) \cdot [(\mathbf{A}(\mathbf{x^i}) + \mathbf{K}(\mathbf{x^j})) \cdot \delta\mathbf{x} \\ &\quad + (\hat{\mathbf{M}}(\mathbf{x^j}) - \mathbf{M}(\mathbf{x^i})) \cdot \dot{\mathbf{x}}^{\mathbf{d}} + (\hat{\mathbf{N}}(\mathbf{x^j}) - \mathbf{N}(\mathbf{x^i}))]. \end{aligned} \tag{5.49}$$

In the following we assume the modeling error

$$\begin{aligned} \Delta &= \sum_{\mathbf{i}}\sum_{\mathbf{j}} w^{\mathbf{i}}(\mathbf{x^d}) \cdot w^{\mathbf{j}}(\mathbf{x^d}) \\ &\quad \cdot \mathbf{M^{-1}}(\mathbf{x^i}) \cdot [(\hat{\mathbf{M}}(\mathbf{x^j}) - \mathbf{M}(\mathbf{x^i})) \cdot \dot{\mathbf{x}}^{\mathbf{d}} + (\hat{\mathbf{N}}(\mathbf{x^j}) - \mathbf{N}(\mathbf{x^i}))] \end{aligned} \tag{5.50}$$

to be small enough to keep the linearization intact.

With regard to the design principles discussed in Sect. 4.2.4 we choose the control laws (5.48) in such a way that the system (5.40) is robustly stable regarding approximation errors. In this connection it is important to divide the state space into an appropriate number of fuzzy regions so that on the one hand the fuzzy approximation is fine enough and, on the other hand, the set of fuzzy controller rules is restricted to a reasonable size.

5.2.2 The Two-Link Robot Arm

In this section we refer to the robot structure of Sect. 5.1.2. According to (5.34) we have the equations of motion

$$\mathbf{M}(\mathbf{x}) \cdot \dot{\mathbf{x}} + \mathbf{N}(\mathbf{x}) = \mathbf{u}(\mathbf{x}) \tag{5.51}$$

where

$\mathbf{x} = (x_1, x_2, x_3, x_4)^T = (q_1, \dot{q}_1, q_2, \dot{q}_2)^T$ is the (4×1) state vector
$\mathbf{u}(\mathbf{x})$ is the (4×1) vector of generalized forces and torques
$\mathbf{M}(\mathbf{x})$ is the (4×4) matrix of inertia (invertible)
$\mathbf{N}(\mathbf{x})$ is the (4×1) vector of damping, centrifugal, coriolis, gravitational forces.

The next step is to Lyapunov-linearize (5.51) which results in (5.40) again:

$$\delta\dot{\mathbf{x}} = \mathbf{M}^{-1}(\mathbf{x}^{\mathbf{d}}) \cdot \mathbf{A}(\mathbf{x}^{\mathbf{d}}) \cdot \delta\mathbf{x} + \mathbf{M}^{-1}(\mathbf{x}^{\mathbf{d}}) \cdot \delta\mathbf{u}. \tag{5.52}$$

According to (5.20) we obtain

$$\mathbf{M}^{-1}(\mathbf{x}^{\mathbf{d}}) = \begin{pmatrix} 1 & 0 & 0 & 0 \\ 0 & m_{11}^{-1} & 0 & m_{12}^{-1} \\ 0 & 0 & 1 & 0 \\ 0 & m_{21}^{-1} & 0 & m_{22}^{-1} \end{pmatrix}, \tag{5.53}$$

where the elements m_{ij}^{-1} are functions of the desired state vector

$$\mathbf{x}^{\mathbf{d}} = (x_1^d, x_2^d, x_3^d, x_4^d)^T = (q_1^d, \dot{q}_1^d, q_2^d, \dot{q}_2^d)^T. \tag{5.54}$$

The matrix $\mathbf{A}(\mathbf{x}^{\mathbf{d}})$ of (5.52) is derived as

$$\mathbf{A}(\mathbf{x}^{\mathbf{d}}) = \begin{pmatrix} 0 & 1 & 0 & 0 \\ A_{21} & A_{22} & A_{23} & A_{24} \\ 0 & 0 & 0 & 1 \\ A_{41} & A_{42} & A_{43} & A_{44} \end{pmatrix}_{\mathbf{x}=\mathbf{x}^{\mathbf{d}}}, \tag{5.55}$$

where

$$\begin{aligned}
A_{21} &= -\frac{\partial n_1}{\partial x_1} = -[x_4^2 m_2 l_1 l_2 \cos(x_1 - x_3) - (m_1 + m_2) g l_1 \cos x_1], \\
A_{22} &= -\frac{\partial n_1}{\partial x_2} = -K_{x_1}, \\
A_{23} &= -\frac{\partial n_1}{\partial x_3} = -[-x_4^2 m_2 l_1 l_2 \cos(x_1 - x_3)], \\
A_{24} &= -\frac{\partial n_1}{\partial x_4} = -[2 x_4 m_2 l_1 l_2 \sin(x_1 - x_3)], \\
A_{41} &= -\frac{\partial n_2}{\partial x_1} = -[-x_2^2 m_2 l_1 l_2 \cos(x_1 - x_3)], \\
A_{42} &= -\frac{\partial n_2}{\partial x_2} = -[-2 x_2 m_2 l_1 l_2 \sin(x_1 - x_3)], \\
A_{43} &= -\frac{\partial n_2}{\partial x_3} = -[x_2^2 m_2 l_1 l_2 \cos(x_1 - x_3) - m_2 g l_2 \cos x_3], \\
A_{44} &= -\frac{\partial n_2}{\partial x_4} = -K_{x_3}.
\end{aligned} \tag{5.56}$$

Recall that the control law corresponding to (5.52) was

$$\delta\mathbf{u} = \mathbf{K}(\mathbf{x}^{\mathbf{d}}) \cdot \delta\mathbf{x}, \tag{5.57}$$

(see (5.41)) where $\mathbf{K}(\mathbf{x^d})$ has to be designed such that

$$\tilde{\mathbf{A}} = \mathbf{M}^{-1}(\mathbf{x^d}) \cdot (\mathbf{A}(\mathbf{x^d}) + \mathbf{K}(\mathbf{x^d})),$$

has negative eigenvalues. Moreover, according to (5.47) one has to design $\mathbf{M}$ different matrices $\mathbf{K}(\mathbf{x^j})$. To do so we choose the eigenvalues for each center of a fuzzy region to be the same

$$\mathbf{p} = (-100, -5, -250, -3)^T. \tag{5.58}$$

Furthermore, we partition $q_1, \dot{q}_1, q_2, \dot{q}_2$ as shown in Table 5.2.2. The corresponding membership functions are shown in Fig. 5.11.

This leads to $3 \times 2 \times 3 \times 2 = 36$ different fuzzy regions with the same number of gain matrices $\mathbf{K}(\mathbf{x^j})$. However, it must be emphasized that the number of fuzzy rules is reduced to at least 9 different rules because of specific symmetries of matrix $\mathbf{A}$ regarding x_2 and x_4. Matrix $\mathbf{K}(\mathbf{x^j})$ has the following structure

Table 5.3. Partitioning of the fuzzy state space

variable	linguistic term	centers of regions
q_1	Low, Med, High	(-1.047, 0, 1.047)
$\dot{q}_1$	N, P	(-1.57, 1.57)
q_2	Low, Med, High	(0.524, 1.57, 2.617)
$\dot{q}_2$	N, P	(-1.57, 1.57)

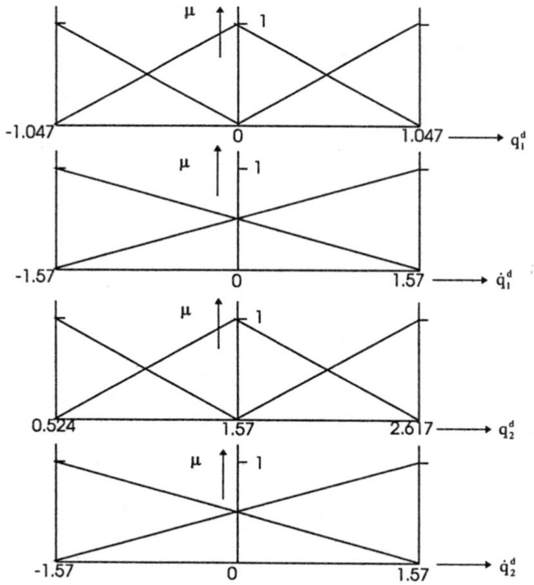

Fig. 5.11. Membership functions for q_1, $\dot{q}_1$, q_2, and $\dot{q}_2$

$$\mathbf{K}(\mathbf{x^j}) = \begin{pmatrix} 0 & 0 & 0 & 0 \\ k_{21} & k_{22} & k_{23} & k_{24} \\ 0 & 0 & 0 & 0 \\ k_{41} & k_{42} & k_{43} & k_{44} \end{pmatrix}^j , \tag{5.59}$$

so that

$$\delta\mathbf{u}(\mathbf{x^j}) = \begin{pmatrix} 0 \\ k_{21}\cdot\delta q_1 + k_{22}\cdot\delta\dot{q}_1 + k_{23}\cdot\delta q_2 + k_{24}\cdot\delta\dot{q}_2 \\ 0 \\ k_{41}\cdot\delta q_1 + k_{42}\cdot\delta\dot{q}_1 + k_{43}\cdot\delta q_2 + k_{44}\cdot\delta\dot{q}_2 \end{pmatrix}^j . \tag{5.60}$$

The mechanical parameters of the robot are

$m_1 = 1.5$ kg,
$m_2 = 1$ kg,
$l_1 = 0.2$ m,
$l_2 = 0.2$ m,
$K_{q1} = 10$ kg m^2 s^{-1},
$K_{q2} = 10$ kg m^2 s^{-1}.

The pole placement routine leads to 36 fuzzy controller rules shown below.

Rule 1: *if* q_1^d = Low *and* $\dot{q}_1^d$ = N *and* q_2^d = Low *and* $\dot{q}_2^d$ = N *then*
$u_1 = -123.6033\cdot\delta q_1 - 15.4631\cdot\delta\dot{q}_1 - 15.4399\cdot\delta q_2 - 0.8376\cdot\delta\dot{q}_2$ *and*
$u_2 = -3.2263\cdot\delta q_1 - 0.0358\cdot\delta\dot{q}_1 - 14.4916\cdot\delta q_2 + 5.8652\cdot\delta\dot{q}_2$.

Rule 2: *if* q_1^d = Low *and* $\dot{q}_1^d$ = N *and* q_2^d = Low *and* $\dot{q}_2^d$ = P *then*
$u_1 = -123.6033\cdot\delta q_1 - 15.4631\cdot\delta\dot{q}_1 - 15.4399\cdot\delta q_2 - 0.8376\cdot\delta\dot{q}_2$ *and*
$u_2 = -3.2263\cdot\delta q_1 - 0.0358\cdot\delta\dot{q}_1 - 14.4916\cdot\delta q_2 + 5.8652\cdot\delta\dot{q}_2$.

Rule 3: *if* q_1^d = Low *and* $\dot{q}_1^d$ = N *and* q_2^d = Med *and* $\dot{q}_2^d$ = N *then*
$u_1 = -120.8947\cdot\delta q_1 - 15.2611\cdot\delta\dot{q}_1 - 4.2759\cdot\delta q_2 + 2.8419\cdot\delta\dot{q}_2$ *and*
$u_2 = 38.8270\cdot\delta q_1 + 8.6862\cdot\delta\dot{q}_1 - 7.5294\cdot\delta q_2 + 6.0870\cdot\delta\dot{q}_2$.

Rule 4: *if* q_1^d = Low *and* $\dot{q}_1^d$ = N *and* q_2^d = Med *and* $\dot{q}_2^d$ = P *then*
$u_1 = -120.8947\cdot\delta q_1 - 15.2611\cdot\delta\dot{q}_1 - 4.2759\cdot\delta q_2 + 2.8419\cdot\delta\dot{q}_2$ *and*
$u_2 = 38.8270\cdot\delta q_1 + 8.6862\cdot\delta\dot{q}_1 - 7.5294\cdot\delta q_2 + 6.0870\cdot\delta\dot{q}_2$.

Rule 5: *if* q_1^d = Low *and* $\dot{q}_1^d$ = N *and* q_2^d = High *and* $\dot{q}_2^d$ = N *then*
$u_1 = -120.8947\cdot\delta q_1 - 15.2611\cdot\delta\dot{q}_1 - 4.2759\cdot\delta q_2 + 3.0393\cdot\delta\dot{q}_2$ *and*
$u_2 = 38.8270\cdot\delta q_1 + 8.4888\cdot\delta\dot{q}_1 - 5.8302\cdot\delta q_2 + 6.0870\cdot\delta\dot{q}_2$.

Rule 6: *if* q_1^d = Low *and* $\dot{q}_1^d$ = N *and* q_2^d = High *and* $\dot{q}_2^d$ = P *then*
$u_1 = -120.8947\cdot\delta q_1 - 15.2611\cdot\delta\dot{q}_1 - 4.2759\cdot\delta q_2 + 3.0393\cdot\delta\dot{q}_2$ *and*
$u_2 = 38.8270\cdot\delta q_1 + 8.4888\cdot\delta\dot{q}_1 - 5.8302\cdot\delta q_2 + 6.0870\cdot\delta\dot{q}_2$.

Rule 7: *if* q_1^d = Low *and* $\dot{q}_1^d$ = P *and* q_2^d = Low *and* $\dot{q}_2^d$ = N *then*
$u_1 = -123.6033 \cdot \delta q_1 - 15.4631 \cdot \delta\dot{q}_1 - 15.4399 \cdot \delta q_2 - 0.8376 \cdot \delta\dot{q}_2$ *and*
$u_2 = -3.2263 \cdot \delta q_1 - 0.0358 \cdot \delta\dot{q}_1 - 14.4916 \cdot \delta q_2 + 5.8652 \cdot \delta\dot{q}_2$.

Rule 8: *if* q_1^d = Low *and* $\dot{q}_1^d$ = P *and* q_2^d = Low *and* $\dot{q}_2^d$ = P *then*
$u_1 = -123.6033 \cdot \delta q_1 - 15.4631 \cdot \delta\dot{q}_1 - 15.4399 \cdot \delta q_2 - 0.8376 \cdot \delta\dot{q}_2$ *and*
$u_2 = -3.2263 \cdot \delta q_1 - 0.0358 \cdot \delta\dot{q}_1 - 14.4916 \cdot \delta q_2 + 5.8652 \cdot \delta\dot{q}_2$.

Rule 9: *if* q_1^d = Low *and* $\dot{q}_1^d$ = P *and* q_2^d = Med *and* $\dot{q}_2^d$ = N *then*
$u_1 = -120.8947 \cdot \delta q_1 - 15.2611 \cdot \delta\dot{q}_1 - 4.2759 \cdot \delta q_2 + 2.8419 \cdot \delta\dot{q}_2$ *and*
$u_2 = 38.8270 \cdot \delta q_1 + 8.6862 \cdot \delta\dot{q}_1 - 7.5294 \cdot \delta q_2 + 6.0870 \cdot \delta\dot{q}_2$.

Rule 10: *if* q_1^d = Low *and* $\dot{q}_1^d$ = P *and* q_2^d = Med *and* $\dot{q}_2^d$ = P *then*
$u_1 = -120.8947 \cdot \delta q_1 - 15.2611 \cdot \delta\dot{q}_1 - 4.2759 \cdot \delta q_2 + 2.8419 \cdot \delta\dot{q}_2$ *and*
$u_2 = 38.8270 \cdot \delta q_1 + 8.6862 \cdot \delta\dot{q}_1 - 7.5294 \cdot \delta q_2 + 6.0870 \cdot \delta\dot{q}_2$.

Rule 11: *if* q_1^d = Low *and* $\dot{q}_1^d$ = P *and* q_2^d = High *and* $\dot{q}_2^d$ = N *then*
$u_1 = -120.8947 \cdot \delta q_1 - 15.2611 \cdot \delta\dot{q}_1 - 4.2759 \cdot \delta q_2 + 3.0393 \cdot \delta\dot{q}_2$ *and*
$u_2 = 38.8270 \cdot \delta q_1 + 8.4888 \cdot \delta\dot{q}_1 - 5.8302 \cdot \delta q_2 + 6.0870 \cdot \delta\dot{q}_2$.

Rule 12: *if* q_1^d = Low *and* $\dot{q}_1^d$ = P *and* q_2^d = High *and* $\dot{q}_2^d$ = P *then*
$u_1 = -120.8947 \cdot \delta q_1 - 15.2611 \cdot \delta\dot{q}_1 - 4.2759 \cdot \delta q_2 + 3.0393 \cdot \delta\dot{q}_2$ *and*
$u_2 = 38.8270 \cdot \delta q_1 + 8.4888 \cdot \delta\dot{q}_1 - 5.8302 \cdot \delta q_2 + 6.0870 \cdot \delta\dot{q}_2$.

Rule 13: *if* q_1^d = Med *and* $\dot{q}_1^d$ = N *and* q_2^d = Low *and* $\dot{q}_2^d$ = N *then*
$u_1 = -128.7644 \cdot \delta q_1 - 15.6650 \cdot \delta\dot{q}_1 - 26.6040 \cdot \delta q_2 - 4.3197 \cdot \delta\dot{q}_2$ *and*
$u_2 = -45.2796 \cdot \delta q_1 - 8.9551 \cdot \delta\dot{q}_1 - 19.7547 \cdot \delta q_2 + 5.6435 \cdot \delta\dot{q}_2$.

Rule 14: *if* q_1^d = Med *and* $\dot{q}_1^d$ = N *and* q_2^d = Low *and* $\dot{q}_2^d$ = P *then*
$u_1 = -128.7644 \cdot \delta q_1 - 15.6650 \cdot \delta\dot{q}_1 - 26.6040 \cdot \delta q_2 - 4.3197 \cdot \delta\dot{q}_2$ *and*
$u_2 = -45.2796 \cdot \delta q_1 - 8.9551 \cdot \delta\dot{q}_1 - 19.7547 \cdot \delta q_2 + 5.6435 \cdot \delta\dot{q}_2$.

Rule 15: *if* q_1^d = Med *and* $\dot{q}_1^d$ = N *and* q_2^d = Med *and* $\dot{q}_2^d$ = N *then*
$u_1 = -126.0558 \cdot \delta q_1 - 15.4631 \cdot \delta\dot{q}_1 - 15.4399 \cdot \delta q_2 - 0.8376 \cdot \delta\dot{q}_2$ *and*
$u_2 = -3.2263 \cdot \delta q_1 - 0.0358 \cdot \delta\dot{q}_1 - 12.7924 \cdot \delta q_2 + 5.8652 \cdot \delta\dot{q}_2$.

Rule 16: *if* q_1^d = Med *and* $\dot{q}_1^d$ = N *and* q_2^d = Med *and* $\dot{q}_2^d$ = P *then*
$u_1 = -126.0558 \cdot \delta q_1 - 15.4631 \cdot \delta\dot{q}_1 - 15.4399 \cdot \delta q_2 - 0.8376 \cdot \delta\dot{q}_2$ *and*
$u_2 = -3.2263 \cdot \delta q_1 - 0.0358 \cdot \delta\dot{q}_1 - 12.7924 \cdot \delta q_2 + 5.8652 \cdot \delta\dot{q}_2$.

Rule 17: *if* q_1^d = Med *and* $\dot{q}_1^d$ = N *and* q_2^d = High *and* $\dot{q}_2^d$ = N *then*
$u_1 = -123.3472 \cdot \delta q_1 - 15.2611 \cdot \delta\dot{q}_1 - 4.2759 \cdot \delta q_2 + 2.8419 \cdot \delta\dot{q}_2$ *and*
$u_2 = 38.8270 \cdot \delta q_1 + 8.6862 \cdot \delta\dot{q}_1 - 5.8302 \cdot \delta q_2 + 6.0870 \cdot \delta\dot{q}_2$.

Rule 18: *if* $q_1^d =$ Med *and* $\dot{q}_1^d =$ N *and* $q_2^d =$ High *and* $\dot{q}_2^d =$ P *then* $u_1 = -123.3472 \cdot \delta q_1 - 15.2611 \cdot \delta\dot{q}_1 - 4.2759 \cdot \delta q_2 + 2.8419 \cdot \delta\dot{q}_2$ *and* $u_2 = 38.8270 \cdot \delta q_1 + 8.6862 \cdot \delta\dot{q}_1 - 5.8302 \cdot \delta q_2 + 6.0870 \cdot \delta\dot{q}_2$.

Rule 19: *if* $q_1^d =$ Med *and* $\dot{q}_1^d =$ P *and* $q_2^d =$ Low *and* $\dot{q}_2^d =$ N *then* $u_1 = -128.7644 \cdot \delta q_1 - 15.6650 \cdot \delta\dot{q}_1 - 26.6040 \cdot \delta q_2 - 4.3197 \cdot \delta\dot{q}_2$ *and* $u_2 = -45.2796 \cdot \delta q_1 - 8.9551 \cdot \delta\dot{q}_1 - 19.7547 \cdot \delta q_2 + 5.6435 \cdot \delta\dot{q}_2$.

Rule 20: *if* $q_1^d =$ Med *and* $\dot{q}_1^d =$ P *and* $q_2^d =$ Low *and* $\dot{q}_2^d =$ P *then* $u_1 = -128.7644 \cdot \delta q_1 - 15.6650 \cdot \delta\dot{q}_1 - 26.6040 \cdot \delta q_2 - 4.3197 \cdot \delta\dot{q}_2$ *and* $u_2 = -45.2796 \cdot \delta q_1 - 8.9551 \cdot \delta\dot{q}_1 - 19.7547 \cdot \delta q_2 + 5.6435 \cdot \delta\dot{q}_2$.

Rule 21: *if* $q_1^d =$ Med *and* $\dot{q}_1^d =$ P *and* $q_2^d =$ Med *and* $\dot{q}_2^d =$ N *then* $u_1 = -126.0558 \cdot \delta q_1 - 15.4631 \cdot \delta\dot{q}_1 - 15.4399 \cdot \delta q_2 - 0.8376 \cdot \delta\dot{q}_2$ *and* $u_2 = -3.2263 \cdot \delta q_1 - 0.0358 \cdot \delta\dot{q}_1 - 12.7924 \cdot \delta q_2 + 5.8652 \cdot \delta\dot{q}_2$.

Rule 22: *if* $q_1^d =$ Med *and* $\dot{q}_1^d =$ P *and* $q_2^d =$ Med *and* $\dot{q}_2^d =$ P *then* $u_1 = -126.0558 \cdot \delta q_1 - 15.4631 \cdot \delta\dot{q}_1 - 15.4399 \cdot \delta q_2 - 0.8376 \cdot \delta\dot{q}_2$ *and* $u_2 = -3.2263 \cdot \delta q_1 - 0.0358 \cdot \delta\dot{q}_1 - 12.7924 \cdot \delta q_2 + 5.8652 \cdot \delta\dot{q}_2$.

Rule 23: *if* $q_1^d =$ Med *and* $\dot{q}_1^d =$ P *and* $q_2^d =$ High *and* $\dot{q}_2^d =$ N *then* $u_1 = -123.3472 \cdot \delta q_1 - 15.2611 \cdot \delta\dot{q}_1 - 4.2759 \cdot \delta q_2 + 2.8419 \cdot \delta\dot{q}_2$ *and* $u_2 = 38.8270 \cdot \delta q_1 + 8.6862 \cdot \delta\dot{q}_1 - 5.8302 \cdot \delta q_2 + 6.0870 \cdot \delta\dot{q}_2$

Rule 24: *if* $q_1 =$ Med *and* $\dot{q}_1^d =$ P *and* $q_2^d =$ High *and* $\dot{q}_2^d =$ P *then* $u_1 = -123.3472 \cdot \delta q_1 - 15.2611 \cdot \delta\dot{q}_1 - 4.2759 \cdot \delta q_2 + 2.8419 \cdot \delta\dot{q}_2$. $u_2 = 38.8270 \cdot \delta q_1 + 8.6862 \cdot \delta\dot{q}_1 - 5.8302 \cdot \delta q_2 + 6.0870 \cdot \delta\dot{q}_2$.

Rule 25: *if* $q_1^d =$ High *and* $\dot{q}_1^d =$ N *and* $q_2^d =$ Low *and* $\dot{q}_2^d =$ N *then* $u_1 = -126.3119 \cdot \delta q_1 - 15.6650 \cdot \delta\dot{q}_1 - 26.6040 \cdot \delta q_2 - 4.1223 \cdot \delta\dot{q}_2$ *and* $u_2 = -45.2796 \cdot \delta q_1 - 9.1525 \cdot \delta\dot{q}_1 - 19.7547 \cdot \delta q_2 + 5.6435 \cdot \delta\dot{q}_2$.

Rule 26: *if* $q_1^d =$ High *and* $\dot{q}_1^d =$ N *and* $q_2^d =$ Low *and* $\dot{q}_2^d =$ P *then* $u_1 = -126.3119 \cdot \delta q_1 - 15.6650 \cdot \delta\dot{q}_1 - 26.6040 \cdot \delta q_2 - 4.1223 \cdot \delta\dot{q}_2$ *and* $u_2 = -45.2796 \cdot \delta q_1 - 9.1525 \cdot \delta\dot{q}_1 - 19.7547 \cdot \delta q_2 + 5.6435 \cdot \delta\dot{q}_2$.

Rule 27: *if* $q_1^d =$ High *and* $\dot{q}_1^d =$ N *and* $q_2^d =$ Med *and* $\dot{q}_2^d =$ N *then* $u_1 = -126.3119 \cdot \delta q_1 - 15.6650 \cdot \delta\dot{q}_1 - 26.6040 \cdot \delta q_2 - 4.3197 \cdot \delta\dot{q}_2$ *and* $u_2 = -45.2796 \cdot \delta q_1 - 8.9551 \cdot \delta\dot{q}_1 - 18.0555 \cdot \delta q_2 + 5.6435 \cdot \delta\dot{q}_2$.

Rule 28: *if* $q_1^d =$ High *and* $\dot{q}_1^d =$ N *and* $q_2^d =$ Med *and* $\dot{q}_2^d =$ P *then* $u_1 = -126.3119 \cdot \delta q_1 - 15.6650 \cdot \delta\dot{q}_1 - 26.6040 \cdot \delta q_2 - 4.3197 \cdot \delta\dot{q}_2$ *and* $u_2 = -45.2796 \cdot \delta q_1 - 8.9551 \cdot \delta\dot{q}_1 - 18.0555 \cdot \delta q_2 + 5.6435 \cdot \delta\dot{q}_2$.

Rule 29: *if* q_1^d = High *and* $\dot{q}_1^d$ = N *and* q_2^d = High *and* $\dot{q}_2^d$ = N *then*
$u_1 = -123.6033 \cdot \delta q_1 - 15.4631 \cdot \delta \dot{q}_1 - 15.4399 \cdot \delta q_2 - 0.8376 \cdot \delta \dot{q}_2$ *and*
$u_2 = -3.2263 \cdot \delta q_1 - 0.0358 \cdot \delta \dot{q}_1 - 11.0933 \cdot \delta q_2 + 5.8652 \cdot \delta \dot{q}_2$.

Rule 30: *if* q_1^d = High *and* $\dot{q}_1^d$ = N *and* q_2^d = High *and* $\dot{q}_2^d$ = P *then*
$u_1 = -123.6033 \cdot \delta q_1 - 15.4631 \cdot \delta \dot{q}_1 - 15.4399 \cdot \delta q_2 - 0.8376 \cdot \delta \dot{q}_2$ *and*
$u_2 = -3.2263 \cdot \delta q_1 - 0.0358 \cdot \delta \dot{q}_1 - 11.0933 \cdot \delta q_2 + 5.8652 \cdot \delta \dot{q}_2$.

Rule 31: *if* q_1^d = High *and* $\dot{q}_1^d$ = P *and* q_2^d = Low *and* $\dot{q}_2^d$ = N *then*
$u_1 = -126.3119 \cdot \delta q_1 - 15.6650 \cdot \delta \dot{q}_1 - 26.6040 \cdot \delta q_2 - 4.1223 \cdot \delta \dot{q}_2$ *and*
$u_2 = -45.2796 \cdot \delta q_1 - 9.1525 \cdot \delta \dot{q}_1 - 19.7547 \cdot \delta q_2 + 5.6435 \cdot \delta \dot{q}_2$.

Rule 32: *if* q_1^d = High *and* $\dot{q}_1^d$ = P *and* q_2^d = Low *and* $\dot{q}_2^d$ = P *then*
$u_1 = -126.3119 \cdot \delta q_1 - 15.6650 \cdot \delta \dot{q}_1 - 26.6040 \cdot \delta q_2 - 4.1223 \cdot \delta \dot{q}_2$ *and*
$u_2 = -45.2796 \cdot \delta q_1 - 9.1525 \cdot \delta \dot{q}_1 - 19.7547 \cdot \delta q_2 + 5.6435 \cdot \delta \dot{q}_2$.

Rule 33: *if* q_1^d = High *and* $\dot{q}_1^d$ = P *and* q_2^d = Med *and* $\dot{q}_2^d$ = N *then*
$u_1 = -126.3119 \cdot \delta q_1 - 15.6650 \cdot \delta \dot{q}_1 - 26.6040 \cdot \delta q_2 - 4.3197 \cdot \delta \dot{q}_2$ *and*
$u_2 = -45.2796 \cdot \delta q_1 - 8.9551 \cdot \delta \dot{q}_1 - 18.0555 \cdot \delta q_2 + 5.6435 \cdot \delta \dot{q}_2$.

Rule 34: *if* q_1^d = High *and* $\dot{q}_1^d$ = P *and* q_2^d = Med *and* $\dot{q}_2^d$ = P *then*
$u_1 = -126.3119 \cdot \delta q_1 - 15.6650 \cdot \delta \dot{q}_1 - 26.6040 \cdot \delta q_2 - 4.3197 \cdot \delta \dot{q}_2$ *and*
$u_2 = -45.2796 \cdot \delta q_1 - 8.9551 \cdot \delta \dot{q}_1 - 18.0555 \cdot \delta q_2 + 5.6435 \cdot \delta \dot{q}_2$.

Rule 35: *if* q_1^d = High *and* $\dot{q}_1^d$ = P *and* q_2^d = High *and* $\dot{q}_2^d$ = N *then*
$u_1 = -123.6033 \cdot \delta q_1 - 15.4631 \cdot \delta \dot{q}_1 - 15.4399 \cdot \delta q_2 - 0.8376 \cdot \delta \dot{q}_2$ *and*
$u_2 = -3.2263 \cdot \delta q_1 - 0.0358 \cdot \delta \dot{q}_1 - 11.0933 \cdot \delta q_2 + 5.8652 \cdot \delta \dot{q}_2$.

Rule 36: *if* q_1^d = High *and* $\dot{q}_1^d$ = P *and* q_2^d = High *and* $\dot{q}_2^d$ = P *then*
$u_1 = -123.6033 \cdot \delta q_1 - 15.4631 \cdot \delta \dot{q}_1 - 15.4399 \cdot \delta q_2 - 0.8376 \cdot \delta \dot{q}_2$ *and*
$u_2 = -3.2263 \cdot \delta q_1 - 0.0358 \cdot \delta \dot{q}_1 - 11.0933 \cdot \delta q_2 + 5.8652 \cdot \delta \dot{q}_2$.

In the following we present some simulations showing the behavior of the system under control with different parameter fluctuations. The desired robot trajectory is

$$(q_1^d, \dot{q}_1^d, q_2^d, \dot{q}_2^d) = (0.5 - 0.5 \cdot \sin 3t, -0.5 \cdot 3 \cdot \cos 3t, 1.57 + 0.5 \cdot \sin 3t, 0.5 \cdot 3 \cdot \cos 3t). \quad (5.61)$$

Figure 5.12 shows the simulation result for perfect compensation at the operating points and a payload $m_2 = 1$ kg. The resulting errors are in the range $(-0.02, 0.02)$.

Figure 5.13 shows a simulation for partial compensation ($\hat{u}_i^d = 0.9 \cdot u_i^d$, $i = 1, 2$) and a payload $m_2 = 1$ kg.

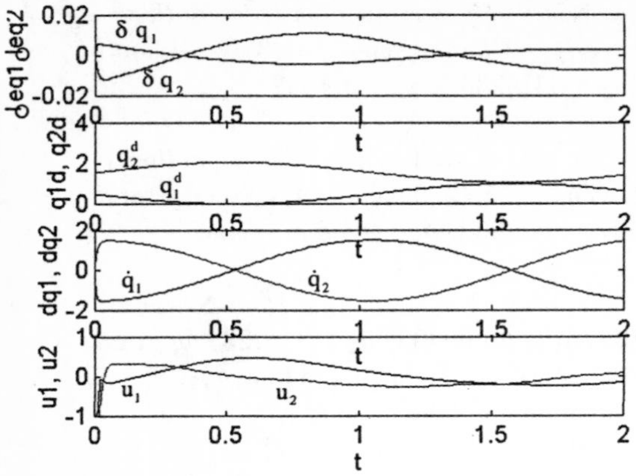

Fig. 5.12. Simulation results for $\omega = 3\ \mathrm{s}^{-1}$, $m_2 = 1$ kg and perfect compensation ($\hat{u}_i^d = 1.0 \cdot u_i^d$, $i = 1, 2$)

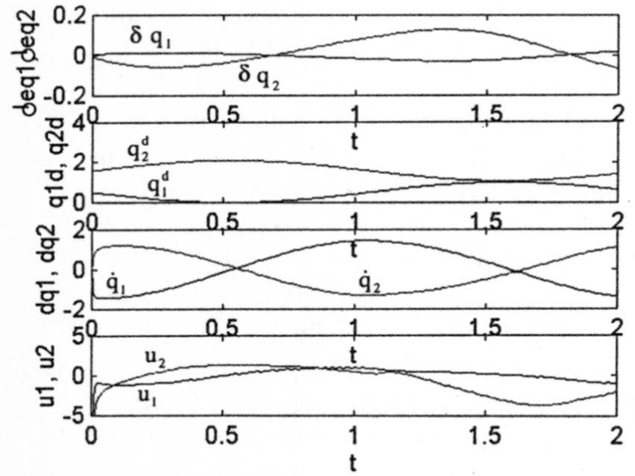

Fig. 5.13. Simulation results for $\omega = 3\ \mathrm{s}^{-1}$, $m_2 = 1$ kg and partial compensation ($\hat{u}_i^d = 0.9 \cdot u_i^d$, $i = 1, 2$)

Figure 5.14 refers to an example where u_i^d are over-compensated at the operating points ($\hat{u}_i^d = 1.1 \cdot u_i^d$, $i = 1, 2$). In this case the system becomes unstable.

When slowing down the frequency with which the robot links move from $\omega = 3\ \mathrm{s}^{-1}$ to $\omega = 3\ \mathrm{s}^{-1}$ we reach again a stable behavior. The new desired robot trajectory is then

$$(q_1^d, \dot{q}_1^d, q_2^d, \dot{q}_2^d) =$$

$$(0.5 - 0.5 \cdot \sin(1t), -0.5 \cdot \cos t, 1.57 + 0.5 \cdot \sin 1t, 0.5 \cdot 1 \cdot \cos t). \quad (5.62)$$

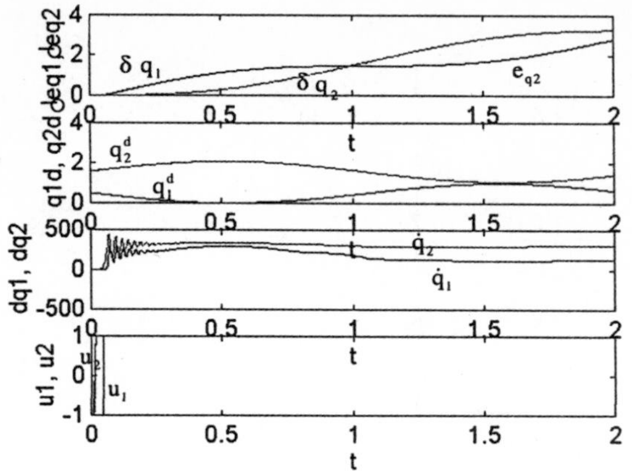

Fig. 5.14. Simulation results for $\omega = 3\ \mathrm{s}^{-1}$, $m_2 = 1$ kg and partial compensation ($\hat{u}_i^d = 1.1 \cdot u_i^d$, $i = 1, 2$)

The corresponding simulation results are shown in Fig. 5.15.

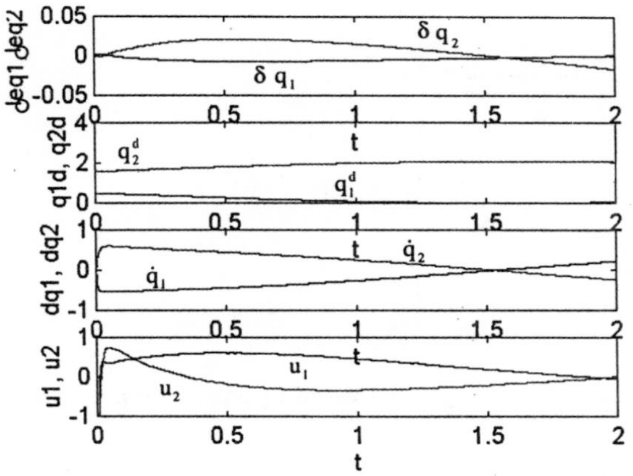

Fig. 5.15. Simulation results for $\omega = 1\ \mathrm{s}^{-1}$, $m_2 = 1$ kg and partial compensation ($\hat{u}_i^d = 1.1 \cdot u_i^d$, $i = 1, 2$)

Figures 5.16 and 5.17 refer to examples with different payloads, but with perfect compensation. The errors δq_1 and δq_2 are in the range $(-0.05, 0.05)$ for $m_2 = 2.5$ kg and $(-0.01, 0.01)$ for $m_2 = 0.2$ kg.

For what concerns stability analysis, it should be pointed out that the desired trajectory and, with that, system matrix $\tilde{\mathbf{A}}$ are slowly time varying. The largest time constants of the robot links controlled are $\tau_{q_1} = 0.2$ s and $\tau_{q_2} = 0.33$ s. In contrast, the time period of the introduced sinusoidal signal is

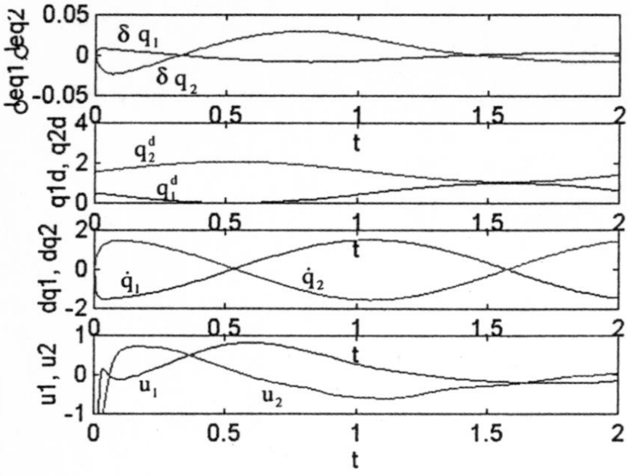

Fig. 5.16. Simulation results for $\omega = 3\ \mathrm{s}^{-1}$, $m_2 = 2.5$ kg and perfect compensation $(\hat{u}_i^d = 1.0 \cdot u_i^d,\ i = 1, 2)$

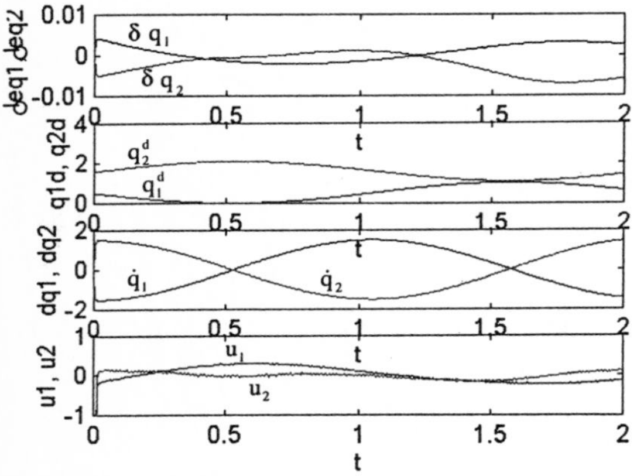

Fig. 5.17. Simulation results for $\omega = 3\ \mathrm{s}^{-1}$, $m_2 = 0.2$ kg and perfect compensation $(\hat{u}_i^d = 1.0 \cdot u_i^d,\ i = 1, 2)$

$\tau_{signal} = 2\pi/\omega = 2.09$ s which is 6–10 times longer than the time constants of the links. Therefore, one can assume that the desired exogeneous trajectory is slowly time varying, which is the basic condition for using the frozen-time stability analysis.

References

1. Babuska, R., and Verbruggen, H.B., "Estimation of Composite Linear Models from Data via Fuzzy Clustering", unpublished paper submitted to *European Journal of Control.*
2. Babuska, R., and Verbruggen, H.B., "A New Identification Method for Linguistic Fuzzy Models", *Proceedings FUZZ-IEEE/IFES'95*, Yokohama, Japan, March 20–24, 1995, pp. 905–912.
3. Babuska, R., and Verbruggen, H.B., "Comparing Different Methods for Premise Identification in Sugeno-Takagi Models", *Proceedings EUFIT'94*, Aachen, Germany, September 20–23, 1994, pp. 1188–1192.
4. Bastian, A. "Towards a Fuzzy System Identification Theory", *Proceedings IFSA'95*, Sao Paolo, Brazil, July 21–28, 1995, pp. 69–72.
5. Boverie, S. et al, "Fuzzy Logic Control for High Order Systems", *Proceedings FUZZ-IEEE'93*, San Francisco, CA, March 28–April 1, 1993, pp. 117–121.
6. Cook, P.A., *Nonlinear Dynamic Systems*, Prentice Hall International (UK), 1994.
7. Driankov, D., Hellendoorn, H., and Reinfrank, M., *An Introduction to Fuzzy Control*, Springer-Verlag, Berlin, 1993. 2nd, rev. ed. 1996.
8. Foellinger, O., *Regelungstechnik*, Huethig Buch Verlag, Heidelberg, 1990.
9. Herrera, F, Lozano, M., and Verdegay, J.L., "Design of Control Rules Base Based on Genetic Algorithms", *Proceedings IFSA'95*, Sao Paolo, Brazil, July 21–28, 1995, pp. 265–268.
10. Hwang, G.-C., and Li, S.-C., "A Stability Approach to Fuzzy Control Design for Nonlinear Systems", *Fuzzy Sets and Systems*, **48**(1992), 279–287.
11. Kawaji, S., and Matsunaga, N., "Fuzzy Control of VSS Type and Its Robustness", *Proceedings IFSA'91*, Brussels, Belgium, July 7–12, 1991, pp. 81–88.
12. Kim, W.C., Kwon, W.H., and Kim, H.D., "Stability Analysis of Linguistic Fuzzy Model Systems", *Proceedings of the American Control Conference*, San Francisco, CA, pp. 777–780, 1993.
13. Marin, J.P., and Titli, A., "Comparative Analysis of Stability Methods for Fuzzy Controllers", *Proceedings EUFIT'94*, Aachen, Germany, September 20–23, 1994, pp. 1183–1187.
14. Moon, B.S., "Equivalence Between FLC and PI Controllers for Single Input Systems", *Fuzzy Sets and Systems*, **69**(2)(1994), 105–113.
15. Nichols, R.A., Reichert, R.T., anf Rugh, W.J., "Gain Sceduling for H-Infinity Controllers: A Flight Control Example", *IEEE Transactions on Control Systems Technology*, **1**(2)(1993), 69–79.
16. Palm, R., "Sliding Mode Fuzzy Control", *Proceedings FUZZ-IEEE'93*, San Diego, CA, March 8–12, pp. 519–526.
17. Palm, R., Driankov, D, and Rehfuess, U., "Lyapunov Linearization Based Design of Takagi–Sugeno Controllers ", *Proceedings FUZZ-IEEE'95*, Sao Paolo, Brazil, July 21–28, 1995, pp. 513–516.

18. Palm, R., "Robust Control by Fuzzy Sliding Mode", *Automatica*, **30**(9), 1994, 1429–1437.
19. Palm, R., "Tuning of Scaling Factors in Fuzzy Controllers Using Correlation Functions", *Proceedings FUZZ-IEEE'93*, San Francisco, CA, 1993, March 28–April 1, pp. 691–696.
20. Park, M., Seunghwan, Ji, and Mignon, P., "A New Approach to the Identification of a Fuzzy Model", *Proceedings FUZZ-IEEE/IFES'95*, Yokohama, Japan, March 20–24, 1995, pp. 2159–2164.
21. Press, W.H., et al., *Numerical Recipes in C*, Cambridge University Press, Cambridge, 1990.
22. Ray, K.S., and Majumder, D.D., "Application of Circle Criteria for Stability Analysis of Linear SISO and MIMO Systems Associated with Fuzzy Logic Controller", *IEEE Transactions on Systems, Man, Cybernetics*, **14**(2)(1984), 345–349.
23. Ray, K.S., Ananda, S., and Majumder, D.D., "L-Stability and the Related Design Concept for SISO Linear Systems Associated with Fuzzy Logic Controller", *IEEE Transactions on Systems, Man, Cybernetics*, **14**(1992), 932–939.
24. Rehfuess, U., and Palm, R., "Design of Takagi–Sugeno Controllers Based on Linear Quadratic Control", *Proceedings First International Symposium on Fuzzy Logic*, Zurich, Switzerland, May 26–27, 1995, pp. C10–C15.
25. Rugh, W.J., "Analytical Framework for Gain Scheduling", *IEEE Control Systems Magazine*, **11**(1)(1991), 79–84.
26. Shamma, J.S., *Analysis and Design of Gain Scheduled Control Systems*, PhD Thesis No. LIDS-TH-1770, Lab. for Information and Decision Sciences, MIT, Cambridge, MA 02139, 1988.
27. Skeppstedt, A., Ljung, L., and Milnert, M., "Construction of Composite Models from Observed Data", *International Journal of Control*, **55**(1992), 141–152.
28. Slotine, J.-J., and Weiping Li, *Applied Nonlinear Control*, Prentice Hall, Englewood Cliffs, NJ 07632, 1991.
29. Smith, S.M., "A Variable Structure Fuzzy Logic Controller with Runtime Adaptation", *Proceedings FUZZ-IEEE'94*, Orlando, FL, July 26–29, 1994, pp. 983–988.
30. Su, Mu-Cun et al, "Rule Extraction Using a Novel Class of Fuzzy Degraded Hyperellipsoidal Composite Neural Networks", *Proceedings FUZZ-IEEE/IFES'95*, Yokohama, Japan, March 20–24, 1995, pp. 233–238.
31. Sugeno, M., and Kang, G.T., "Fuzzy Modelling and Control of Multilayer Incinerator", *Fuzzy Sets and Systems*, **18**(1986), 329–346.
32. Sugeno, M., and Kang, G.T., "Structure Identification of a Fuzzy Model", *Fuzzy Sets and Systems*,**28**(1988), 15–33.
33. Sugeno, M., and Tanaka, K., "Successive Identification of Fuzzy Model and its Application to Prediction of Complex System", *Fuzzy Sets and Systems*, **42**(1991), 315–344.
34. Takagi, T., and Sugeno, M., "Fuzzy Identification of Systems and Its Applications to Modelling and Control", *IEEE Transactions on Systems, Man, Cybernetics*, **15**(1)(1985), 116–132.
35. Tanaka, K., and Sano, M., "Concept of Stability Margin for Fuzzy systems and Design of Robust Fuzzy Controllers", *Proceedings FUZZ-IEEE'93*, San Francisco, CA, March 28–April 1, 1993, pp. 29–34.
36. Tanaka, K., and Sugeno, M., "Stability Analysis and Design of Fuzzy Control Systems", *Fuzzy Sets and Systems*, **45**(1992), 135–156.
37. Tang, K.L., and Mulholland, R.J., "Comparing Fuzzy Logic with Classical Control Designs", *IEEE Transactions on Systems, Man, Cybernetics*, **17**(6)(1987), 1085–1087.

38. Utkin, V.J., "Variable Structure Systems: A Survey", *IEEE Transactions Automatic Control*, **22**(1977), 212–222.
39. Vergara, V., and Moraga, C., "Optimal Fuzzy Identification Models", *Proceedings IFSA '95*, Sao Paolo, Brazil, July 21–28, 1995, pp. 109–112.
40. Vidyasagar, M., *Nonlinear Systems Analysis*, Prentice Hall, Englewood Cliffs, NJ 07632, 1993.
41. Wakileh, B.A.M., and Gill, K.F., "Use of Fuzzy Logic in Robotics", *Computers in Industry*, **10**(1988), 35–46.
42. Wang, Li-Xin, *Adaptive Fuzzy Systems and Control*, Prentice Hall, Englewood Cliffs, NJ 07632, 1994.
43. Yen, J., and Gillespie, W., "Integrating Global and Local Evaluations for Fuzzy Model Identification Using Genetic Algorithms", *Proceedings IFSA '95*, Sao Paolo, Brazil, July 21–28, 1995, pp. 121–124.
44. Zhou, K., and Khargonekar, P., "Stability Robustness for Linear State-Space Models with Structured Uncertainty", *IEEE Transactions on Automatic Control*, **32**(7)(1987), 621–623.

Index

Druck: STRAUSS OFFSETDRUCK, MÖRLENBACH
Verarbeitung: SCHÄFFER, GRÜNSTADT

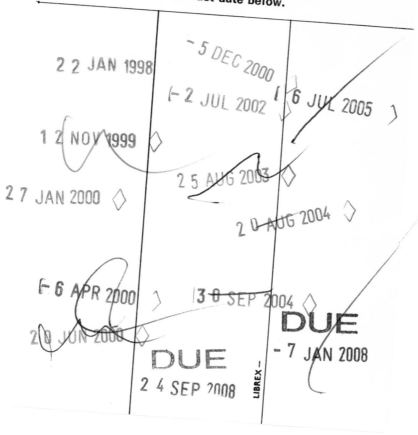